Biology of Neuroglia

Compiled and Edited by

WILLIAM F. WINDLE, Ph.D., Sc.D.

Chief, Laboratory of Neuroanatomical Sciences
National Institute of Neurological Diseases and
    Blindness
National Institutes of Health
Public Health Service
Department of Health, Education and Welfare
Bethesda, Maryland

Biology of Neuroglia

CHARLES C THOMAS · PUBLISHER
Springfield · *Illinois* · *U.S.A.*

CHARLES C THOMAS · PUBLISHER

BANNERSTONE HOUSE

301-327 East Lawrence Avenue, Springfield, Illinois, U.S.A.

Published simultaneously in the British Commonwealth of Nations by

BLACKWELL SCIENTIFIC PUBLICATIONS, LTD., OXFORD, ENGLAND

Published simultaneously in Canada by

THE RYERSON PRESS, TORONTO

Library of Congress Catalog Card Number: 57-12559

Printed in the United States of America

Contributors

RAYMOND D. ADAMS, M.D., Bullard Professor of Neuropathology, Harvard University Medical School and Chief, Neurological Services, Massachusetts General Hospital, Boston, Mass.

R. WAYNE ALBERS, PH.D., Section on Neurocytology, Laboratory of Neuroanatomical Sciences, National Institute of Neurological Diseases and Blindness, Bethesda, Md.

ANGELO BAIRATI, M.D., Professor of Anatomy, Director of the Institute of Anatomy, University of Milan, Milan, Italy.

ROBERT H. BROWNSON, PH.D., Assistant Professor of Anatomy, Medical College of Virginia, Richmond, Va.

JAN CAMMERMEYER, M.D., Chief, Section on Experimental Neuropathology, Laboratory of Neuroanatomical Sciences, National Institute of Neurological Diseases and Blindness, Bethesda, Md.

CARMINE D. CLEMENTE, PH.D., Assistant Professor of Anatomy, University of California, School of Medicine, Los Angeles, Calif.

MAYNARD M. COHEN, M.D., PH.D., Associate Professor of Neurology, University of Minnesota School of Medicine, Minneapolis, Minn.

ISAAC COSTERO, M.D., Professor of Pathology, National University of Mexico, Chief Pathologist, National Institute of Cardiology, Mexico City, Mexico.

EDWARD W. DEMPSEY, PH.D., SC.D., Professor of Anatomy, School of Medicine, Washington University, St. Louis, Mo.

K. A. C. ELLIOTT, PH.D., SC.D., Associate Professor of Experimental Neurology and Biochemistry, Montreal Neurological Institute, McGill University, Montreal, Can.

LOUIS B. FLEXNER, M.D., Professor of Anatomy and Director, Institute of Neurological Sciences, School of Medicine, University of Pennsylvania, Philadelphia, Pa.

PAUL GLEES, M.D., D.PHIL., a. p. Professor, University Lecturer and Demonstrator, Department Laboratory of Physiology, Oxford, England.

J. FRANCIS HARTMANN, PH.,D., Associate Professor, Institute of Anatomy, University of Minnesota, Minneapolis, Minn.

WALTHER HILD, M.D., Research Associate, Tissue Culture Laboratory, University of Texas Medical Branch, Galveston, Tex.

HEINRICH KLÜVER, PH.D., Professor of Experimental Psychology, Divi-

v

sion of the Biological Sciences, University of Chicago, Chicago, Ill.

SEYMOUR S. KETY, M.D., Associate Director in Charge of Research, National Institute of Neurological Diseases and Blindness and National Institute of Mental Health, Bethesda, Md.

SAUL R. KOREY, M.D., Professor of Neurology, Department of Medicine, Division of Neurology, Albert Einstein College of Medicine, Yeshiva University, New York, N. Y.

HELMUT LEONHARDT, M.D., Privatdozent, Anatomical Institute, University of Erlangen, West Germany.

RICHARD LINDENBERG, M.D., Director of Neuropathology and Legal Medicine, Department of Mental Hygiene, Central Anatomic Laboratory, Baltimore, Md.

CHARLES E. LUMSDEN, M.D., Professor of Pathology, Leeds University, Leeds, England.

SARAH A. LUSE, M.D., American Cancer Society Fellow in Anatomy, Washington University School of Medicine, St. Louis, Mo.

NATHAN MALAMUD, M.D., Associate Professor of Psychiatry and Neuropathology, University of California School of Medicine, San Francisco, Calif.

MARGARET R. MURRAY, PH.D., Associate Professor of Anatomy, Columbia University College of Physicians and Surgeons, New York, N. Y.

JOHN I. NURNBERGER, M.D., Professor of Psychiatry and Director, The Institute of Psychiatric Research, University of Indiana Medical Center, Indianapolis, Ind.

SANFORD L. PALAY, M.D., Associate Professor of Anatomy, Yale University School of Medicine, New Haven, Conn.

CHARLES M. POMERAT, PH.D., Professor of Cytology and Director, Tissue Culture Laboratory, University of Texas Medical Branch, Galveston, Tex.

ALFRED POPE, M.D., Associate Professor of Neuropathology, Harvard Medical School, Boston. Neuropathologist, McLean Hospital, Waverly, Mass.

LEON ROIZIN, M.D., Assistant Professor of Neuropathology, Columbia University College of Physicians and Surgeons, New York, N. Y.

AUGUSTUS S. ROSE, M.D., Professor of Medicine (Neurology), University of California School of Medicine, Los Angeles, Calif.

ARNOLD B. SCHEIBEL, M.D., Assistant Professor of Psychiatry and Anatomy, University of California School of Medicine, Los Angeles, Calif.

MADGE E. SCHEIBEL, M.D., Research Associate, Departments of Psychiatry and Anatomy, University of California School of Medicine, Los Angeles, Calif.

ROBERT D. TSCHIRGI, M.D., PH.D., Associate Professor of Physiology and Anatomy, University of California School of Medicine, Los Angeles, Calif.

BETTY GEREN UZMAN, M.D., Associate Pathologist, Children's Medical Center, Boston, Mass.

WILLIAM F. WINDLE, PH.D., SC.D., Chief, Laboratory of Neuro-anatomical Sciences, National Institute of Neurological Diseases and Blindness, Bethesda, Md.

ABNER WOLF, M.D., Professor of Neuropathology, Columbia University, College of Physicians and Surgeons, New York, N. Y.

DIXON M. WOODBURY, PH.D., Associate Research Professor of Pharmacology, University of Utah College of Medicine, Salt Lake City, Utah.

Preface

EMPHASIS on the intrinsic structure of the central nervous system is usually placed on the neurons and their connections. The other elements, especially the neuroglia cells, have received all too little attention by physiologists and morphologists alike. To try to correct this and stimulate new studies which might result in shedding light on the function of these cells, the National Advisory Neurological Diseases and Blindness Council sponsored a "Conference on the Biology of Neuroglia" which was held at the National Institutes of Health in Bethesda, Maryland in March, 1956. A committee, composed of Drs. Jan Cammermeyer, John I. Nurnberger, Sanford L. Palay, Charles M. Pomerat, Arnold B. Scheibel and the Editor of this monograph was appointed to organize a program and recommend names of other participants. It proposed consideration of four main topics; namely, relation of neuroglia cells to neurons, relation of neuroglia cells to blood vessels and to the blood-brain barrier, structure and function of neuroglia cells in vitro and biochemical aspects of neuroglia cells. In addition it recommended that a geographically representative group of clinical neuropathologists be invited to attend the conference and to conduct a "Neuropathological Symposium on Neuroglia" immediately afterwards to reassess the role of this tissue in disease processes in light of new concepts which might be developed during the conference.

The present monograph is based on the transcriptions of the recorded proceedings. Nine keynote papers have been supplemented by revised and, in some instances, amplified discussions on topics of especial interest, to form the principal chapters. Round table discussions are reproduced in appropriate places in relation to the main topics. The last two chapters of the book summarize the "Neuropathological Symposium on Neuroglia."

Editorial responsibility fell largely upon the shoulders of the secretarial staff of the Laboratory of Neuroanatomical Sciences and especially Mrs. Elizabeth W. Snowden who transcribed most of the proceedings and prepared the final manuscript. We are appreciative of their excellent work. The task was agreeably enhanced by fine co-operation on the part of all contributors. The editor assumes full responsibility for deletions from original copy and for reorganization of illustrations (and elimination of a number of them for the sake of economy). The principal aims were to achieve uniformity without sacrificing individuals' styles of writing, to fill in certain omissions and to co-ordinate the citations of literature. No attempt was made to provide a complete bibliography on the neuroglia but the list is representative and contains most key references. To achieve the first aim we adopted a single style in respect to spelling, use of numerals, abbreviations and subheadings. The current editions of *Webster's New International Dictionary Unabridged* and the *American Illustrated Medical Dictionary* were used as authorities. A long form was chosen for bibliographic references, the abbreviations of periodical names being those of the *Current List of Medical Literature* or, in cases of journals no longer published, the *Index Catalog of the Library of the Surgeon General's Office.*

It is a pleasure to acknowledge the fine co-operation of the publishers who have spared no effort to produce a book of attractive appearance. It is noteworthy that the present monograph is the third in a series of publications of Symposia in Neurology, the previous ones being *Regeneration in the Central Nervous System* and *New Research Techniques of Neuroanatomy.*

WILLIAM F. WINDLE
Laboratory of Neuroanatomical Sciences
National Institutes of Health
Bethesda 14, Maryland

Introduction to the Conference

WILLIAM F. WINDLE

IT MAY BE said of the neuroglia, like the weather, that everyone discusses it but no one does anything about it. This conference provides another opportunity to discuss it but we hope it will lead also to some action, for research on the nervous system cannot proceed much farther until we have more accurate knowledge about all its elements, their origin, fine structure and interrelations—and that includes the neuroglia. A good way to start may be to outline the material that is commonly presented to our students as "the essential facts about the neuroglia" and see how little it has changed in the last half century.

Neuroglia—literally, nerve glue—is declared to be the supportive or connective tissue of the central nervous system, leading one to think of it as something comparable with fibroelastic connective tissue in other regions. It is said to be made up of cells and fibers. Some teachers even still talk about the old concept of Weigert (1895) concerning separateness of protoplasm and gliofibrils. Students commonly learn of the syncytial nature of the neuroglia cells as depicted by Hardesty ('04) and Held ('09). Fact and fancy are often mixed in our teaching.

The cells of the neuroglia are said to fall into three types, though many will admit in addition the ependyma cells and even such special forms as the pituicytes. The three types are astrocytes (fibrous and protoplasmic), oligodendrocytes and microglia cells. Except that the names used to designate them have changed this classification represents little advance in the last half century.

Although Virchow had described the neuroglia as a tissue in 1846 and Deiters recognized its cellular components as being different from nerve cells in 1865, it was Golgi's introduction of the silver method in 1873 that made possible the first clarification of cell form and relationship to blood vessels. By 1900 most of the knowledge with which we currently indoctrinate our students had accumulated. Spider cells or fibrous astrocytes, mossy cells or protoplasmic astrocytes, both with footplates attaching to blood vessels and pia mater, were known. The contribution of ependyma cells to the neuroglia was well recognized. Other non-nervous elements, called mesoglia cells, had been described in 1900 by Robertson. These obscure cells undoubtedly included both the oligodendrocytes and microglia cells. The latter were most clearly defined and their transformation into macrophages noted.

It is interesting that Ramon y Cajal failed to grasp the full extent of the then current knowledge of the neuroglia when he wrote his great *Histologie du Système Nerveux*. Not until later did he speak of a third element, that of Robertson, and raise the question whether or not it should be considered a neuroglia cell. Del Río Hortega's clear demonstration of the oligodendrocyte in 1921 led to a violent controversy with his teacher, Ramon y Cajal, which forced him to leave the Madrid laboratory; but the world of science quickly accepted del Río Hortega's findings. Since that time until the immediate present there has been little noteworthy change in the story of the neuroglia—none as it is described in the textbooks of histology and neurology.

Contents

Biology of Neuroglia

The Neuroglia-Neuronal Relationships

Chapter 1

Neurons and Neuroglia Cells as Seen With the Light Microscope

MADGE E. AND ARNOLD B. SCHEIBEL*

WHEN WE examine sections of brain tissue from mammalian vertebrates stained by the Golgi technique, in addition to nerve cell bodies, axons, dendrons and variable numbers of astrocytes, we also see orange staining spheres ranging in size from 6 to 9μ. They are fairly regular in shape and size for any one area, though they are occasionally oval or pear shaped, and once in a while bear small buds as if some kind of simple division were in progress. They can be found in both gray and white matter. In the gray matter they are seen in large numbers throughout the fields of neuropil surrounding the nerve cell bodies and the first portion of their dendrons, in classical satellite positions. In the white matter they are found among the nerve fiber masses, frequently lined up in short rows and often of somewhat larger size than those of the gray matter.

We first noticed them in the inferior olivary nucleus during the course of a study of the intrinsic structure of that nucleus (Scheibel and Scheibel, '55), somewhat later in the brain stem reticular formation (Scheibel, '55) and since then have recognized them in all portions of the central nervous system including spinal cord, cranial nerve nuclei, cerebrum and cerebellum. Their size, shape, distribution and geographical relations to nerve cells and axons point to their being the nuclei of oligodendrocytes.

Careful focusing through the tissue sections often reveals narrow, asymmetric rims of unstained refractile material, while an

* Supported in part by a grant from the National Institute of Neurological Diseases and Blindness.

occasional fortunate impregnation colors this rim and a group of sparsely ramified nodular processes similar to the classic drawings of del Río Hortega ('28) and Penfield ('32a). When these observations are controlled through the use of the silver carbonate methods specific for oligodendrocytes, and by modified Bielschowsky, Bodian and Nissl techniques, and when careful comparisons are made of nuclear morphology, geographical distribution, relations to neuronal elements and patterns of processes, no doubt can remain that the orange staining bodies represent the nuclei of oligodendrocytes; they apparently become chromated without reducing the silver, while their scanty cytoplasm and processes generally remain completely uncolored.

We were surprised to find that these oligodendrocyte nuclei frequently bore on their surfaces small round button or ringlike forms. It became evident that these structures were axonal, they were, in fact, indistinguishable from the familiar *boutons en passage* and *boutons terminaux* of the nerve cell synapse. The possibility that axons synapse with certain types of neuroglia cells should not, in retrospect, have proven as disturbing as it did at first. Certainly, neuroglia cells and neurons deriving originally from the same stem cells must have many basic similarities. In addition, no well documented functions exist for any of the neuroglia cells, so that a set of observations apparently linking them intimately to nerve cells should not have seemed unacceptable. Then too, as we later found in scanning the literature, De Castro ('51) had described contacts between preganglionic axon terminals and glioid cells in peripheral autonomic ganglia; and it is practically bromidic to suggest that nature frequently effects similar solutions to similar problems, no matter how diverse the organisms or environments.

Nevertheless, the gulf between neurons and neuroglia cells seemed so emphatic that we were reluctant to go along with these observations for almost three years, preferring to assume that the ring and buttonlike forms on the surface of the oligodendrocyte nuclei were either intrinsic structures of the cells themselves or small footlike contacts from adjacent neuroglia cells—perhaps even artifacts of the impregnation.

Prolonged study of sections from the brains of several thousand cats, dogs, rabbits, rats and mice, plus a smaller amount of monkey and human material, has definitely ruled out the possibility that all these structures are artifacts. Some of the contacts are undoubtedly glial contacts—as we will show later—which introduce some intriguing functional possibilities of their own. However, careful study of modified Bielschowsky and cresyl violet counterstained Bodian material clearly corroborates the fact that axon terminals effect contact with oligodendrocytes as well as with nerve cells. Study of a small number of sections from lesion material stained by various silver methods reveals degenerating preterminal or terminal axons making contact with oligodendrocytes.

From a number of points of view, then, the data appear clear that nerve cells can establish terminal or in passage contact with oligodendrocytes, at least. We add the qualifying phrase, since some of our observations suggest that axons may also come into intimate physical contact with other types of neuroglia cells, especially the ependyma surrounding the cerebral aqueduct.* However, the evidence here is incomplete and will not be referred to again in the present communication.

We hope that these observations will stimulate the electron microscopist to look more deeply into structural evidence of relations between neurons and neuroglia cells as the neurochemists are beginning to examine possible biochemical relations between them.

Before presenting the actual data, one point should be emphasized. We are not suggesting glial interposition between axons and neuron somata and dendrons or, in other words, between pre- and post-synaptic elements. We have never seen any evidence of such interposition—although De Castro ('51) has championed this point of view—and the electron microscope clearly shows that such interposition does not, in fact, exist. We are stating rather that, on the basis of our observations, a separate system of neuronal-glial synapselike contacts exist through the application of axonal *boutons en passage* and *boutons terminaux* to the cytoplasm and/or nucleus of the oligodendrocyte.

---

* Based on unpublished data.

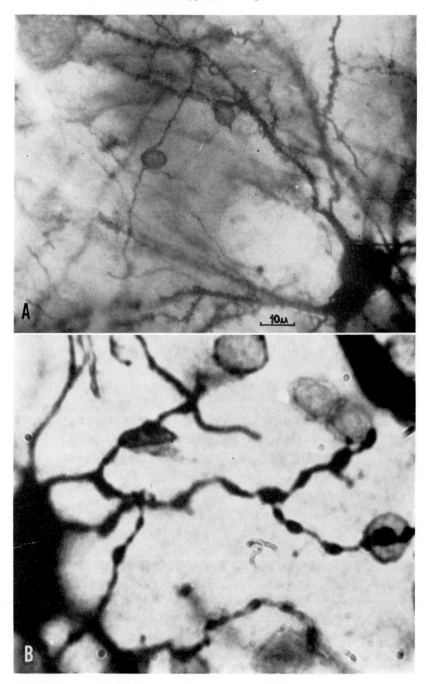

Figure 1A shows a typical field of frontal cortex in the young monkey as visualized by the rapid Golgi method. In addition to the cortical cell which has been impregnated, several small spheroidal oligodendrocyte nuclei can be seen scattered through the cortical neuropil. Individual axons bend over the surface of these bodies, sometimes broadening out into the familiar *boutons en passage* as they do, while elsewhere, enlargements on the terminal segments of axons are seen in contact with the oligodendrocytes. We do not as yet know whether any areas of cortex are especially rich in such relations. However, in general, the dense neuropil formed by the terminal arborization of specific afferent fibers in layer 4 appears to contain high concentrations of the oligodendrocytes with correspondingly large numbers of such neuronal-glial contacts. It would seem desirable to have quantitative data, not only on oligodendrocyte concentrations in the various areas and layers of the cerebral cortex, but throughout the neuraxis. Quite apart from the intrinsic interest of such information would be the obvious contribution it might subsequently make to the quantitative biochemistry of the various portions of the central nervous system.

Figure 1B shows a Golgi type II cell of the cerebral cortex whose multiple nodular, ramifying axons make contact with a number of oligodendrocyte nuclei in the vicinity. The apparent closeness of physical contact between some of the axonal enlargements and the nuclear membrane, especially in the case where the contacts are seen in silhouette at one edge of the neuroglia cell

---

←◄◄◄

FIGURE 1. A. A neuron and oligodendrocytes in frontal cortical fields of a young rhesus monkey, showing the relation of one neuroglia cell to a horizontally running axon, another to a dendron. Rapid Golgi method; magnification, 150 ×.

B. A Golgi type II neuron from the frontal cortex of a young rhesus monkey. The multiple, nodular, ramifying axon breaks up in the vicinity of the cell body and effects terminal and *en passage* contacts with a number of adjacent oligodendrocytes. Two of the terminal attachments appear very closely applied to the nucleus, as seen in silhouette, although it is impossible to determine with this method whether an intervening thin layer of glial cytoplasm exists between the terminal and nucleus (see text). Rapid Golgi method; magnification, 440 ×.

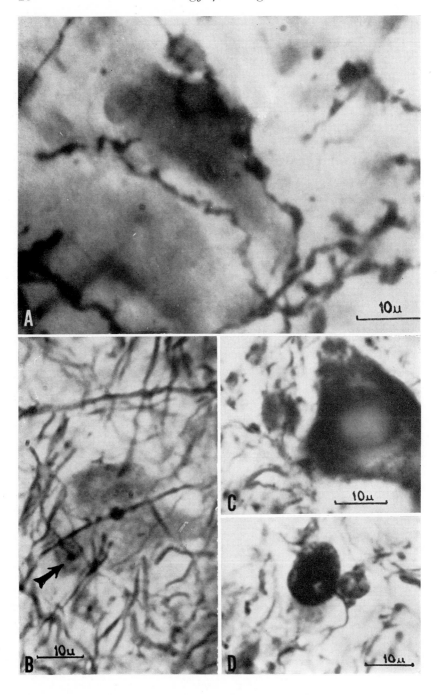

rather than in superimposition upon its surface, has made us wonder whether the nerve fibers may not actually penetrate the thin cytoplasmic mantle of the neuroglia cell to effect direct contact with the nucleus. Let us hasten to point out that our own methods are too gross and the resolving power at our command inadequate to the task of deciding this question. This we must leave for the electron microscopist. However, it is interesting to recall that De Castro ('51) has made the definite statement that, in the peripheral autonomic ganglia, terminal preganglionic axons penetrate the cytoplasm of the glioidal cells to reach the nucleus. In any case, in Figures 2 to 4 we see examples of *boutons en passage* and *boutons terminaux* in contact with oligodendrocytes. Figure 3B is an oil immersion photograph which again stresses the closeness of contact between boutons and oligodendrocytes. Unfortunately, the picture is of poor quality because of difficulties involved in photographing tissue cut at 100μ to 150μ at high magnification.

Figure 3A shows a single oligodendrocyte in the inferior olivary nucleus of a puppy receiving a single terminal from an axon of moderate thickness. In the original preparation, the axon could

---

←

FIGURE 2. A. A large motor neuron and 2 adjacent satellite oligodendrocytes in the ventral horn of the spinal cord of a 2 week old kitten. An axon effects several synaptic contacts *en passage* with the neuron soma; several similar contacts (by smaller boutons) and one terminal contact with one of the 2 oligodendrocytes are shown. The cellular elements are stained lightly, due to secondary diffusion of silver, while the nerve fibers are heavily blackened by the original impregnation. Golgi method; magnification, 440 ×.

B. A medium sized reticular neuron and satellite oligodendrocytes in the lower brain stem of an adult cat. Three terminating fibers are seen on the surface of the neuron while one bouton bearing terminal is seen (*arrow*) on the surface of the oligodendrocyte. Bodian method; 8μ section; oil immersion photograph; magnification, 1200 ×.

C. A large reticular neuron and satellite oligodendrocyte in the lower brain stem of an adult cat. A number of terminal axons and *boutons terminaux* are seen on the surface of the oligodendrocyte. Bodian method; 25μ section, counterstained with cresyl violet; magnification, 1200 ×.

D. A nerve cell and satellite oligodendrocyte in the superior olivary nucleus of an adult cat. A single treminal axon makes at least one contact with the neuroglia cell before terminating on surface of the neuron (obscured in photograph). Bodian method; 20μ section; magnification, 1200 ×.

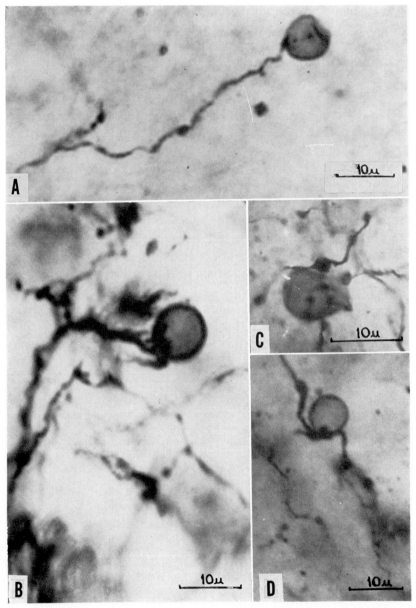

FIGURE 3. A. An oligodendrocyte receiving a single *bouton terminal* from an axon terminal in the inferior olivary nucleus of a 10 day old puppy. Collaterals of this axon could be followed in the original preparation to

be followed and several collaterals could be seen leaving it to terminate on nerve cell bodies. In Figure 3B a rather thick axon emits a collateral system, then breaks up and places three *boutons terminaux* on a single oligodendrocyte. Although we seldom see more than two or three contacts effected by any one fiber with an oligodendrocyte, in some areas such as the *substantia gelatinosa* of spinal cord, we have seen as many as 5 buttons or rings from the same axonal filament on the surface of a single oligodendrocyte.

Figure 2A is a photograph of a ventral horn neuron and satellite oligodendrocyte in the spinal cord of a kitten. An axon passes over the surface of the neuron, effecting synaptic contact by means of 6 or 8 *boutons en passage*. After giving off a small terminal branch, it continues, making subsequent contact with the oligodendrocyte by means of several *boutons en passage* and at least one *bouton terminal*. Figure 5 is a drawing of a spinal cord section in the kitten in which a number of axons, entering from the fiber bundles of the dorsal column and the adjacent tract of Lissauer, arborize in the *substantia gelatinosa,* making various patterns of contact with nerve cells and oligodendrocytes.

These two illustrations (Figs. 2A and 5) are significant in that they show clearly that those axons which enter into the synapse-like contact with oligodendrocytes do not constitute a separate axonal system devoted to the innervation of neuroglia cells.

←◀◀◀

synaptic terminations on nerve cell bodies. Rapid Golgi method; magnification, 660 ×.

B. An oligodendrocyte receiving 3 *boutons terminaux* from one collateralizing axon in the basal ganglia of a 2 week old kitten. Rapid Golgi method; magnification, 660 ×. (From Scheibel and Scheibel ('55); courtesy *Journal of Comparative Neurology.*)

C. An oligodendrocyte receiving at least one *bouton en passage* and one *bouton terminal* in the inferior olivary nucleus of a one month old puppy. Rapid Golgi method; 100µ section; oil immersion photograph, magnification, 1500 ×.

D. An oligodendrocyte in the medial portion of the lower brain stem reticular formation receiving a typical *bouton en passage* from an axon, presumably unmyelinated, in a young kitten. Rapid Golgi method; magnification, 660 ×.

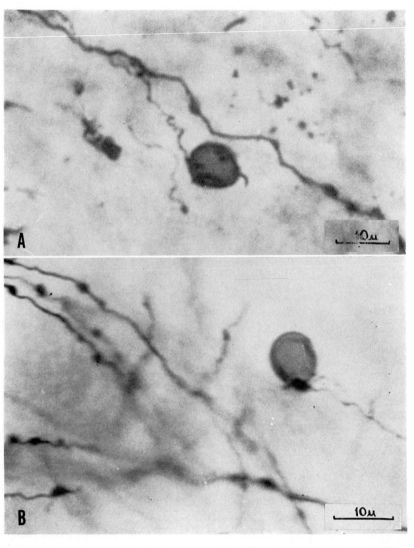

FIGURE 4. A. An oligodendrocyte in the white matter of the cerebellum of a young kitten receiving a *bouton terminal* from a fine collateral which emanates from adjacent heavy axons, one of which is impregnated. Rapid Golgi method; magnification, 660 ×.

B. An oligodendrocyte adjacent to tegmento-olivary tract fibers in a young puppy. It receives a large *bouton terminal* from a fine axon running at the periphery of a bundle. Rapid Golgi method; magnification 660 ×. (From Scheibel and Scheibel ('55); courtesy, *Journal of Comparative Neurology.*)

Rather, both neural and glial elements are innervated by the same axonal system and must therefore be expected to receive samples of the same "information" at approximately the same time.

It seems clear that similar relations exist, to some extent at least, in the long fiber bundles and in white matter in general. Several kinds of contact between unmyelinated axon terminals and oligodendrocytes have been seen. One type is illustrated in Figure 4A, where a fine collateral leaves a thicker, possibly myelinated axon and, after following a somewhat irregular course, terminates on an interfascicular oligodendrocyte. Contacts also appear to be made between unmyelinated long tract fibers and oligodendrocytes by means of *boutons en passage*, an example of which is seen in Figure 4B.

It would appear doubtful, on the whole, that the large number of oligodendrocytes which lie in and among the fibers of myelinated tracts could be affected directly by the latter because of the thick myelin investments about the individual tract fibers. One method of establishing effective interaction may be that shown in Figure 4A; careful examination under oil immersion objectives of Bodian stained sagittal brain stem sections of an adult cat reveals such fine collaterals coming from pyramidal and parapyramidal fibers and apparently effecting contact with interfascicular oligodendrocytes. However, the number of such fibers that we have seen is so small that other methods of interaction must be postulated.

We wonder whether the pattern of cytoplasmic processes established by del Río Hortega's ('28) types III and IV oligodendrocytes may not offer a clue to another method of interaction between myelinated axons and neuroglia cells. These two subtypes are described as having rather elaborate processes which spiral for long distances around individual or small groups of axons. The investment of the axon is far from complete, leaving endless lacunae and bare areas on its surface. Del Río Hortega suggested that the oligodendrocyte and its processes may play some role in the nutrition and maintenance of the myelin sheath. If this is true, it would seem to be a peculiar structural adaptation to such a function.

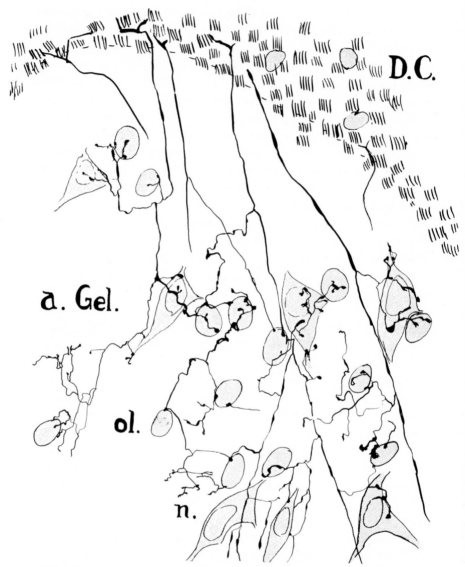

FIGURE 5. Drawing of a section through the substantia gelatinosa of the cervical spinal cord of a 2 week old kitten. Axons emerging from the dorsal columns *(D. C.)* and adjacent tract of Lissauer, penetrate the substantia gelatinosa *(a. Gelat.)* and terminate in various boutons on nerve cells *(n.)* and oligodendrocytes *(ol.)*. It is interesting to note that neuroglia cells and nerve cells receive innervation from the same axons. Rapid Golgi method; magnification, approximately 100 ×.

We suggest an alternative hypothesis. Assuming that the functions of the oligodendrocyte in white matter, whatever they may be, are analogous to those in gray matter, then one of the remarkable facts about the structural organization and relations of oligodendrocytes and neurons in the gray matter, is the apparent provision made for transmitting information from neurons to oligodendrocytes via bouton synapse systems. If transmission of some kinds of data to the oligodendrocyte were equally important in the white matter, then the coiled cytoplasmic processes of oligodendrocytes spiraling about the myelinated axons may be effectively arranged to detect, via induction, the field phenomena surrounding action potentials moving down the axons, smoothly or via jumps from node-to-node (Tasaki, '53) as the saltatory theory demands. Whether the induction of minute currents in the coils of oligodendrocyte cytoplasm is significant is unknown, but the possibility seems worthy of consideration.

In addition to the neuronal-glial relations already discussed, two other types of structural relations also may reflect on the function of the oligodendrocytes. We refer to their relations with the dendrons of nerve cells and with the processes of fibrous and protoplasmic astrocytes.

Figures 6A, C and D show the contacts effected by oligodendrocytes with the dendrons of an inferior olivary nerve cell, a lateral reticular formation nerve cell and with the apical dendron of a cortical neuron. In each case, fine spicules which appear to be dendronal spines bridge across from the dendron shaft to the neuroglia cell, and seem to come into direct contact with the nucleus. Whether the cytoplasmic mantle of the neuroglia cell is penetrated or not, the intimacy of the relationship is beyond question. When modifications of the Golgi method enabling more regular impregnation of glial processes are used, these can be seen to lie along or wind loosely around the dendrons, thus intensifying the intimate character of the relationship. A variation of this type of contact occurs where the nucleus of the neuroglia cell appears to burrow into the dendron, forming a small pocket for itself (Fig. 6B).

The relationship of the oligodendrocyte with the processes of protoplasmic and fibrous astrocytes appears to have as general a

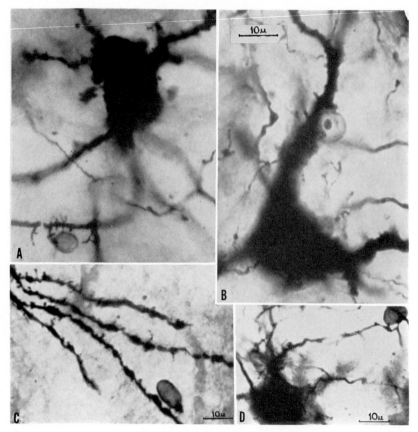

FIGURE 6. A. An oligodendrocyte (bottom of photograph) receiving contacts from several spines of the dendron of an inferior olivary nerve cell of
a young kitten. Part of the dendron is out of focus. Rapid Golgi method;
magnification, 660 ×. (From Scheibel and Scheibel ('55); courtesy, *Journal
of Comparative Neurology.*)

B. An oligodendrocyte which appears to be partly buried in a niche in
the first part of the dendron of a neuron in the lateral reticular formation
of a young puppy. Rapid Golgi method; magnification, 660 ×.

C. An oligodendrocyte which appears to receive at least one spinous
contact from an apical dendron of a small pyramidal cell in the sensory-
motor cortex of a young cat. Rapid Golgi method; magnification, 660 ×.

D. An oligodendrocyte which receives at least 2 contacts from the spines
of an inferior olivary nerve cell dendron in a 10 day old kitten. Rapid
Golgi method; magnification, 660 ×. (From Scheibel and Scheibel '55);
courtesy, *Journal of Comparative Neurology.*)

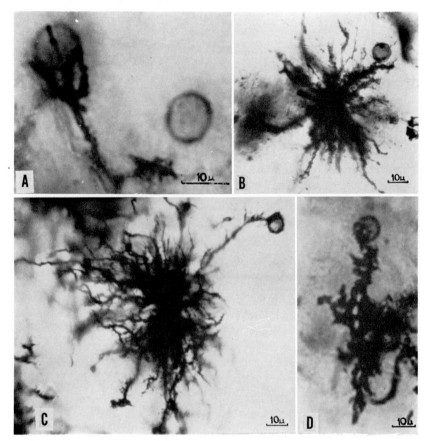

FIGURE 7. A. A terminal expansion of a fibrillary astrocyte partly surrounds an oligodendrocyte in the white matter of the cerebellum of an adult cat. Rapid Golgi method; magnification, 660 ×.

B. A protoplasmic astrocyte in the white matter of the cerebral cortex of a young cat, one of the processes of which effects terminal contact with an oligodendrocyte. Rapid Golgi method; magnification, 440 ×.

C. A fibrous astrocyte in the lower brain stem of a young kitten, one of the processes of which effects terminal contact with an oligodendrocyte. Notice several other footlike expansions visible on the tips of other processes. Modification of the rapid Golgi method; magnification, 150 ×.

D. Contact between a protoplasmic astrocyte process and an oligodendrocyte in the cerebellar white matter of a young puppy. Rapid Golgi method; magnification, 440 ×.

pattern of distribution as those already described. The long, somewhat varicose or nodulated processes of the fibrous astrocyte may terminate on oligodendrocytes with either a blunt tip or expansion resembling a small vascular endfoot, or else the heavier fronds of the protoplasmic variety may wrap partly or completely about the oligodendrocyte. Figure 7 shows examples of astrocyte-oligodendrocyte relations of the type that are seen throughout the central nervous system. Because of the highly elective nature of the Golgi impregnation, it is not possible to estimate what proportion of astrocytes are in contact with oligodendrocytes at any one time. However, what tissue culture techniques have revealed about the plasticity of form of astrocyte tips, and the apparent motility of oligodendrocytes (Pomerat, '52) suggest that such relations may be dynamic and changing through time.

The present data indicate that the oligodendrocyte shares a rather unique bilateral relationship with nerve cell somata, dendrons and terminal portions of axons, on the one hand, and with astrocytes, on the other. Considering first the axon to oligodendrocyte relationship, we have already seen that the same axon system innervates both the post-synaptic neuron and the satellite oligodendrocyte. If it is not the function of the oligodendrocyte to transmit information the way neurons do (and we are not necessarily suggesting that it is), then the information transmitted to the oligodendrocyte must serve another purpose, perhaps one auxiliary to and necessary for the process of neural conduction. From what is known about the physiology and chemistry of oligodendrocytes, what could that purpose be?

In the past, suggestions as to function of the neuroglia have been based largely on inference drawn from morphology and structural interrelationships. To mention a few examples, Penfield ('32a) quotes Ramon y Cajal as speculating that the perineuronal satellite lives in perfect symbiosis with the neuron. For Achucarro ('18), the oligodendrocytes resembled unicellular glands, perhaps similar to the cells of the pineal body. During nervous activity, he suggested, they might pump secretions into the blood stream, producing the somatic tones that often go along with neural activity. Del Río Hortega ('28) was impressed by the close relationship of oligodendrocytes to the formation and maintenance of myelin. To some of the recent workers, among them

De Castro ('51) and Bairati ('48-9), the suggestion has seemed pertinent that the oligodendrocyte may act as an isolator or insulator of synaptic areas on the surface of nerve cells. Each of these suggestions has points in its favor, yet each runs into difficulties.

Perhaps the most popular theory at present is that of the relationship of the oligodendrocyte to myelin, and we would like to point out briefly why we are dissatisfied with it. In the first place, oligodendrocytes are numerous in neuropil areas, characterized by the presence of preterminal and terminal axons, nerve cells and dendrons, all of which, so far as we know, are completely without myelin. From the phylogenetic point of view, some kind of myelinated fiber exists, according to Kappers, Huber and Crosby ('36) as early as the Arthropoda whereas oligodendrocytes are not identifiable as such until the vertebrate line is reached; Klüver ('55) suggests that they are not recognizable until vertebrates become warm blooded. Finally, from the ontogenetic point of view, myelin first appears in the spinal cord of the developing human fetus about the fourth or fifth month. Oligodendrocytes are supposed to appear somewhat later and not in greatest numbers until close to the time of birth. For these reasons, the suggestion that the oligodendrocyte is uniquely related to the formation and/or maintenance of myelin is not completely satisfactory.

Some recent data relating to the chemistry of oligodendroglia may shed light on the function of these cells when considered in view of the structural interrelationships already discussed. Ashby, Garzoli and Schuster ('52) suggested that there were significant amounts of carbonic anhydrase in oligodendrocytes while Cavanaugh, Thompson and Webster ('54) found large amounts of pseudocholinesterase in white matter, which they believe is primarily neuroglial, and more especially in the oligodendrocytes. In the past decade, Klüver ('55) has described the presence of porphyrins in the nervous system which appear to be localized to the oligodendrocytes. If substances such as pseudocholinesterases, carbonic anhydrase and porphyrins are present in significantly high concentrations in the oligodendrocyte, these may give us some clues as to its function.

Throughout the organism, porphyrin-containing compounds

and carbonic anhydrase are related to respiratory function. The former compounds not only constitute essential parts of the oxygen carriage system of the red cells as hemoglobin but also of a number of enzyme systems related to electron transfer, such as the cytochromes. Just as oligodendrocytes apparently contain significantly high concentrations of porphyrin and carbonic anhydrase, the erythrocytes are rich in porphyrin-bearing compounds and carbonic anhydrase.

Although we know of no evidence, either physiological or biochemical, linking oligodendrocytes with respiratory (or with any other) function, we hazard the following suggestions as to their role in the central nervous system. We wonder whether the presence of carbonic anhydrase may not implicate them in the process of removal of carbon dioxide from the immediate surroundings of the active neuron; also, whether the high concentration of porphyrins may not be related to the problems of electron transport from active neural foci, granting that the relationship may involve several interposed steps involving enzyme synthesis. If such "clean-up" functions relative to the high rate of neuronal metabolic processes were one of the roles oligodendrocytes played, they might be activated by diffusion gradients of such metabolic products across the nerve cell membrane and into the immediate surroundings of the neuroglia cell. However, in a system as complex as brain tissue, where the essence of activity involves rapidly occurring events, necessitating rapid recovery cycles, a more efficient system of communication than the simple diffusion gradient of the metabolites themselves might be advantageous. Perhaps the bouton systems coming directly from the neuron-innervating terminal axon, such as we have described, may fulfill this function. We could hypothesize that each satellite oligodendrocyte received samples of the impulse patterns coming to the adjacent neurons, thereby being prepared for the approximate amount of "clean-up" work in the next fraction of time. What such "preparation for work" might be is anybody's guess. One possibility might involve changes in permeability of the oligodendrocyte membrane, a function in which the observed high pseudocholinesterase content might be involved.

Similar patterns of activity might apply to the white matter where glial "sensing" of the amount or intensity of neural activity in the immediate environment might occur through previously hypothesized minute currents induced in the loose coils of oligodendrocyte cytoplasm spiraling around the medullated axons.

We suggest such possibilities, not because they are strongly favored by data collected so far, but rather to stress the fact that we are now almost at a point where dynamic functional interpretations may begin to be made, on the basis of synthesis of microscopic and submicroscopic structure, with neurochemistry. Our need now is for biochemical and enzymatic analyses to be performed, if possible, on pure cultures of oligodendrocytes obtained either by microdissection from living tissue, by one of a number of the techniques of differential separation or else from tissue culture. These data must be used conjointly with those obtained from relatively crude neurohistological methods such as ours, which stress structural interrelationships, and with the finer methods of the electron microscopist. As the increasingly critical technique of the latter brings neurochemistry within the domain of the descriptive morphologist, and vice versa, there should emerge more meaningful interpretations of the functional significance of this enigmatic tissue.

ADDENDUM

Some time after the conference, a note on a cholinergic "local hormone" mechanism in the cat's brain by Desmedt ('56), was called to our attention. Making use of the fact that acetoChE is predominantly associated with neurons and butyroChE (or pseudoChE) with neuroglia cells, this author observed: " . . . A combined electrophysiological and enzymological study, using a number of selective inhibitors of these enzymes, gave the rather unexpected result that selective inactivation of butyroChE produces a typical activation pattern of the brain rhythms as well as behavioral arousal in the sleeping cat (Desmedt and LaGrutta, '55). This result suggests that the neuroglia is effectively participating in the regulation of the chemical milieu of nerve cells. . . ." He concluded by wondering ". . . how this humoral mechanism can be 'set' to any particular level if it does indeed participate in the control of the ever-changing excitatory state by regulating local chemical gradients." We suggest that the neuroglial "setting" mechanism about which he speculated may be the axon-oligodendrocyte synaptic system which we have demonstrated.

Chapter 2

An Electron Microscopical Study Of Neuroglia*

SANFORD L. PALAY†

WHENEVER the electron microscopist starts work in a new area he must establish criteria for identifying the structures which he encounters. The electron microscopy of the neuroglia is currently in just this stage of development. Recognition of neuroglia cells at the light microscopical level usually depends upon the size, shape and position of the cells, generally in preparations in which no other cellular elements are demonstrated and often in preparations which are selective for a particular type of cell. Furthermore, the methods employed for distinguishing the various types of neuroglia cells provide little or no information about their internal structures and generally demonstrate only silhouettes or skeletal images (Pomerat, '52). These are few enough clues for light microscopy, but in electron microscopy the situation is rendered much more complex by the following facts: (a) In adequately preserved tissues all of the components—nervous and glial—are revealed together in a single preparation; (b) sections thin enough to be useful in the electron microscope are too thin for demonstration of the characteristic silhouette of the cell; (c) internal structure is more striking than general configuration and therefore more useful for recognition; and (d) the areas which can be examined in contiguity are limited by the smallness of the specimen, by the necessary thinness of the section, and by

* This study was aided by Grant No. B-849 from the National Institute of Neurological Diseases and Blindness, National Institutes of Health, United States Public Health Service.

† Present address: National Institute of Neurological Diseases and Blindness, National Institutes of Health, Bethesda 14, Maryland.

611,018 W 723
C. 1

the grid upon which the sections are supported in the microscope.

These operational conditions mean that criteria must be sought at the level of the electron microscope to supplement those already available from light microscopy. Of the latter criteria perhaps the most useful may be the location of the different types of glial cells, their relations with one another and with other entities such as blood vessels, nerve cells and nerve fibers. Careful application of these simple positional characteristics may lead to delineation of distinguishing features that will be identifying in electron micrographs. It must not, however, be assumed that absolute categories can be constructed, for even in light microscopy numerous varieties of neuroglia cell types have been found which cannot honestly be placed in one category or another.

MATERIALS AND METHOD

This paper is a preliminary report of an electron microscopical study of the neuroglia in selected regions from the central nervous system of Sprague-Dawley rats. The regions studied included the floor of the fourth ventricle, the cerebral and cerebellar cortices and the infundibular stem of the neurohypophysis. All animals were lightly anesthetized by an intraperitoneal injection of nembutal and the brain was exposed by removing the occipital portions of the calvarium. The fixative was then injected into the fourth ventricle while the animal was still breathing. Small fragments of tissue were fixed in chilled buffered osmium tetroxide (pH 7.3-7.5), dehydrated by passage through increasing concentrations of methanol and embedded in a prepolymerized mixture (9:1) of butyl and methyl methacrylates. Most of the rats were adult, but the cerebellum of one 14 day old rat was also examined. Thin sections were cut on a Porter-Blum microtome (Sörvall) and examined in an RCA EMU 2E electron microscope at original magnifications of from 4000 to 9000 times. Photographic enlargements were made as desired.

In an attempt to increase the number of neuroglia cells, craniotomies were performed in 6 female rats, and a single wound was made in the cerebral cortex of each rat by means of a hot needle. All except one of these rats were littermates. The

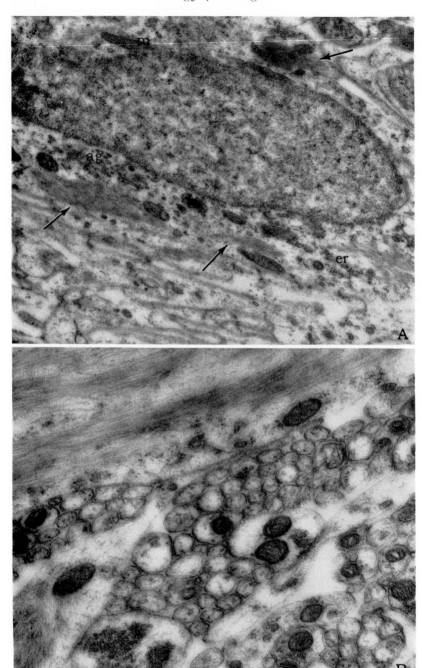

animals all survived the operation without revealing any functional deficit. At the time of autopsy, 24 to 31 days after the lesions were placed, no sign of infection, or even hyperemia, was evident about the lesions. The specimens were fixed by injecting the fixative into the brain substance surrounding the lesion and allowing the fixative to well up in the center of the cortical defect. The margins of the defect were removed, trimmed into small fragments and treated as mentioned in the previous paragraph.

OBSERVATIONS

It would be prudent to begin with an element of the neuroglia the identification of which cannot be questioned—the ependyma lining the ventricles. The ependyma consists of a single layer of cuboidal or short columnar cells, the free surfaces of which are crowned with cilia and the bases of which are drawn into tapering processes that extend into the depths of the brain substance. Because the cilia have no unusual characteristics (Fawcett and Porter, '54), they will not be described here. The internal structure of the ependymal cell, however, is shown in Figure 8A, which is an electron micrograph of a section passing obliquely through the ependyma covering the floor of the fourth ventricle. The oval profile of the highly granular nucleus, in the upper half of the micrograph, is surrounded by a narrow band of cytoplasm

---

FIGURE 8. A. Electron micrograph of an oblique section through an ependymal cell from the floor of the fourth ventricle of the rat. The nucleus occupies most of the upper half of the figure and is surrounded by cytoplasm containing small mitochondria (m), ergastoplasm (er), agranular reticulum (ag), and compact bundles of fine filaments (arrows). Beneath the ependymal cell lie the elongated profiles of the astrocytic processes which comprise the internal limiting membrane. Magnification, 22,600 ×.

B. Electron micrograph of a section through the internal limiting membrane of the medulla of the rat. Part of a basal ependymal process sweeps across the upper left. Within it bundles of long, delicate, nearly parallel filaments can be seen. Immediately beneath the ependymal process the feltwork of the internal limiting membrane appears, with almost all of the constituent astrocytic processes shown in transverse section. The clustered circular profiles enclose small tubular or vacuolar structures and occasionally a mitochondrion. Two presynaptic terminals are included in the feltwork. Magnification, 33,700 ×.

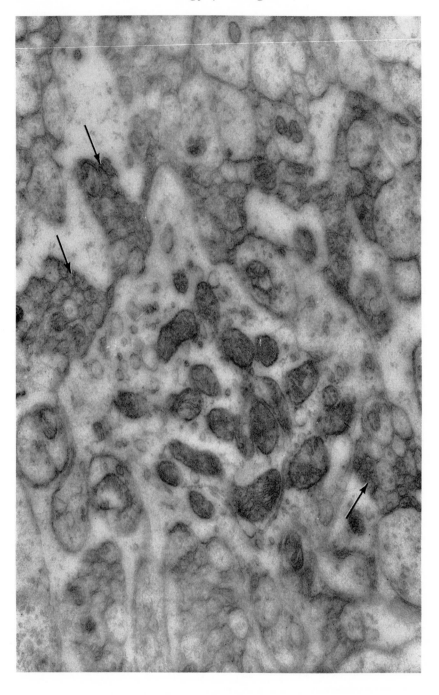

crowded with small slender mitochondria *(m)*, the clustered fine granules and vesicles of ergastoplasm *(er)*, and the packed agranular vesicles of the Golgi complex *(ag)*. In addition, the cytoplasm contains numerous fine filaments that are often aggregated into dense swirling masses. In Figure 8A several bundles of these filaments are shown and in Figure 8B they appear at a higher magnification in a section of an ependymal process. The filaments are 90 to 95 Å in diameter and of indefinite length. In some places they have a finely beaded appearance. They generally occur as bundles of roughly parallel constituent filaments, sometimes filling nearly the entire perinuclear cytoplasm and sweeping into the basal process. In such cells, mitochondria, ergastoplasm and endoplasmic reticulum are located in the interstices among the bundles of filaments and in the peripheral cytoplasm. The nature of these filaments is completely unknown but we may presume that they represent a fine filamentous protein, perhaps related to keratin.

The subependymal, internal limiting glial membrane is also shown in Figure 8B. Lying against the root of the basal ependymal process is a narrow zone consisting of roughly circular profiles about 165 mµ in diameter, and appressed one against the other. These profiles represent sections of the expansions, processes and fibers of astrocytes that are densely intertwined to form the internal limiting membrane. Inside many of these profiles lie still smaller circular and oval profiles which represent sections of minute vacuoles, vesicles or tubules. Occasionally a mitochondrial profile fills nearly the entire section of the astrocytic process. Although these astrocytic processes are packed very closely, small but typical nerve terminals can be found among them, extensions of the underlying neuropil.

←━

FIGURE 9. Electron micrograph of a transverse section through the dendron of a Purkinje cell in the molecular layer of the cerebellar cortex from a rat two weeks old. The center of the figure is occupied by the profile of the branching dendron, containing a cluster of mitochondria and tubules of the endoplasmic reticulum. Packed profiles of the end knobs of Fañanás glia *(arrows)* are arrayed about the periphery of the dendron. The resemblance between these packets and those of th subependymal, internal limiting membrane is evident. Magnification, 29,600 ×.

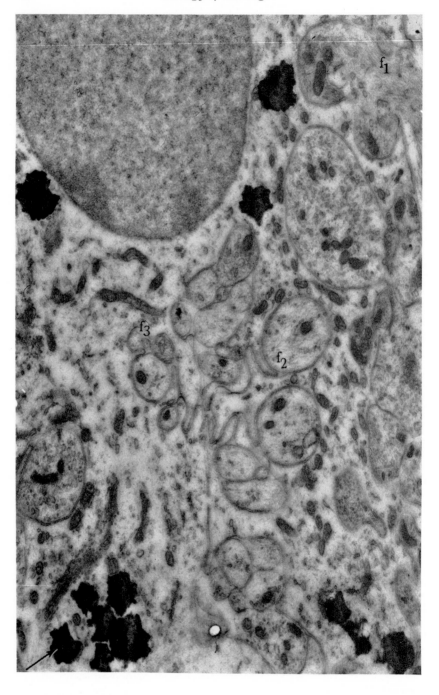

There are few places in the central nervous system where astro-cytic processes are so concentrated as they are in the subependy-mal limiting membrane. However, in the cerebellar cortex a pe-culiar and characteristic protoplasmic astrocyte, known as the Fañanás cell, gives off clustered stubby expansions that can be recognized by their distinctive location. This astrocyte extends a few long processes from the Purkinje cell layer towards the super-ficial surface of the molecular layer, and each of the processes is beset with tiny spicules or rounded knobs. The processes come into close relationship with the dendronal expansions of the Pur-kinje cell, which they appear to support in some way. This rela-tionship is shown in Figure 9 in which a large transverse section of a Purkinje cell dendron occupies the center of the field. It con-tains a cluster of mitochondria, some vesicles, tubules, and cister-nae of the endoplasmic reticulum and fine nucleoprotein granules. It sends out a number of smaller branches in all directions and receives at its surface a few synaptic terminals. Surrounding the dendron are patches of small rounded profiles with a mean diame-ter of 165 mμ and with characteristics similar to those of the astrocytic profiles in the subependymal limiting membrane. The profiles are usually clustered closely against the Purkinje cell dendron, in agreement with the position of Fañanás glia accord-ing to light microscopy (Fañanás, '16).

Clusters of rounded profiles resembling those in the subepen-dymal glial membrane and in the cerebellar cortex, also occur in other regions of the gray matter and Luse ('56a) has described them in association with a relatively large nonneuronal cell char-

---

←

FIGURE 10. Electron micrograph of a section through a pituicyte in the hypothalamohypophysial tract of the rat. The nucleus occupies the left upper corner of the figure. Dense, irregularly shaped lipid droplets *(arrow)* are found within the cytoplasm, in addition to the usual organelles, mito-chondria, ergastoplasm and agranular reticulum. The surface of the pitui-cyte is highly convoluted to form a complex pattern of furrows and con-duits, through which pass the unmyelinated nerve fibers of the hypothala-mohypophysial tract. Some of these fibers (f_1) are only partially enfolded into the pituicyte, others (f_2) are completely and individually enclosed. Still other nerve fibers (f_3) are enclosed as small bundles. Magnification, 15,900 ×.

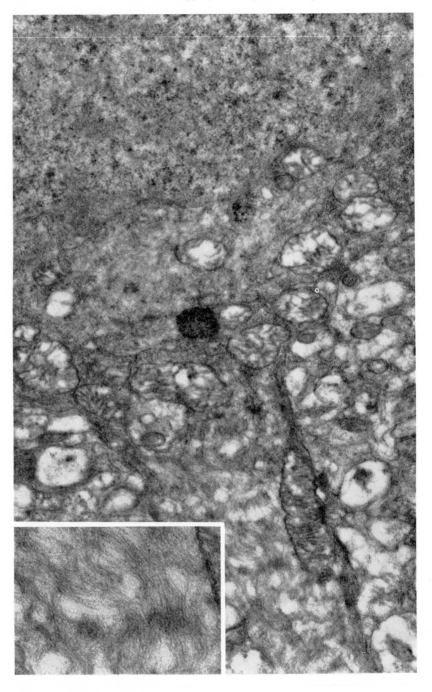

acterized by scanty, relatively dense cytoplasm and an oval, indented nucleus. In favorably oriented sections some of these profiles can be demonstrated to be continuous with the cytoplasm of this cell. This finding corroborates the identification of this cell as the protoplasmic astrocyte. The circular profiles are interpreted as sections of the highly infolded surface of the astrocyte and its expanded processes, which may be considered as flowing and motile ruffles, as shown in cinematographic records of glia in tissue culture (Pomerat, '52).

The astrocytic processes are disposed between neurons and nerve fibers, lying intermingled among them rather than ensheathing them. Although this arrangement is typical for the central nervous system there is at least one region where the astrocytes enclose the nerve fibers very much as Schwann cells in the peripheral nervous system. This region is in the infundibular stem of the neurohypophysis. Here the unmyelinated fibers of the hypothalamo-hypophysial tract lie in furrows or tunnels impressed in the surfaces of the pituicytes as shown in Figure 10 (Palay, '57). The pituicytes are generally considered as specialized neuroglia (Romeis, '40), but in the infundibulum they appear much like Schwann cells in relation to the nerve fibers (Gasser, '55). Many fibers are completely enclosed in the cytoplasm of the pituicyte separated only by the apposed plasma membranes of their respective surfaces, whereas other nerve fibers are only partially embedded. This intimate arrangement persists until the fibers of the tract reach the hilar zones of the neurohypophysis, where the more usual relationship typical of the central nervous system reappears. Here the pituicytes and their processes are

---

←◀◀◀

FIGURE 11. Electron micrograph of a section through a reactive astrocyte and one of its processes at the margin of a healing cortical wound in the cerebrum of a rat. The highly granular nucleus occupies the upper third of the figure. The cytoplasm contains many mitochondria and crowds of fine dense granules. Two small collections of extremely dense, presumably lipid-protein, inclusions lie below the nucleus. Within the perinuclear cytoplasm and nearly filling the process, which extends into the lower half of the figure, are numerous delicate long filaments. Magnification, 26,360 ×. The inset shows the filaments at a higher magnification; 63,400 ×.

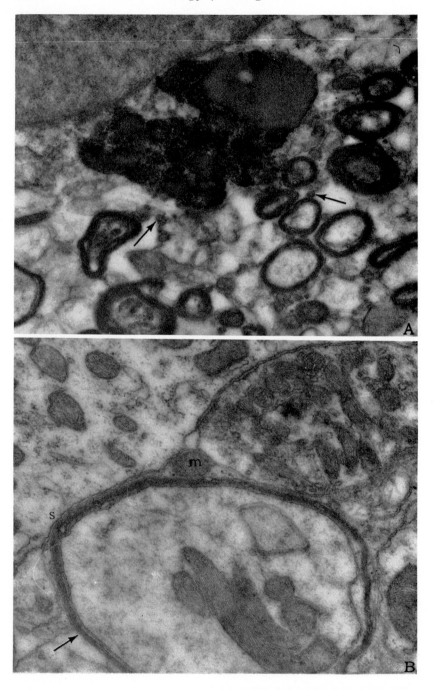

merely interwoven with the preterminal branches and endings of the nerve fibers.

Numerous astrocytes may be found in the healing margins of cortical wounds made with a hot needle. Figure 11 is an electron micrograph of a section through one of these reacting astrocytes. Around the oval, densely granular nucleus is a relatively thin layer of cytoplasm containing the usual organelles—mitochondria, agranular reticulum, and ergastoplasm. The latter is remarkable for its high proportion of fine nucleoprotein granules, dispersed almost uniformly between nuclear membrane and plasma membrane in all the spaces unoccupied by other organelles. Numerous clusters of small, dense masses, irregular in shape and size, are also distributed in the cytoplasm. Each cluster is enclosed by an apparently single, thin membrane. Because of their density, these inclusions are interpreted as lipid-protein coacervates; they may represent masses of pigment, perhaps derived from lipid. The cell pictured in Figure 11 also illustrates another cytoplasmic component of these reacting astrocytes. This is a fine fibrillar material in the form of tiny filaments about 90 Å in diameter. In the perinuclear cytoplasm, these filaments display no preferential orientation, but in the processes, as shown in Figure 11, the filaments are disposed lengthwise and nearly parallel with one an-

---

←◀◀◀

FIGURE 12. A. Electron micrograph of a section through a microglia cell in the margin of a healing cortical wound from the cerebrum of a rat. The cytoplasm contains a large, complex mass of various density and configuration. Among the surrounding myelinated fibers are small numbers of minute circular profiles *(arrows)* which probably represent transverse sections through the processes of the microglia cell. Magnification, 27,800 ×.

B. Electron micrograph of a section through a small myelinated fiber in the medulla of a rat. The edge of a small neuron lies in the upper left corner and a presynaptic *bouton terminal* lies in the upper right corner. The myelin sheath of the nerve fiber consists of eight layers. The two outermost layers are clearly the limiting membrane of a glial expansion which is added to the sheath just above the arrow. The expansion becomes attenuated *(s)* so that it is indistinguishable from the rest of the myelin sheath. In the center of the figure it becomes enlarged to include a mitochondrion *(m)* and then rapidly thins again. The figure shows the contribution of a glial expansion (presumably oligodendroglial) to the formation of a myelin sheath. Magnification, 31,000 ×.

other. The cell process is nearly filled by the host of fine filaments. Such cytoplasmic ultrastructure is probably to be correlated with the appearance of the fibrous astrocyte as visualized in stained preparations with the light microscope.

Small cells containing elongated nuclei and dense, heterogeneous, cytoplasmic masses also occur in the neighborhood of healing cortical wounds. The size, shape and content of these cells identify them as microglia (Fig. 12A). The dense inclusions consist of fine granules, rounded larger masses and packets of thin, parallel, sheetlike material. It is reasonable to suggest that these inclusions arise from phagocytized myelin of injured nerve fibers. In the neighborhood of the microglia cells extremely small protoplasmic processes are located (Fig. 12A). These measure about 60 to 80 mµ in diameter, or about half the size of the processes associated with the astrocytes. Mitochondria are rarely found inside of them, but tubular and vesicular elements are frequent. Thus, the processes of microglia can be distinguished principally on the basis of their size from those of the macroglia.

Of all the neuroglia cells, the oligodendrocyte is the most difficult to identify with certainty in electron micrographs. The principal reason for this difficulty is that faultless fixation has not yet been achieved. A small rounded cell with a nearly spherical nucleus and scanty cytoplasm can be found among myelinated fibers in the white matter of the brain. According to the usual criteria for identifying oligodendrocytes (Penfield, '32a), these interfascicular cells should belong to that type. However, it is precisely here that the greatest disagreement among electron microscopists centers. In my own preparations, the cytoplasm of the cells in this location is crowded with dense nucleoprotein granules and small vacuoles. The processes associated with these cells are few in number and are often in contact with the surrounding myelinated nerve fibers. In some instances the myelinated fibers appear to be embedded in the cytoplasm of the interfascicular cells. If this identification is correct, this close association of myelin and the oligodendrocyte suggests that this cell plays a role in myelination in the central nervous system analogous to that of the Schwann cell in the peripheral nervous system (Geren, '54; Geren and Schmitt, '55).

Figure 12B is an electron micrograph of a transverse section through a small myelinated fiber in the medulla of the rat. The myelin sheath consists of apparently concentric, dark, circular lines surrounding the axon. At the position indicated by the arrow, the sheath consists of seven dark lines, the innermost of which represents the axolemma. Just above the arrow two additional lines are added, and it can be seen that these two lines delimit the profile of a protoplasmic process or expansion which here becomes continuous with the myelin sheath. As this profile is traced over the surface of the sheath it becomes very thin and at the position marked by the letter *s*, it is indistinguishable from the sheath. At the position of the letter *m*, the profile expands again to enclose a mitochondrion and then it rapidly becomes attenuated again, merging with the sheath. Similar appearances can be found quite frequently in myelinated nerve fibers of the central nervous system. They indicate that myelin is composed of a convoluted and attenuated protoplasmic sheet bounded by its cell membrane, which because of the thinness of the intervening protoplasm appears as a doublet. The origin of the protoplasmic sheets comprising the myelin of the central nervous system is probably oligodendroglial, but an ontogenetic study is necessary for final determination of their source and mode of formation.*

CONCLUSION

The materials presented in this paper indicate some of the problems confronting the electron microscopist in his study of the neuroglia. Aside from the purely technical problems, his major concern at present is to establish firm criteria for the identification of the neuroglia cell types. Once this has been accomplished, the morphological relations among the neuroglia cells, neurons and nerve fibers can be readily elucidated.

One conclusion, however, is clear even from this preliminary study. The protoplasmic expansions of the neuroglia cells constitute the glial fibers seen in the conventional light microscopic preparations. The glial fibers are not extracellular, but are cyto-

---

* Since this paper was presented, Luse ('56b) has reported an electron microscopical study of the formation of myelin in the central nervous system.

plasmic in nature. They probably should be interpreted as lacy frills or ruffles composed of thin protoplasmic expansions extending from the cell body and capable of undergoing flowing movements such as those revealed in tissue culture. Where fine fibrils are present, as in the fibrous astrocyte, these filaments lie entirely within the protoplasmic boundaries. Thus, the electron microscopic findings support the contention of del Río Hortega ('16) that the gliofibrils are cytoplasmic differentiations corresponding to neurofibrils in neurons, myofibrils in muscle cells and tonofibrils in epithelial cells. Indeed, the impressive close-packing of the protoplasmic elements in the central nervous system leaves very little room for extracellular structures of any kind.

ROUND TABLE DISCUSSION

DR. WINDLE: The two papers this morning have dealt with structure of neuroglia cells, as depicted by one of the oldest and one of the newest techniques. It is clear that we must be attentive to both and not discard the old in the rush to embrace the new.

DR. FLEXNER: I would just like to discuss Dr. Scheibel's suggestion that the neuroglia cell may act as a modifier of the rate of oxidation of the nerve cell by way of its porphyrin. In the first place if one uses the Madi reagent, the concentration of cytochrome and cytochrome oxidase in a nerve cell, examined either in fresh tissue or in frozen tissue, appears to be considerably higher than it is in the neuroglia cell. I can't give quantities more exact than 4+, 2+—that sort of thing. So I would suppose that it is unnecessary to assume that the nerve cell is in need of aid of that kind from any outside source. Secondly, let's suppose I am wrong about that; in order for electrons to be transferred between the nerve cell and the neuroglia cell, one would have to have an oxidation reduction system present in both the membrane of the nerve cell and that of the neuroglia cell. This would be pretty tough to demonstrate, it seems to me.

DR. SCHEIBEL: We appreciate your reaction Dr. Flexner. As we mentioned, it was just a suggestion. The porphyrins of the oligodendrocyte need not be actually in or of the cytochrome series but related to progenitors. Neither one of us is a chemist; we are speaking in the freest sense of the word. As to the necessity for two membranes in contact carrying on this oxidation reduction system, structural evidence suggests that the oligodendrocyte wraps its processes, which are probably quite flat and filamentous, very intimately over the surface of the neuron, the dendron as well as over the axon. So your second criticism is an apt one but need not be a limiting factor. The intimacy of the contact, I think, is sufficient to allow for that kind of oxidation reduction reaction in two opposing membranes to occur from a structural point of view. Our own techniques of course show only what we assume to be the nuclei but different techniques also stain the cytoplasm; with them the picture is clouded, so far as the axonal bouton details are concerned, because the cytoplasmic elements of the oligodendrocytes are so closely intertwined on the surface of the neuron and its cell processes.

DR. KLÜVER: No doubt Dr. Flexner knows more about oxidation than I do, but his remarks remind me of a discussion I had many years ago with Leonor Michaelis at the Rockefeller Institute. I had just discovered free porphyrins in the white matter (Klüver, '44a, b) and asked him whether coproporphyrin, for instance, could possibly play a role in the oxygen uptake of certain structures in the myelinated fiber masses of warm-blooded animals. I was not surprised when he replied that in his opinion a metal-free porphyrin could play no such role. I then recalled that Hinsberg and collaborators ('37, '39) had found that under certain conditions porphyrins, including coproporphyrin, exert strong inhibitory effects on the antioxidation of a mixture of linoleic and linolenic acids. This led me to inquire whether free porphyrins may serve as inhibitors in depressing respiration or conceivably play a role in some balance of reaction rates. Michaelis felt that such a possibility should be seriously considered. In fact, the work of Granick and Gilder ('45, '46), dealing with the influence of iron-free porphyrins or of hematin and other iron porphyrins on the growth of smooth strains of *Hemophilus influenzae*, led to the hypothesis that coproporphyrin may function as an inhibitor of aerobic cell respiration, thus determining the relative degree of oxidation or anaerobiosis. It is possibly significant that free porphyrins occurring in plant or animal tissues often occur in an environment deficient in oxygen. As regards the "physiological porphyria" associated with embryonic, fetal and early postnatal phases in mammals, it is of interest that conditions of "partial physiological anaerobiosis" (Needham, '42) may prevail towards the end of fetal life. Studies of porphyrin metabolism in yeast have led to the conclusion that coproporphyrin may be partly associated with lack of oxygen in the cells (Kench and Wilkinson, '46). The porphyrins (coproporphyrin and legcoproporphyrin) which I found to be present in the root nodules of various leguminous plants (Klüver, '48, '49, '54) apparently occur in tissues with a relatively low oxygen uptake. The pO_2 has been reported to be particularly low in the central nodular tissue (Smith, '49). Furthermore, the white matter of the central nervous system which exhibits a porphyrin fluorescence spectrum in mammals and birds has an oxygen consumption that falls far below that of the gray matter. In view of the possible relations between free porphyrins and neuroglia cells, certain results obtained by Pomerat and his collaborators in studying the in vitro growth of the chick embryonic spinal cord are also of special interest (Hudspeth, Swann and Pomerat, '50). These investigators found that cellular migration was stimulated by a low oxygen content, but abolished by a high oxygen content. For instance, the greatest number of migrating cells at 48 hours developed in a gas mixture consisting of 94 per cent N_2, 4 per cent CO_2 and 2 per cent O_2. The majority of these migrating cells were identified as neuroglia cells. In connection with reports that there are significant amounts of carbonic anhydrase in oligodendrocytes, I should like to recall that my own work has led to the suggestion that at least some of the porphyrin in the white matter may be present as zinc complex (Klüver, '55). It would therefore be of great interest to determine the zinc content of the different types of neuroglia cells. The recent demonstration of zinc in certain regions of the Ammon's horn in various mammals has furnished no indications as to the particular cellular elements that may be involved.

DR. ELLIOTT: This discussion about porphyrins reminds me of Pappenheimer's ('47) study. I think it was on the neurotoxin of diphtheria and the production of porphyrins and their toxic action. The thought that porphyrins may be regulators of metabolism through interfering, say, with cytochrome *b*, as was Pappenheimer's idea, seems quite attractive, but I would like to ask whether we can think of porphyrins or any other materials being transferred from an oligodendrocyte to the neuron. Is this type of contact such that chemical materials, in one form or another, can be transferred from cell to cell?

DR. DEMPSEY: The same thought occurred to me in relation to what Dr. Flexner said. I believe we must think of some kind of a transfer mechanism between the glial and the neural elements since, to a degree, the neuron is isolated from its blood supply. It does not come directly in contact with the blood vessels, but a neuroglia cell is interposed. It seems obvious that, for the nerve cell to exist, material must be transferred to and from it; it therefore must be transferred through neuroglia cells by some mechanism, the nature of which I have not the faintest idea.

DR. KOREY: It does not appear obligatory to pass nutriments from the vascular system through a series of neuroglia cells to the neuron. Intercellular diffusion may be an acceptable process.

Has there been any direct evidence that porphyrins are in neuroglia cells?

DR. KLÜVER: So far, there is no direct evidence that porphyrins are actually located in the neuroglia cells. However, various lines of evidence suggest that the occurrence of free porphyrins in the white matter and in the glial segments of cranial nerves is in some way related to the oligodendrocytes (Klüver, '44c, '51, '55). It does not seem possible to determine the absence or presence of porphyrin in single oligodendrocytes, by even the most sensitive techniques, since we are dealing with amounts as small as 2 or 3 micrograms of coproporphyrin per 100 grams. I should like to recall that the physical chemists on the Manhattan Project, in their fluorophotometric determinations of uranium, got into difficulties when trying to work at levels below 0.0001 microgram (Price, Ferretti and Schwartz, '53).

DR. KOREY: One hundred grams of what type of material?

DR. KLÜVER: One hundred grams of white matter, although it is certain that pure white matter has not been used in these determinations.

DR. KOREY: From 100 grams of white matter we may be able to

provide some 3 to 5 grams of glial material. True, these are far from intact but it is conceivable that a sufficient amount of the neuroglia tissue may be obtained for porphyrin analysis.

DR. KLÜVER: I hope so, although for the time being I take a dim view of settling the problem of porphyrins in single neuroglia cells by direct determinations.

DR. NURNBERGER: We have been talking about the possible metabolic interrelationships between neuroglia cells and neurons and I wonder if we should not question whether a morphological relationship has been established. In dealing with any kind of a technical procedure, whether it is histochemical, cytochemical or optical microscopical, one has to face the limitations of that procedure. Looking at these Golgi stained sections and trying to appraise them, we may tend to forget that they are thick sections, perhaps 25μ to 50μ thick. You must consider the resolving power of a refracting system and also the focal depth of your objective; does proximity, shown in your photomicrographs, sufficiently establish a structural interrelationship which would really justify the discussion of a functional interrelationship. I frankly don't see it established by the tools that you have used.

DR. CLEMENTE: Recently Dr. Genis-Galvez and I have made some observations on the degeneration and modes of termination of optic nerve fibers in the diencephalon of the cat. We were looking for the degenerating terminal rings that have been described by Glees ('46); we observed some of the nerve terminals at some distance from diencephalic neurons and in intimate relationship to the neuroglia cells. In certain cases it seemed as though some optic fibers actually terminated on the somas of neuroglia cells in the lateral geniculate body.

MRS. SCHEIBEL: In response to Dr. Nurnberger, we recognize the limitations of the Golgi method. The sections were even thicker, averaging 100μ for the Golgi sections, while control material ranged from 10 to 20μ. The criteria and type of material we have used in describing neuronal-neuroglial relations were those used by Ramon y Cajal and others in establishing the neuronal synapse, upon which most of our present neurological concepts are based. It is possible that, as our techniques become more refined, we may have to revise our concepts of the synapse, both neuronal and neuroglial.

In defense of the data, we must point out that some of the synapselike contacts we have described are seen in such a way as to make it highly unlikely that the thickness of the tissue would compromise the validity of the observation. We agree that when one sees one or several boutons applied directly over the cell in question, it is often difficult to decide between coincidental apposition or proximity on the one hand, and true, functionally meaningful contact on the other. However, we frequently observe contact between axonal bouton and oligodendrocyte at the very edge of the cell so that the contact may be studied as if in silhouette, with cell body and bouton in approximately the same plane of focus. At times, with critical focusing of the immersion objective, there is seen a slight indentation in the surface of the cell where the bouton contact is made. It would be difficult to deny the structural intimacy of such a contact. This is about the best we can do at present.

DR. WINDLE: The use of stereoscopic caps on eyepieces of the binocular compound microscope will aid one in determining relationships. I have found them indispensable for studies of developing fiber tracts in embryos stained with silver.

DR. NURNBERGER: The only point I made was that, with critical focusing as you use it with the material you have, you are not justified to infer structural contiguity.

DR. FLEXNER: Do you ever have any doubts, as you look at these cells, whether you are dealing with an oligodendrocyte or a small nerve cell? Are you never bothered by difficulties of identification?

MRS. SCHEIBEL: I would not say that we are not bothered by it, since the oligodendrocyte shows up rather differently depending on the stain used. However, with the rapid Golgi method, the oligodendrocyte is the only element which consistently appears as an orange staining sphere. We do not know why the cytoplasmic envelope becomes orange rather than black. This staining idiosyncrasy, combined with the rather characteristic shape of the nucleus and a fairly lengthy experience makes us reasonably certain of our identification. Even the cerebellar granule cells which closely resemble the oligodendrocytes, take a black impregnation with this method, so that the possibilities of misidentification in the rapid Golgi technique are gratifyingly small.

Identification may be more questionable in other types of preparations and here a number of additional factors are taken into consideration such as location, size, relation to other elements of the central nervous system, etc.

DR. POMERAT: In answer to Dr. Flexner, certainly it is difficult at times to distinguish in living preparations of the cerebellum between granule cells and oligodendrocytes.

DR. KLÜVER: In connection with the difficulties of identifying oligodendrocytes, I wonder about the phylogenetic distribution of these cells. In a paper published a few months ago, Prince ('55) referred to oligodendrocytes in the optic nerves of reptiles, amphibians and fishes. On the other hand, I have been told by eminent comparative neurologists that true oligodendrocytes do not occur below the mammals and the birds.

DR. GLEES: I asked Dr. Berta Scharrer about that, when writing my book. She said it is too difficult to be certain what an oligodendrocyte is in lower animals.

DR. UZMAN: This is a problem which has confronted our work in studying the Schwann cell and axon interrelationships in peripheral nerve fibers of invertebrates. When one examines such lower forms as squids and lobsters, it is very difficult to know what specific criteria in the way of staining reactions to use in identifying what would correspond to an oligodendrocyte of the human nervous system. A case in point is the satellite cells of the neurosecretory apparatus of the eye stalk of the mollusk. These satellite cells appear to bear the same relationship to the neurosecretory fibers as do Schwann cells to the leg nerve fibers. It is difficult to assign the nomenclature derived from the study of human brain to forms so widely divergent. Perhaps the most important criteria for recognizing similarities of supporting cells in different types of nervous systems must be based on their analogous positioning, rather than identity of staining properties.

DR. BROWNSON: I am interested in the arrangement of the satellite with long attachments to cell bodies of neurons. I wonder if our classic interpretation of the perineuronal satellite cell as being in close proximity to the cell body is outdated by the picture of this long oligodendrocyte attachment. If we are to count satellite cells and interpret satellitosis on the above mentioned basis, we might incorporate many more astrocytes into this picture. If we look back into a recent publication (Glees, '55) we find that maybe 40 per cent of the cortex is made up of astrocytes, then more of our satellite cells might be astrocytes and it might be in keeping to think of the astrocyte as contributing more to metabolic activity of neurons. I hope that Mrs. Scheibel will comment on this. Do the astrocytes have some special attraction to the neuron as do the oligodendrocytes?

MRS. SCHEIBEL: Both astrocytes and oligodendrocytes may be seen adjacent to nerve cells. In addition, both glia cell types may bear intimate contact relationships with each other. We have not seen axonal boutons on astrocytes. The astrocyte, via its processes is often in direct contact with blood vessels, neurons and oligodendrocytes, while the satellite oligodendrocyte appears to be related only secondarily to the vascular tree through the astrocyte. So the astrocyte appears to act, morphologically at least, as the middle man between the blood supply and the cellular elements. From the structural point of view, we would guess that the functions of these two neuroglia cells are different.

DR. BROWNSON: I am particularly interested in satellitosis (Brownson, '56) and have made differential counts (Fig. 13). A high proportion of the satellite cells, so-called (if we include a larger area around the neuron) are apparently astrocytes. This is in agreement with Kryspin-Exner ('52) who reported that astrocytes comprise in the vicinity of 40 per cent, oligodendrocytes more than 50 per cent and microglia cells something like 6 to 10 per cent of total cortical neuroglia cells.

DR. SCHEIBEL: We may have a morphological basis for some kind of bucket carrying reaction from blood vessels by astrocytes to oligodendroglia to neurons. We also know from work of Ramon y Cajal ('13) and De Castro ('51) that there is a more direct bucket brigade from blood vessels via astrocytes directly to neurons. It appears as if both the astrocyte and oligodendrocyte very thickly plaster their processes onto the surface of cell bodies, whatever that means. The point of differentiation may be the fact that we have found that the oligodendrocytes which are in the process of plastering their processes on a cell body also received innervation from the axons which may be thought of as presynaptic to that same cell body. This makes it look like the oligodendrocyte may be receiving some modicums of the same

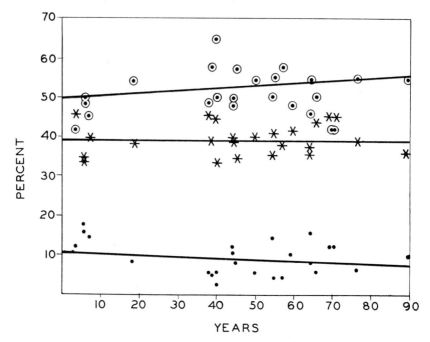

○ – OLIGODENDROGLIA
✴ – ASTROGLIA
● – MICROGLIA

FIGURE 13. Percentage of perineuronal satellite cell types in the motor cortex of human brains at various ages. (From Brownson ('56); courtesy, *Journal of Neuropathology and Experimental Neurology.*)

kind of information which will be transferred synaptically to neurons. Perhaps the function of the oligodendrocytes in this "bucket brigade" is qualitatively different than that of the astrocyte but, certainly, it is not surprising. We agree that both types of cells are either in satellite or near satellite position to the neuron.

DR. BROWNSON: That is what I meant. I was attempting to avoid thinking that the satellite cells are always oligodendrocytes.

The greater the distance out from a neuron, the greater the numbers of astrocytes to be included. The classic description holds that an oligodendrocyte is a satellite if it is touching a neuron. If we find only a foot process plastered onto the cell wall and a long tenuated extension out into the extraneuronal tissue, we might say that this neuroglia cell is still a satellite cell.

DR. CAMMERMEYER: When tissue is prepared under special conditions intended to minimize swelling, the relationship of neuroglia cells to neurons becomes more apparent. The usual 10 per cent formalin, which is hypotonic, and subsequent alcohol treatment both contribute to distortion. Consequently the neuroglia cell nuclei appear dark and shrunken and are displaced from the juxtaneuronal position to the edge of an artificially enlarged perineuronal space. With the use of either the perfusion solution of Koenig, Groat and Windle ('45) or 10 per cent formalin in normal saline, the nuclei are large and uniform in size, shape and staining qualities and they remain in relative positions. As a supplement to normal animal material, it is useful to study pathological material from cases of liver cirrhosis with terminal hepatic coma; under such conditions the astrocyte nuclei are known to undergo selective hypertrophy throughout all gray matter (Adams and Foley, '53). Microscopical sections prepared from such sources contained a cell population in which identification of astrocytes and oligodendrocytes was relatively simple. Two observations made under these conditions raised some doubts as to the validity of the usual concept (Müller, '30) that oligodendrocytes are the only elements to constitute satellite cells: (a) single unquestionable astrocytes were situated next to neurons; and (b) numerous oligodendrocytes, clustered around a large motor neuron of the spinal cord, were in fact seen to bear a closer relationship to a contiguous capillary than to the neuron. In addition, single oligodendrocytes and single astrocytes were seen in juxtaposition to the neuron. On this basis the increased number of oligodendrocytes may be a response to vascular deficiency and therefore termed paraneural vascular perigliosis. Since the reaction is not related to neuronal abnormality the terms neuronal satellitosis and neuronophagia should be dismissed.

As an afterthought to the discussion of the paper given by

Drs. Scheibel, I would like to ask whether they have formulated any idea about the origin of so-called amyloid bodies which some of their orange bodies resembled?

MRS. SCHEIBEL: We have not seen any orange staining structures other than the nuclei of oligodendrocytes.

DR. GLEES: The role of the neuroglia as a metabolic carrier has been questioned. The possibility of intracellular transportation has been denied or, at least, it has been said it could go around the neuroglia cells. Has Dr. Palay seen any of these glial terminations around neurons containing mitochondria? In case he has, might this imply that they act as conveyors?

DR. PALAY: All that I have seen is that among the synaptic terminals around a neuron there are small cytoplasmic processes which look just like those of astrocytes or the branches of oligodendrocytes interspersed among the other elements. They are in close contact with the neuron but they seem to have no special arrangement and usually they do not contain mitochondria. I think that is because the mitochondria are infrequent in the processes. If an exchange does occur, I do not see why it could not occur through the cytoplasmic processes because the mitochondria need not be right at any particular site to yield their energy within a few micra. It is noteworthy that the distance between cellular elements in the central nervous system is extremely small. It is something of the order of 200 to 300 Å and probably that apparent space is even enlarged by some unknown amount of shrinkage so that the true interstitial space, which I am sure Dr. Dempsey will speak about later and which I don't want to say anything more about, is an extremely narrow space and would have room only for a capillary type of film.

DR. DEMPSEY: In your opinion would it be a suitable place for diffusion phenomena to be well exhibited?

DR. PALAY: I would think not, unless you had some mechanism for providing pressure to push it, or suction on the other end to pull it, along this system.

DR. KOREY: There would be a flow of material by virtue of concentration gradients with one end of the system providing glucose, for example, and the other consuming it.

Dr. Palay: The problem would only be to know whether the rate of transfer is sufficient to account for the utilization of it.

Dr. Korey: I would believe that many transcellular passages, true intracellular penetration and exit, would add to the energy requirements of a system a great deal. Analogies to the mechanisms operative in the vascular system may not apply to the nervous system where the type of cells and the geometry are so exceedingly different.

Dr. Dempsey: Isn't that just what has to happen when a substance moves through the endothelium of the capillary?

Dr. Windle: To get back on morphological grounds, does anyone wish to discuss types of neuroglia cells?

Chapter 3

Two Views Concerning Criteria for Identification of Neuroglia Cell Types by Electron Microscopy

PART A

J. FRANCIS HARTMANN

DR. PALAY echoed a sentiment which was expressed last evening by Dr. Dempsey and in which I heartily concur, that those of us in electron microscopy are bothered at the moment by a lack of suitable criteria for identifying the various components of the central nervous system seen in electron micrographs. I should like to lay before this group the criteria that Dr. Marilyn G. Farquhar and I have used in attempting to identify some of the neuroglia cell types in our electron micrographs of the central nervous system. Some of this work was presented before the American Association of Anatomists a year ago (Farquhar, '55).

Our identification of neuroglia cell types has been based chiefly on the classical descriptions in the light microscope literature summarized by Penfield ('32a) for astrocytes and oligodendrocytes and by del Río Hortega ('32) for the microglia cells.

⮞

FIGURE 14. Electron micrograph showing nuclear and cytoplasmic characteristics of a typical oligodendrocyte (O) contrasted with those of a typical astrocyte (A). It will be noted that the nucleus of the former is smaller, denser and more nearly round than the nucleus of the latter. In addition, the oligodendrocyte cytoplasm is much more sparse and dense than that of the astrocyte which is clear and watery. Magnification, 10,400 ×. (From Farquhar and Hartmann ('57); courtesy, *Journal of Neuropathology and Experimental Neurology.*)

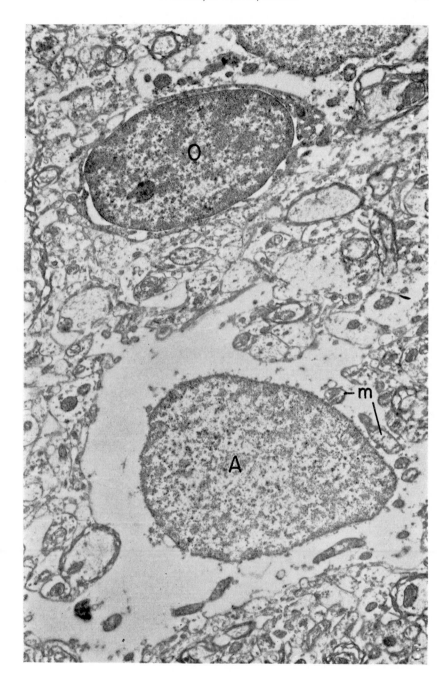

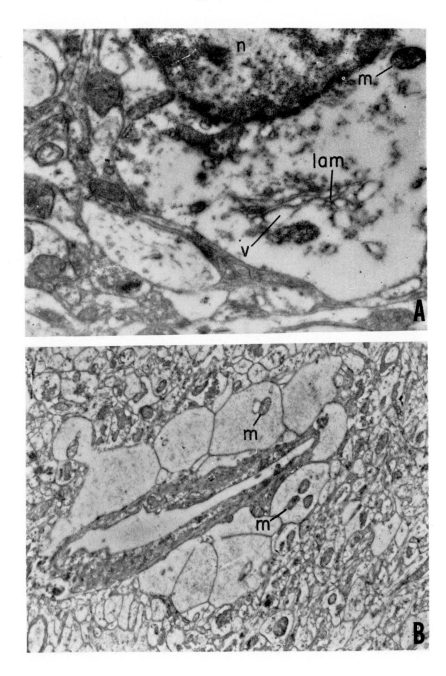

Criteria that have been found most useful for identification of astrocytes are the size, shape and density of the nucleus and the striking frequency with which processes are found in intimate relationship to the capillaries. Penfield ('32a) has summarized this group of astrocyte features in the following manner: "The astrocyte nucleus is irregularly oval. It is larger than oligodendroglia or microglia nuclei and has chromatin which is smaller in amount." He writes further that astrocyte processes "are attached to blood vessels by one or many perivascular feet," and that the perivascular feet contain "protoplasm difficult to stain by most methods." The large cells with large vesicular nuclei and nearly empty cytoplasm seen in electron micrographs of cerebral cortex correspond very closely to these classical concepts of astrocyte structure (Figs. 14 and 15).

Penfield indicated that oligodendrocytes may be distinguished from astrocytes by their "rounder and smaller" nuclei and "smaller cell body with smaller, more delicate expansions." In addition, the cytoplasm of oligodendrocytes is "granular and small in amount." The frequent location of oligodendrocytes as perineuronal satellites which "often seem to rest in little hollows between neuron expansions" or as interfascicular neuroglia "in rows between the medullated sheaths" is another feature which helps to distinguish oligodendrocytes from other types. All of these structural features have been used by us to distinguish oligodendrocytes in electron micrographs (Fig. 14).

←⫷

Figure 15. A. A portion of an astrocyte from the cerebral cortex of an adult rat. Part of the nucleus (*n*) can be seen in the upper part of the figure. In the cytoplasm, several mitochondria (*m*) can be identified. The Golgi complex at this magnification can be seen to consist of paired electron-dense lamellae (*lam*) and vacuoles (*v*). Magnification, 21,800 ×.

B. A section through a capillary in the cerebral cortex of the rat. The capillary is virtually surrounded by pale astrocyte ctyoplasm which is partitioned into compartments. The partitions probably represent the cell borders of a number of different astrocyte processes, the latter containing a few mitochondria (*m*) and some fine flocculent background material. Magnification, 10,000 ×. (From Farquhar and Hartmann ('57); courtsey, *Journal of Neuropathology and Experimental Neurology.*)

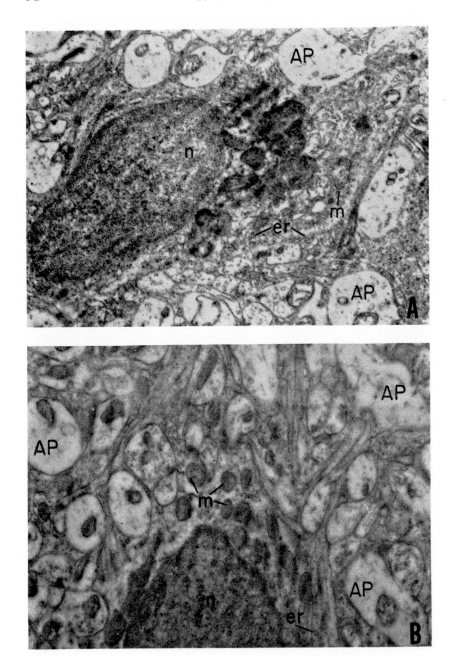

Inasmuch as the nature (length, width, density) of the processes of microglia cells are known to vary considerably with phagocytic activity, nuclear characteristics were found to be of more value in the identification of microglia cells. Del Río Hortega ('32) described the nuclei of microglia cells as "polymorphic" and as having "abundant chromatin contents." In addition, he stressed the fact that in the so-called resting stage the processes of microglia cells are "covered with very numerous thin twigs." The numerous fine branches that he describes are quite evident in electron micrographs (Fig. 16).

In Figure 15B appears a capillary of the cerebral cortex; and we find that what would probably be interpreted in light microscope studies as pericapillary space is in reality subdivided into compartments by membranes so thin as to escape detection at the resolution limit of the light microscope. It is our interpretation that these are limiting membranes of astrocyte processes. The presence of mitochondria between the membranes, and the same finely granular background density that we associate with astrocyte cytoplasm are offered in support of this view.

The presence of mitochondria in microglia cells, as seen with the electron microscope, is a very constant finding and is in con-

---

FIGURE 16. A. A microglia cell from the cerebral cortex of an adult rat. The nucleus (*n*) is elongated in shape and the particles which make up its background are evenly distributed and uniformly dense. Irregular inclusions of dense material, presumably phagocytosed debris, are prominent in the cytoplasm. A number of mitochondria (*m*), canaliculi of the endoplasmic reticulum (*er*) and small particles can also be seen. The outline of the microglia cell border is very irregular, for a number of processes can be seen extending into the surrounding tissue. Above and below the microglia cell, several pale cytoplasmic processes of astrocytes (*AP*) cut in cross section are identifiable. Magnification, 15,000 ×.
B. Part of a microglia cell from the cerebral cortex of an adult rat is seen here at higher magnification. The nucleus (*n*), mitochondria (*m*), canaliculi of the endoplasmic reticulum (*er*) and small cytoplasmic particles are seen. Many cytoplasmic processes of the microglia cell branch out in every direction and give rise to small secondary branches. Several larger pale processes of astrocytes (*AP*) are out in cross section. Magnification, 15,900 ×. (From Farquhar and Hartmann ('57); courtesy, *Journal of Neuropathology and Experimental Neurology.*)

tradiction to the statement so often repeated in the light microscope literature that mitochondria are absent from microglia cells
(Fig. 16B).

Although the illustrations of neuroglia cell types presented here
are considered to be typical for each cell type, many intermediate
or intergrading forms can be seen in electron micrographs, not all
of which can be explained on the basis of plane of section alone.
Hence it is felt that the neuroglia cells must show much more
variation in form than has heretofore been entirely appreciated.

PART B

Sarah Luse

By light microscopy in pathological material the oligodendrocyte
has for years been identified in hematoxylin and eosin and other
usual stains by its pale cytoplasm. This is particularly striking
in the presence of anoxia, in edema of the brain and in the
oligodendroglial tumors. The oligodendrocyte has a uniformly
round or ovoid nucleus with a surrounding halo of unstained
cytoplasm. In contradistinction, the cytoplasm of the astrocyte
can be stained by hematoxylin and eosin and also by the PAS
and other techniques which stain the acidophilic cytoplasm of
the gemistocytic astrocyte. Surrounding many of the blood vessels in hematoxylin and eosin preparations there is, as has been
pointed out by electron microscopy, a clear space wherein one
can see some material by electron microscopy but by light microscopy is an unstained region. However, both in tumors and normal central nervous tissue stained by hematoxylin and eosin, a
foot process can frequently be seen attached to the vessel wall
and this foot process is stained acidophilically, not the unstained
type of material that is seen in the cytoplasm of the oligodendrocyte. Penfield and other workers have pointed out that the oligodendrocyte often is a satellite to the surface of the blood vessel
and that often this cell has processes that pass by, surround or
go around the wall of the capillary or the blood vessel, whereas
the astrocyte is a cell which may be far distant from the vessel
and sends one or two processes out as end-feet. This does not
mean that the entire wall of the vessel must be surrounded by

such end-foot processes. Other processes also surround the vessel. In electron microscopy, as in light microscopy, we have found that the oligodendrocytes are often lined up in rows and those cells which we have identified in that way are similar to these that Dr. Hartmann calls protoplasmic astrocytes and which I call oligodendrocytes. In order to further substantiate this, I have examined tumors, neoplasms of the well differentiated type, by electron microscopy. The oligodendroglia tumor, which by light microscopy of the same tumor is made up of the cells with the clear halo, is by electron microscopy made up of the cells with pale cytoplasm. These cells are lined up in rows as I have mentioned. We certainly see them adjacent to the walls of vessels as has been previously mentioned. In the young animal where myelination of the nervous system is just beginning, these cells with pale cytoplasm are very prominent and actually appear to increase in number as the myelination begins.

In identifying the astrocyte foot, which can be seen by light microscopy, we have noted that attached to the margins of many vessels there are intricately folded membranes which certainly are reminiscent of the undulating folding membranes which Dr. Pomerat has shown by phase microscopy of the astrocyte. These come out and attach to some portion of the vessel wall while pale processes may be seen elsewhere on the same vessel wall. The pale processes are considered as those of the oligodendrocytes. In low grade astrocytic tumors there are two types of astrocytes. The fibrous astrocyte is readily identified by fine fibrils in its processes. Some of the fine fibrils are within processes, the cytoplasmic membranes of which are folded and refolded in a complicated manner. Other cells with the plicated membranes are present and are similar to those cells which we have identified as protoplasmic astrocytes.

ROUND TABLE DISCUSSION

Dr. Windle: This places the matter of identifying neuroglia cells in electron micrographs squarely before you for discussion.

Dr. Clemente: Dr. Daniel Pease has submitted one of his electron micrographs of the cerebral cortex. The watery type cytoplasmic processes seen in Dr. Hartmann's pictures are duplicated in Dr. Pease's electron micrograph (Fig. 17). Capillaries are surrounded by what he has interpreted as astrocytic end-feet—some, almost complete encapsulation by the watery processes.

Dr. Glees: When looking at one individual nucleus, using electron microscopy, it is impossible to say that it is one particular type of neuroglia cell. There is great difficulty even under the light microscope. When one makes differential counts, one has to go over to low power and one has to check on a lot of histological fields to get one's bearings again. Under high power (oil immersion), it is increasingly difficult to make a definite statement and, if one had only very high power, I doubt that he would dare to label a particular nucleus to belong to an astrocyte, protoplasmic or fibrous, or to an oligodendrocyte.

Dr. Luse: I think that is certainly true and the mechanism which we must use in order to do this is to check, by phase microscopy, adjacent sections which may also later be stained by some of the methods which can be applied to methacrylate sections as well as by using, not only the high power magnifications of the electron microscope, but the lowest power available. A low power lens might well be used, and with it we could examine the sections at approximately 300 or 400× magnification for orientation, as well as at a higher magnification later.

Dr. Lumsden: It seems to me evident on observing living cells in tissue culture that the nuclear shape is largely determined by movements of the cell, i.e., either by the rate and direction of locomotion of the whole cell, or by the direction of flow of the

———————————————————————————————————————

⤜⤜→

Figure 17. Part of a low power electron micrograph showing a cerebral capillary sectioned longitudinally. A sheath of watery cytoplasm nearly covers the vessel. Mitochondria may be found in this, and partitions exist. This sheath corresponds to the layer of astrocytic feet that can be observed by conventional microscopy. Nearby is a cell with identical watery cytoplasm, bigger than any other type to be found in nervous tissue except large neurons, which is an astrocyte. (From Pease, Maynard and Schultz, University of California, Los Angeles.)

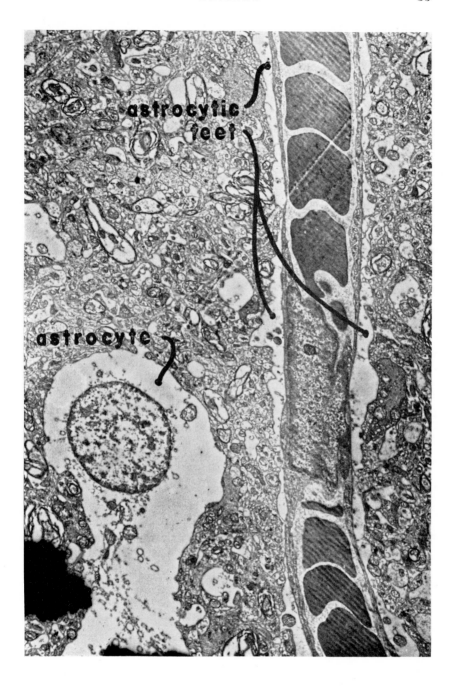

cytoplasm when this only occurs and the cell body is not displaced as a whole. Thus, to take the extreme example, the great polymorphism of the nuclei of the highly ameboid forms of cell, like the microgliocyte, is a direct expression of the high mobility of this type of cell. However, more sedentary types of cell, like astrocytes, also show nuclear elongation during active migration of the cell and rounding up of the nucleus on return to a sedentary or stationary phase. A second factor in determining nuclear shape in astrocytes, as seen in culture conditions, is the elaboration of the intracytoplasmic products or secretions. These remarks, of course, apply in the case of neuroglia cells to conditions in culture, where the factors to which I have alluded probably apply more than in vivo in the normal adult organ. In the intact organ, tissue pressure forces modify, not only the direction and rate of cell movements (and hence nuclear shape), but also the shape of the nuclei of sedentary cells. The shape of the nucleus is thus a secondary, not a specific, characteristic of the cell.

DR. PALAY: I think that there is probably not so much disagreement as would seem to be expressed by saying that what one group calls an astrocyte is an oligodendrocyte to another group. There are some important characteristics of the material which has been presented that have to be considered. The fixation of tissue in the nervous system is of the utmost importance before we can identify cellular elements. After looking at cells in tissue culture, and particularly the beautiful films that we saw last night, I wonder about completely empty spaces that appear within the cytoplasmic areas of these cells. If we find clumps of membranous or vacuolar material suspended in a nonstructured cytoplasm and interrupted membranes that are hard to follow across some spaces, perhaps our difficulties in identification are due to the fact that all of the cell is not there and that when we compare such pictures with material stained by the classical methods that give outlines of the cells we may be misled. What we have to do is to join the information we have from tissue culture concerning the flowing, highly irregular and dynamic membranes—surface phenomena—and concerning the internal structures that are visible in these living cells together with the information we have from methods concerning the general skeletal outline of the cell. I don't think that the silhouettes that are seen in silver preparations represent all the cells. They only tell us what are the thickest parts of the cell, the parts that have not retracted toward the cell body. They give just the scaffolding of the cell, whereas after we have fixed adequately with osmium tetroxide we are at least hoping that we have the whole cell, everything there, and the success of this hope varies somewhat from one preparation to another. So perhaps the argument here is not really as intense as it appears. When completely satisfactory fixation is obtained I believe these differences will tend to disappear.

DR. LUMSDEN: In addition to what Dr. Palay has just said, later in the meeting I will show some electron micrographs of the tips of processes of whole cells from cultures, grown directly on Formvar films and immediately fixed by osmium tetroxide vapor. There one sees the whole matrix of the protoplasm completely filled up.

DR. CAMMERMEYER: There are some other factors involving preparation of material which should be taken into consideration. The proportion of astrocytes to oligodendrocytes may vary with the thickness of the section. In the ventral horn of the cat spinal cord, astrocytes were found to constitute 35 to 55 per cent of all neuroglia cells in sections 10μ thick, but only 23 to 32 per cent in sections 20μ thick. In the third cortical layer of a patient with hepatic coma, the pathologically hypertrophied astrocytes numbered 37 to 55 per cent in sections 10μ thick after either paraffin or celloidin embedding, and 36 to 45 per cent in frozen sections 20μ thick.

The size of astrocyte nuclei as measured planimetrically is also influenced by the histological preparation. As seen in Figure 18, the average area of astrocyte nuclei is greatest in frozen sections of material from a 74 year old man, 4 days in hepatic coma, fixed with 10 per cent formalin in 0.9 per cent NaCl; the area is smaller after use of 10 per cent formalin with less or no saline admixtures. After substitution of 1.2 per cent NaCl, the average area of astrocyte nuclei is reduced too. The smallest area of nuclei was generally noted in the paraffin embedded material; after celloidin embedding, the astrocytes were of intermediate size. This observation contrasts with that on the overall size of the spinal cord which became smaller after celloidin embedding than after paraffin embedding. The size of astrocyte nuclei may be influenced by changes in osmotic pressure of their environment, a mechanism proposed to explain the immediate increase

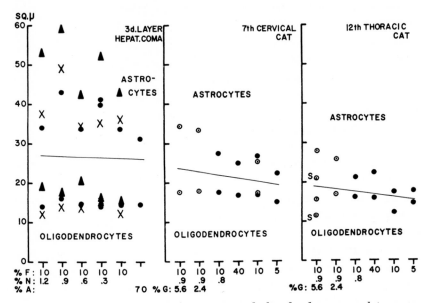

FIGURE 18. Average areas of astrocyte and oligodendrocyte nuclei, measured planimetrically in 200 neuroglia cells of the human cerebral cortex and cat thoracic spinal cord, and in 600 neuroglia cells in the cat cervical spinal cord. Sections of the cat material were stained with gallocyanin at pH 1.64; paraffin and frozen sections of human material were stained at pH 4.5. The symbols indicate: *circle*, paraffin embedded, 20μ; *dot*, paraffin embedded, 10μ; *crosses*, celloidin embedded, 10μ; *triangle*, frozen sections, 20μ. The composition of fixatives is indicated in per cent of formalin, F; sodium chloride, N; ethyl alcohol, A; gum acacia, G. The letter S indicates shrinkage of neuroglia cell nuclei.

in area of astrocyte nuclei after severance of the facial nerve (Cammermeyer, '55a).

The size of astrocyte nuclei is similarly affected in the cat. The highest values were obtained after the perfusion fixation. The area of oligodendrocyte nuclei is influenced by fixation in very much the same manner as for astrocytes but the variations in size are less striking.

DR. POMERAT: Many structures in the living state are highly

mobile. Fixation artifacts have been re-examined by the electron microscopists. Fixatives are only good insofar as they reach structures quickly and with the proper physical chemical attributes. By slow fixation of tissue cultures we can produce the classical pictures one gets with silver preparations. We can also preserve monolayers of cells faithfully by rapid fixation with agents at appropriate concentrations. Like the electron microscopist, in the re-evaluation of technique we come to recognize that the rate of fixation is tremendously important. On the basis of living preparations we can analyze the effect of shrinking of extremely delicate membranes. I should not decry the magnificent achievement of classical neurocytology although, from time to time, we like to refer to it as "silver plated neurology." It is one of the goals of these gatherings to read these results anew in the light of the fine fixation being achieved by electron microscopy.

DR. POPE: I would like to ask two questions of the electron microscopists which I think may have a bearing on the metabolic properties of neuroglia cells. One of these is whether any estimate can be made of the relative number of mitochondria per unit volume of cytoplasm in the various neuroglia cell species compared with the number in large and small neurons. This has some bearing on the point that Dr. Flexner raised. Since mitochondria are sites of oxidative enzyme systems in cells, their relative numbers might be indicative of the relative concentrations of such enzymes and rates of oxidative metabolism in neuroglia cells as compared to neurons. My second question has to do with the film of nucleoprotein which, as I understand it, is located in astrocytes primarily in a perinuclear position. I wonder if Dr. Palay could comment on the relative amount of such material in neuroglia cells as compared with neurons, especially in view of the well-known virtual lack of cytoplasmic basophilia which neuroglia cells show with ordinary aniline dyes. May I ask, also, whether he would consider such a concentration of ribonucleoprotein around the nucleus to be an indication that this is a position in the cell in which protein synthesis is active, as is apparently the case in neurons according to Caspersson.

DR. HARTMANN: In quantitating the mitochondria in neuroglia cells versus nerve cells, the phase microscope would probably be easier to use than the electron microscope. However, identification of mitochondria is a little easier with the electron microscope. Many of us at the moment probably have only an impression and my impression is that neuroglia cells contain fewer mitochondria than do nerve cells.

DR. POMERAT: It is also our impression that the astrocytes do not have as many mitochondria as we see in neurons.

DR. PALAY: I have the impression that, area for area, the nerve cell has a higher concentration of mitochondria than the oligodendrocyte.

DR. CLEMENTE: What can be said about the relative concentrations of mitochondria in astrocytes and oligodendrocytes?

DR. PALAY: My impression was that oligodendrocytes have more; but, again, this must be qualified with the statement that it is very difficult to make a good estimate. A question was whether the ribonucleoprotein granules could have any relation to protein synthesis. It is almost a basic precept in cytology that basophilic cytoplasm has something to do with protein synthesis. The evidence for this is almost direct now, for the uptake of radioactive aminoacids in isolated granules of this size and density is the highest and quickest of all the particulate fractions that can be obtained from cells. Although I do not know of any information about neuroglia cells in particular, I assume that the situation is the same.

DR. CLEMENTE: Would you assume from your electron micrographs that the amount of perinuclear material that you consider protein in the astrocyte is of the same order of magnitude as the perinuclear granules of neurons?

DR. PALAY: This is a little hard to say, again for the same reason that would apply to the mitochondria, because we have only thin sections which are selected from a whole cell. I would say that in these astrocytes there is a very dense concentration of granules around the nucleus and that it is at least as dense as in the Nissl substance, perhaps even greater.

DR. CLEMENTE: Haven't you observed a different organization of this material in the two types of cells?

DR. PALAY: In the Nissl substance they are oriented with relation to the membranes and the granules are oriented in clusters, rows and spirals whereas, in neuroglia cells, the membranes and granules seem to have no immediate relation. They are dispersed fairly uniformly. Also the cytoplasm of the astrocytes may be very thin. It may extend as a film around the nucleus and the absolute quantity present is perhaps not enough to be differentiated in the light microscope from the nucleus. In the light microscope you are dealing with juxtaposition of objects below the resolving power of the microscope and you may not be able to pick up such small amounts.

DR. CLEMENTE: The pictures you showed were of proliferative, reactive astrocytes surrounding a wound. Wouldn't it be reasonable to assume that the nuclear and cytoplasmic inclusions of these cells differ somewhat from a nonreactive astrocyte?

DR. PALAY: That is true; however, if one can jump to the neurohypophysis where you have pituicytes, considered as a variety of the normal protoplasmic astrocyte, I think there, too, you would find a large amount of endoplasmic reticulum and ribonucleoprotein granules. That is characteristic of them.

Chapter 4

Fibrillar Structure of Astrocytes[*]

ANGELO BAIRATI

HISTOLOGISTS generally agree on the existence of filamentous structures in neuroglia cells but little is to be said
about the nature, location and mechanical properties of these
structures. Weigert (1895) maintained that the gliofibrils are
extracellular and therefore comparable with collagen fibrils of
the connective tissue. Most authors on the contrary, according
to Ramon y Cajal and his school, held that gliofibrils are inside
the cells and it is unsettled whether this filamentous material
is an inert paraplasm or should be considered an alloplasmatic
substance, i.e., a particular functional differentiation of the neuroglia cells.

Early investigations on the physical nature of gliofibrils were
carried out by Schmidt ('42) who was able to show a positive
birefringency in the neuroglia cells of the retina and in the spinal
cord of some fishes. He thought this birefringency depended on
the presence of fibrillar protein structures. I have made a more
extensive submicroscopical analysis by means of polarized light,
by phase contrast microscopy, in dark field and by studying the
action of proteolytic enzymes, as well as with electron microscopy (Bairati, '49). These researches confirm the existence of
a filamentous protein structure within the neuroglia cells. The
electron microscopical investigations on normal and pathological
neuroglia cells dissociated by means of ultrasonic vibrations
showed some submicroscopical structures similar to those of the
collagen. On the contrary, Wilke and Kircher ('52) demonstrated
in x-ray diffractograms of the pathological neuroglia cells a pat-

[*] Professor Bairati's discussion was abstracted from his presentation at the
Neuroanatomical Seminar of March 27, 1956.

66

tern similar to that of fibrinogen. These different results depend mainly on the difficulties of having the neuroglia cells in relatively pure state. Generally, the fibrous astrocytes are intimately associated with other elements, which prevents a neat separation of the cells in sufficient number for analysis. I have noticed that the neuroglia cells can be obtained in a relatively pure state from the so-called "corneal laminae" of the ventricular cavities, especially in cases of senile or juvenile hydrocephalus consequent to ventricular obstruction. These laminae can be freed easily from the surrounding nervous tissue. Following a short-ultrasonic treatment of the laminae, neuroglia cells with well preserved perikaryon and larger processes were cleanly isolated. By centrifuging such suspensions in media having a special gradient of density, e.g., a 60 per cent solution of sucrose, entire and fully unimpaired neuroglia cells were obtained.

Investigation with the phase contrast microscope yields interesting results on external morphology of neuroglia cells and of their processes but does not offer any indication of the minute structure (Fig. 19A). After fragmentation of the cells by means of ultrasonic vibrations, division of processes and fracturing of the cell body may result; thus, well expanded processes or thin cytoplasmic layers are obtained, which are more suitable for examination. These materials show a tenuous filamentous pattern at the limit of the resolving power of the microscope. The examination by the phase contrast microscope is necessary for identification of structures obtained by ultrasonic dissociation previous to investigation by electronic microscopy.

Examination in dark field shows a very complicated optical image of the fibrous astrocytes. A clear diffraction of the surface predominates and interferential dots become apparent within the cell body and its processes (Fig. 19B). The structural unhomogeneity, thus revealed, depends on the existence of denser and more diffracting material embedded in a less diffracting medium. These images do not prove the existence of filamentous structures in the neuroglia cells but the azimutal illumination reveals a preferential arrangement of the diffracting material according to the processes' axes whereas they are arranged along various trajectories in the cell body. This pattern is somehow

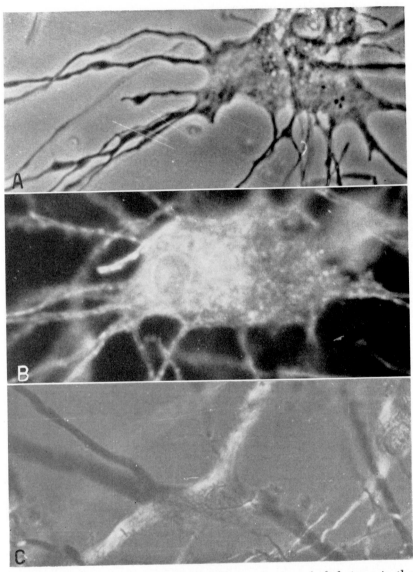

FIGURE 19. Neuroglia cells isolated from a lamina of glial tissue in the brain of a 6 year old patient with infantile hydrocephalus. A. Photomicrograph by phase contrast; magnification, 800 ×. B. Photomicrograph by darkfield; magnification, 1000 ×. C. Photomicrograph with polarized light using Brace's compensator; magnification, 800 ×.

different from that of the common neuroglia cells; in the latter a granular pattern seems to depend on large numbers of globular structures (gliosomes).

Examination in polarized light shows an uniaxial birefringency which is positive, according to the major axis of the processes, and more complexly oriented in the cell body. Birefringent trajectories similar to those observed in dark field may be detected especially in bipolar neuroglia cells. In the latter, the birefringency of one process appears to be continuous with that of the opposite process through the trajectories surrounding the nucleus (Fig. 19C).

The birefringency shows the following characteristics: (a) The positivity according to the major axis of the processes is not inverted by treatment with phenol or other reagents which convert into negative the positive birefringency of collagen protein. (b) It is abolished after moderate swelling in acids and following tryptic hydrolysis. No effect is shown by treatment with other enzymes, such as ribonuclease and hyaluronidase, nor after lipolytic treatment. (c) Textural birefringency is apparent in the largest processes and in the perikaryon. By soaking the cells with fluids having a progressively increasing refractive index, a gradual decrease of birefringency up to a refractive index of 1.5 was observed. However, a fraction of the intrinsic birefringency is maintained. When soaking fluids of still higher refractive indexes are used, the birefringency undergoes a further increment.

Observation with the electron microscope reveals interesting pictures after ultrasonic treatment. The processes and cell body of neuroglia cells split into expanded fragments thin enough to be permeable to electrons. A tenuous network of tiny filamentous structures becomes apparent. These are arranged in narrow and elongated meshes according to the long axis of the cell processes. The thin filaments may be compared to the protofibrils of some other filamentous structures or to the microfilaments of myosine. They are nearly 100 Å in thickness showing a beaded microglobular periodic structure of about 200 Å (Fig. 20). Submicroscopically detectable individual fibrils, such as seen in other biological materials, were never observed. Within the cytoplasm,

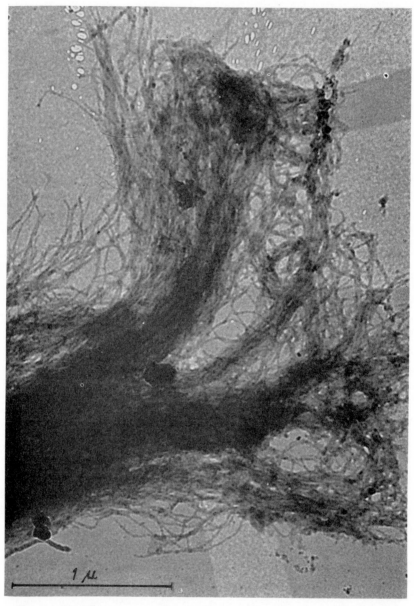

FIGURE 20. Electron micrograph of an astrocyte process, dissociated by means of ultrasonic waves and lipids extracted. The protofibrils, about 100 Å in diameter, have a beaded periodic structure of 200 Å.

thick meshes were seen surrounding spaces containing occasional fragments of cytoplasm and gliosomes.

The observations are in agreement with those with polarized light. Both are consistent with the existence of a submicroscopic composite body and of an intrinsic birefringency. On the contrary, the assumption that the filaments may be collagenlike structures seems not to be strengthened by our observations.

Glial laminae about one millimeter thick were examined by means of the Kristalloflex III, manufactured by Siemens. The x-ray diffractograms show two fundamental bands of diffraction at the distances of 4.6 and 10 Å, which correspond to backbone spacing and side-chain spacing of proteins. These two rings are diffuse, differing from those observed in typical members of keratin class, for instance, β-keratin. Moreover, there is a sharper diffraction ring at the distance of 5.1 Å; all these rings are visible also following lypidic extraction.

Autoclaving at 120°C for a few minutes does not destroy the glial laminae. Following such treatment, the x-ray pattern becomes clearer with sharper delimitation of the bands. The diagram obtained is not comparable with x-ray pattern of collagenlike fibrous proteins. It shows some similarity to the diagrams of some proteins of group KEMF and to that obtained by Wilke and Kircher ('52) in other pathological glial materials. However, we cannot accept the interpretation of these authors.

Analysis of the amino acids of the glial laminae was made by quantitative paper chromatography after hydrolysis with hydrochloric acid 5N for 24 hours at 100°C. We applied two methods, those of McFarren and Mills ('52) and Pernis and Wunderly ('53), which gave similar results. Our aim was to find out whether or not the amino acid composition is similar to that of well-known fibrous proteins. It appears that essential differences between our protein and collagen and elastin may exist. The amino acids represented in collagen, oxyproline, proline and glycine, are virtually absent. The glial protein seems to be characterized by the abundance of dicarboxylic and diamino acids and by scarce amounts of cystine. On the whole, the composition seems to be similar to proteins of KEMF group.

Biology of Neuroglia

CONCLUSION

In the cytoplasm of fibrous astrocytes, a protein has been found which gives rise to a filamentous protofibrillar structure endowed with intrinsic birefringency. The nature of this protein could not definitely be established. It is possible to exclude identity with scleroproteins of the connective tissue. From the diffractographic and chemical data it seems possible that it is similar to the proteins of the group KEMF of Astbury ('33, '53).

The hypothesis that the fibrous astrocytes have well individualized submicroscopical fibrils, similar to collagen fibrils, should be disposed of. The gliofibrils of the histologists are formed when this protein material of the neuroglia cell cytoplasm is shrunk and coagulated after chemical fixation and silver staining. We can affirm that the filamentous structures of the neuroglia cells have biophysical properties essentially different from connective tissue proteins. It is important to emphasize that these filamentous structures are of ectodermal origin and are embedded into the cytoplasm, whereas the connective tissue fibrils are of mesenchymal origin and are placed extracellularly.*

---

* Our more recent researches have determined the nature of the neuroglia cell protein. It is an α-keratin. It appears likely that neuroglia cells, being of ectodermal origin, undergo a partial cytomorphosis as epidermal cells do. The intracellular filamentous structures seem not to be specific to neuroglia cells.

Chapter 5

The Role of Neuroglia Cells in Myelin Formation

BETTY GEREN UZMAN

I HAVE been interested in myelin formation principally in the peripheral nervous system. That peripheral nerve myelin is derived from the infolded surface membrane of the Schwann cell is well documented in our studies of the sciatic nerves of chick embryos and infant mice (Geren, '54; '56). Other investigators have now published evidence which supports this view (Robertson, '55; Wersäll, '56). For more than a year and a half we have worked with developing myelin in the central nervous system, particularly in the dorsal columns of the spinal cords of infant mice. The mode of formation of myelin in the central nervous system is still not clear from our studies. We have been unable to trace a complete spiral in the lamellar structure of myelin in the central nervous system. We have seen what appear to be the beginnings and endings of spirals in relation to the lamellar structure of the myelin sheath. We have not been able on the outer surface of the myelin sheath to trace these connections to cell surfaces of any sort and one of the problems which I think has hindered our work is the problem of the exact delineation of cell surfaces in the central nervous system; this probably due to difficulties in fixation. One may find areas in which cytoplasm appears to be enclosed by a black line, presumably the locus of the cell surface, but we have not been able to show that the tenuous membranes which appear to come off in spiral fashion from myelin in the mouse spinal cord have a direct relation to the cell surfaces of oligodendrocytes or other types of cells. One observation which makes it difficult to apply the same theory of myelin formation in the peripheral nervous system to

73

the central nervous system is the fact that in young mice, very early in the course of myelin formation adjacent myelinated fibers come to lie within 90 Å of each other, which leaves very little room between them for cell surfaces of any kind. In our preparations we have not been able to see an interruption in the period from one fiber to the next. This presents a rather difficult problem if one wishes to assume that at least two cell surfaces must lie between adjacent fibers and must be acting independently. I think that this is evidence that there is some sort of interaction between fibers in myelin formation in the central nervous system. I don't know what it is. That, plus the fact that we have been unable to trace a complete spiral in any section of spinal cord fibers, makes me quite hesitant to try to apply a hypothesis for myelin formation in the peripheral nervous system to the central nervous system. As far as I know, there is no crucial evidence to date indicating that the oligodendrocyte is responsible for myelin formation in the central nervous system.

I think we must also be extremely cautious in assuming that the Schwann cell surface has all the properties of the myelin sheath, or vice versa, just by virtue of the evidence that some sort of structural pattern of a cell surface is used in the formation of myelin in the peripheral nervous system. Such conclusions must be drawn only after detailed experimental analysis.

ROUND TABLE DISCUSSION

DR. WINDLE: Dr. Hild has some comments on the possible role of neuroglia cells in myelination, as seen in tissue cultures.

DR. HILD: It has been pointed out that myelin formation in the central nervous system seems to take place under the influence of oligodendrocytes. This view is in agreement with the opinion expressed by earlier investigators, for instance del Río Hortega, that oligodendrocytes in brain and spinal cord play the same role as do Schwann cells in the peripheral nerves, as far as production and maintenance of myelin is concerned. I wonder whether the close proximity of oligodendrocytes to nerve fibers, sometimes seen in histological sections, is merely coincidental but not necessarily proof of a functional relationship. Even extensive studies, both with the light and the electron microscope, have not yet fully proven a relationship between oligodendrocytes and axons in the central nervous system similar to the association of Schwann cells to peripheral axons.

The tissue culture method offers a different approach to the study of the possible role played by neuroglia cells in the formation of myelin because the original arrangement of glial elements in relation to axons, as they exist in vivo and as they are seen in histologic sections, become altered after a piece of central nervous tissue has been explanted. In other words, the architectural plan of the tissue in situ becomes more and more modified after cultivation. In such experimental situations the properties and potentialities of individual cells can be evaluated more advantageously.

In cultures of kitten cerebellar folia, the deposition of myelin around single axons of Purkinje cells can be seen as early as 18 days after explantation, becoming markedly increased in older cultures.

It is beyond our present goal to describe in detail the morphological peculiarities of myelin formation, as seen in living preparations with phase contrast and polarized light microscopy or after fixation and staining, since we are only concerned here with the relationship of neuroglia cells to axons and with the role that they might play in myelination. Suffice to say that the first appearance of myelin around an axis cylinder consists of a cuff which spreads out in both directions, becoming more definite with time (Fig. 21A). In following the course of a particular axon, frequently one finds several of such collarlike centers of myelogenesis while the rest of the axon between such sites is naked. In the areas of primary deposition of myelin, the axis cylinder seems to contain a considerable amount of filamentous and rod-shaped mitochondria which are less evident in zones where myelination is completed (Fig. 21B). That the structures identified as myelin with phase optics in living preparations do really represent myelin, may be seen in Figure 22A which was photographed with polarized light.

Biology of Neuroglia

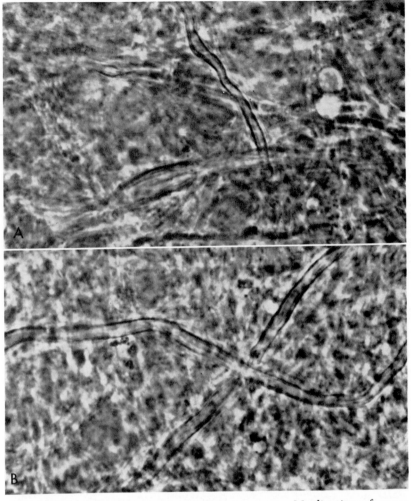

FIGURE 21. Photomicrographs of living neurons. Myelination of axons of Purkinje cells in a 43 day old roller tube culture of kitten cerebellum. A. Early stage. B. Fully myelinated. Phase contrast; magnification, 1500 ×.

In no instance have I seen typical, readily identifiable oligodendrocytes in the immediate vicinity or in adjacent areas where myelination is in progress. Their remote location from the site of primary myelin deposition does not speak in favor of del Río Horetga's conception.

The predominant neuroglia cell type, both in areas where myelin formation takes place as well as other regions of such cultures, are protoplasmic astrocytes. These cells form a three-dimensional network. However, it is impossible to establish a specific relationship between astrocytic processes and nerve fibers running over and through the network (Fig. 22B). At least within the limits of the resolving power of the light microscope, no ensheathment of nerve fibers by astrocytes, spiraling around nerve fibers, or any other peculiar association, similar to the relationship which exists between Schwann cells and peripheral axons, could be seen. Astrocyte processes cross the course of a nerve fiber in all directions without apparent functional interplay between the two elements.

I would like to introduce the working hypothesis that myelin

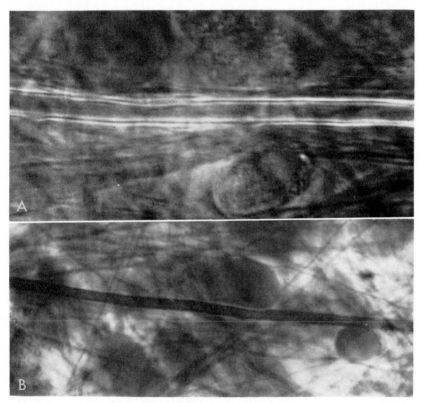

FIGURE 22. A myelinated Purkinje cell axon in a 38 day old roller tube culture of kitten cerebellum. A. Photographed in living culture with polarized light; magnification, 2000 ×. B. The same fiber after treatment according to O. Schultze's osmic acid-hematoxylin method; magnification, 1500 ×.

formation, at least in this experimental material, is accomplished primarily by the axons themselves.

DR. UZMAN: What is the source of the cultures, the age at which myelin appears and the conditions under which these are grown?

DR. HILD: The cultures were from the cerebellar folia of kittens from birth to 4 weeks old. Fragments approximately 2 mm square were explanted in an avian plasma clot on cover slips in roller tubes and fed with a nutrient medium containing 50 per cent Gey's balanced salt solution, 45 per cent human ascitic fluid and 5 per cent embryonic extract. An increased amount of glucose in the nutrient medium seems to act favorably on the maintenance of neurons in these cultures.

DR. MURRAY: How much extra glucose do you use?

DR. HILD: Approximately 200 milligrams per cent more than in the usual culture medium.

DR. GLEES: We found similar myelin formation in peripheral nerve fibers. We studied it in the rabbit's ear after crushing the nerve, waiting for regeneration to occur and then staining fixed sections with sudan black. We never saw Schwann cells in relation to this myelin. As you say, too, myelin segments appeared and part of the nerve fiber remained without Schwann cells. We saw myelin formation beginning where there would be a node of Ranvier later. Have you seen anything like this?

DR. HILD: I never saw anything like a node of Ranvier in tissue culture material. Moreover, I think we all agree that by definition there are no Schwann cells in the central nervous system. Even if we see interruptions of the myelin sheath they do not resemble nodes because the myelin never ends abruptly; it becomes thinner and thinner until it fades away. We have observed myelin extending for 600μ without interruption. Finally, I doubt that a node would occur where myelination is initiated.

DR. GLEES: Yes, but you would have noted something resembling it in the central nervous system.

DR. HILD: No. There is no evidence that there are nodes of Ranvier.

DR. GLEES: Have you seen structures resembling the incisures of Schmidt-Lantermann?

Dr. Hild: I have never observed a structure in my cultures resembling indentations of Schmidt-Lantermann, as in peripheral nerves.

Dr. Rose: How far out from the explant were these pictures taken?

Dr. Hild: The pictures were taken in various areas of the cultures, generally in the zone of outgrowth, since the optical conditions are more favorable there than in the thick parts of the original explant.

Dr. Dempsey: I am not quite clear, Dr. Hild. You say these myelinating fibers are remote from oligodendrocytes and that the nearby cells are not oligodendrocytes, in your opinion. I was not sure whether you said the myelinating fibers are remote from all cells, whether they are completely naked, whether they are not in any association with any cell.

Dr. Hild: The nerve fibers were not remote from all cells, since they usually did not grow out on the cell free area of the glass beyond the zone of outgrowth. What we frequently see, however, is that fibers cross cell free areas of liquefaction within the zone of outgrowth. Myelinated axons have been found spanning 20 to 30μ distances across such cell free areas. What I wanted to point out, however, was that even if there were topographic relationships between axons and surrounding neuroglia cells, it might be very difficult to prove a functional relationship.

Dr. Dempsey: Then myelin is indeed formed by the naked axon?

Dr. Hild: I do not yet have conclusive evidence, but there are many facts which point in this direction.

Dr. Murray: One of the points that you mentioned, which seems to me to point in another direction, is that you saw the myelin produced separately in segments that were not continuous along the same fiber. Is that right?

Dr. Hild: Yes, but the initiation of myelin formation within different centers in the course of a given axon does not necessarily mean that starting from these centers the myelin is deposited by other cells enveloping the nerve fiber. The accumulation of mitochondria in these areas within the axoplasm speaks rather in favor of an increase metabolic activity within this site which could result in the formation of myelin by the axon itself. This may involve a process comparable to that of endochondral ossification, where the replacement of cartilage arises from several centers.

DR. MURRAY: Well, when we saw that occurring on the fibers of spinal ganglion cells of the peripheral nerve, we saw Schwann cells associated with the segments. We took that to mean that there must be a Schwann cell or something extraneous to the nerve fiber itself which was producing this irregular segmental arrangement. We reasoned that if a fiber were going to myelinate wholly as a result of its own initiative, myelination should either start at the soma and move down continuously or go the other way; but where we saw this intermittent myelination of segments, we assumed that it represented response to different environmental conditions along the fiber.

DR. CLEMENTE: Dr. Glees' comment on peripheral nerve fiber regeneration and myelination without benefit of Schwann cells is an observation seen often in tissue cultures of the central nervous system. In peripheral nerve, Williams ('30) re-routed growing nerve fibers in the tail of the tadpole away from the bands of Büngner. The rate of regeneration of these fibers was only 39 per cent of those nerves which re-entered the distal Schwann sheath.

DR. UZMAN: Dr. Ross Harrison in 1924 showed in amphibian larvae that, if the neural crests are removed, the axons may grow peripherally but they never myelinate; as far as he could determine they did not conduct impulses.

DR. MURRAY: One of our problems in trying to run down this relationship of Schwann cells to the myelination of the peripheral fibers is the difficulty of doing quantitative work. Our general observation in cultures of dorsal root ganglia is that at the periphery of the outgrowth, where the fibers are naked, they never become myelinated. In the inner region just beside the explant, which is the preferential area of myelination, we are dealing with a complex felt-work of interwoven cells and fibers. In this we regularly see Schwann cell nuclei lying in indentations at about the middle of a myelin segment. But it seems an impossible task to check all of these segments for the presence of Schwann cell nuclei or to be sure, when we don't see one, that it is not underneath the fiber or obscured by some other cellular elements.

DR. UZMAN: I realize that you are not interested in myelin formation per se, but I can't help commenting that one of the problems of interest in our laboratory is the reconstruction of a three-dimensional view of the forming myelin sheath from a series of electron micrographs of longitudinal sections through the sciatic fibers of one-week old mice. We are particularly interested in the lamellar structure of myelin and the manner in which it terminates or is interrupted, both at nodes of Ranvier and Schmidt-Lantermann clefts. One would expect the Schwann cell surface to act as a natural limit to the myelin sheath, if one can extrapolate from the information gained from the study of transverse sections.

DR. SCHEIBEL: This is a very important point. The perpetuation in the literature of the relationship of myelin formation and oligodendrocyte is potentially damaging because it tends to freeze our thinking. Del Río Hortega said that he saw his type 3 and 4 oligodendrocytes spiraling cytoplasm around naked axis cylinders. We have pointed out previously that oligodendrocytes are extremely rich in completely unmyelinated areas. We must be very hesitant in accepting this idea of the unique relationship of oligodendrocytes to myelin formation in the central nervous system.

DR. COSTERO: I am thinking on this problem as a neuropathologist and from the knowledge of general histology of a common brain tumor. Because the element active in the formation of myelin is said to be the oligodendrocyte in the normal development of the central nervous system, I would be interested in pathological conditions which repeated this phenomenon. I have had the opportunity to examine many oligodendrogliomas, gliomas and inflammatory processes in which the activity of oligodendrocytes was involved. I have never found signs of excessive myelination, supermyelination; I found only demyelination. Why do not oligodendrocytes in tumors produce myelin? This is my suggestion for pathologists. If the actual oligodendrocytes produce myelin in some situations, why can't they participate in some form of myelin production in tumors. In my experience, also, oligodendrogliomas are accompanied by loss of myelin but never overmyelination. Perhaps we haven't yet full knowledge of what may happen in diseases. Also I must admit that some published observations may have escaped my attention. There are some recent studies that seem to be highly pertinent to this problem which indicate that the neuroglia cells need the nerve fibers to produce myelin. In my experience as a pathologist, I am left with the impression that neuroglia cells alone never form myelin.

DR. MURRAY: Dr. Costero, have you ever found myelin production in a neuroblastoma?

DR. COSTERO: No. But I think it is significant that the myelin production occurs after the full development of axons.

DR. LUMSDEN: There exist some instances in neuropathology which do relate to the questions raised by Dr. Costero. The hypermyelination of *status marmoratus* is one. As far as has been determined this appears to be due to transient antenatal damage (anoxic episode ?) to the basal ganglia at a time just prior to the occurrence of myelination. At this stage a good measure of regeneration of the damaged axons appears possible and, in the subsequent presence of large numbers of oligodendrocytes in the hypertrophic phase during the period of active myelination, it looks as though these regenerating axons become hypermyelinated. Another instance of hypermyelination is that of the curious and rare ganglion cell tumor (as it appears) of the cerebellum, designated under a number of different names including that, perhaps not inaptly, of "myelinated neurocytoma" (Duncan and Snodgrass, '43). In this hamartomatous tumorlike condition, the granule cells are hypertrophic and, contrary to the normal, their axons in the molecular layer are myelinated. As far as I can recollect from material which Dr. Duncan was kind enough to show me once, and from another case which I have recently seen at the Maida Vale Hospital (Oppenheimer, '55), this myelin which is abnormally present in the molecular layer is definitely associated with the abnormal presence there of oligodendrocytes in great numbers.

DR. WINDLE: The work of Duncan ('55) in experimental compression of the spinal cord should be mentioned in this connection. He pictured numerous hyperstaining nerve fibers. A possible relation to neuroglia cells has not been established. There are many reports on human material of somewhat similar nature. Druckman ('55) has reviewed them.

The Neuroglia-Vascular Relationship
And the Blood-Brain Barrier

Chapter 6

Perivascular Relationship of the Neuroglia Cells

ANGELO BAIRATI

IT IS AN old concept, widely held since the time of Virchow (1851), that the relationships between nervous tissue and blood vessels are very different in the central nervous system from what can be found in the organs furnished with a connective tissue framework. At that time the existence of a space between the vessel wall and the nervous tissue was, indeed, demonstrated. It is generally known that this space was described in various ways in different sites. It was called the Virchow space, Virchow-Robin space, space of His, and space of Key and Retius by different writers. Following the excellent account of the perivascular space by Schaltenbrand and Bailey ('28), Patek ('44) proposed a revision of these opinions. The fundamental results of many researches have been reviewed in a monograph by Glees ('55) and more recently Woollam and Millen ('55) added further to our knowledge by means of experimental studies.

In view of these studies we can now assume that one discontinuity only exists between vessels and nervous tissue; that is to say that there is one perivascular space which extends from pia mater surrounding the venous and arterial vessels, toward the depth of the nervous tissue. However, it is not yet clear how far this extends. On the contrary, we can take for granted, on the basis of electron microscope researches performed by Wyckoff and Young ('54) and Dempsey and Wislocki ('55), that a perivascular space does not exist at the capillary level. The perivascular space at the pial level communicates with the subarachnoid space and contains cerebrospinal fluid. The morphologist, therefore, has to study two problems: the nature of the lining surface of the

85

Biology of Neuroglia

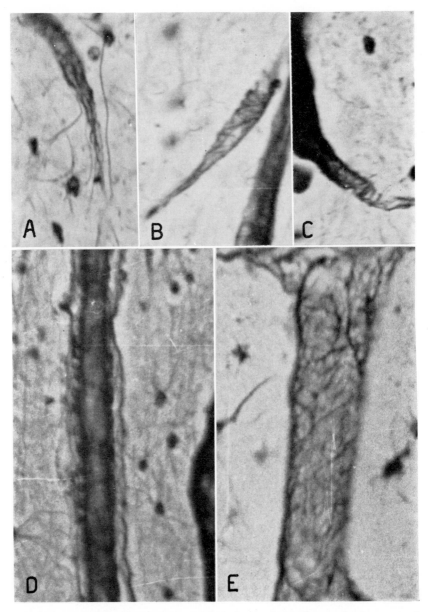

FIGURE 23. Photomicrographs of blood vessels of the cerebral cortex of a 41 year old man; Urechia-Nagy's method. A. B. C. Various aspects of the terminal (Schaltenbrand and Bailey; '28) ring. Magnification, 450 ×. D. First portion of the perivascular space surrounding a little artery of 50μ.

perivascular spaces and the nature and structure of the lining surface existing between blood and nervous tissue at the level of the capillaries. The latter constitutes the morphological problem of the blood-brain barrier.

LINING SURFACES OF THE PERIVASCULAR SPACES

The modalities of delimitation of the perivascular space are not similar throughout the length of a vessel. Two portions are distinguishable, the first one in proximity of the surface of nervous organs, the other around the deep vessels. The latter still presents some uncertainties concerning its magnitude, extension and location. Furthermore, the structures of the lining membranes are evaluated differently by various authors.

There is no doubt about the first portion placed near the pial surface. The recent experiments of Woollam and Millen ('55) confirmed what was well-known from previous investigations. The first portion of perivascular space is funnel shaped and furnished with two walls both composed of connective tissue (Fig. 23D). The internal wall is constituted by a lamina of connective tissue extending from the pia into the depth of the neural tissue. The extension of this lamina varies from site-to-site within the human neuraxis and in animals. In man the longest extension can be demonstrated at the level of the cerebral cortex, around the great vessels of the brain stem and at the perforated substances. The shortest one is the extension into the cerebellar cortex. According to Woollam and Millen, there is a constant relationship between the vessel caliber and the extension of this connective tissue lamina.

The connective tissue sheath of the outer wall of perivascular space shows the structure of a thin basal membrane (Fig. 23E). Parallel or reticulated fibers are found in the cerebral cortex and, among the fibrils, amorphous mucoprotein substance is found as in all connective tissues.

←≪≪

Magnification, 500 ×. E. Fibrillar reticulated structure of the connective tissue membrane forming the outer wall of the first tract of the perivascular space. Magnification, 650 ×.

It is difficult to establish how this connective tissue lamina ends. Schaltenbrand and Bailey ('28) suggested the presence of a terminal ring (Fig. 23A, B, C). The connective tissue of the lamina should then continue as the vascular adventitia. Patek ('44) maintained that this membrane becomes at first fenestrated and finally disappears.

Under the deep surface of the connective tissue membrane a glial layer can be found which is the continuation of the marginal neuroglia of Held covering the surface of the brain. Feet of neuroglia cells there stick to the outer surface of the connective tissue.

At the level of the ring (Schaltenbrand and Bailey, '28) the second portion of the perivascular space is assumed to begin but at this point there originates the previously mentioned discrepancies among various authors. As a matter of fact, Woollam and Millen ('55) even deny the existence of a perivascular space around the small vessels. These authors injected colloidal carbon particles into the subarachnoid space and demonstrated that these carbon particles penetrate only along the great vessels where both connective tissue membranes exist. According to them the true perivascular space can be found only at the level of the larger vessels. Their data show that morphological and experimental researches cannot entirely solve the problem. The divergent opinions may originate from investigations on different animals and may not be based on fundamental differences.

Investigations on man are even more difficult and open to question for two reasons: Histological techniques cannot avoid shrinkage and detachment of structures and direct experimental observations are impossible. Studies on human material are therefore limited to careful histological investigation and to the identification of the nature of the tissues surrounding the intracerebral vessels.

My own investigations were performed by varying the silver staining methods in order to demonstrate both connective tissue structures of the vessels and the glial structures (Bairati, '55). Moreover polarized light experiments were performed and histochemical tests, based on phenolic inversion of birefringency, made it possible to differentiate between collagenous and glial structures (Fig. 24). Investigations made by these techniques show the following features referring to the arrangement of the tissues around the intracerebral vessels:

(a) There are arterioles and venules ranging from 50 to 100μ

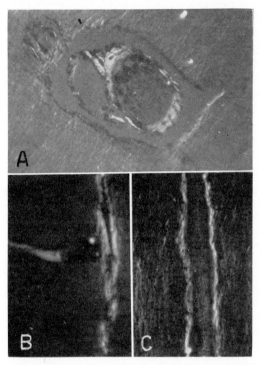

FIGURE 24. Connective tissue and glial structures of the perivascular space of a 22 year old man, photographed with polarized light. A. A blood vessel of the anterior perforated substance; the birefringency of the vessel wall and of the glial membrane is visible. B. Birefringency of the pia mater and the connective tissue funnel of the first tract. C. A little artery of the white matter; a true space is not apparent. Magnification of all photomicrographs, 250 ×.

in diameter which appear to be surrounded by a wide space with an outer surface formed by a fibrous layer. It is necessary to point out that the size of this space has certainly been increased by the histological technique. Cutting of sections, separates the vessel from the fibrous layer, thus proving that stable structural connections do not exist. This fibrous layer is made of

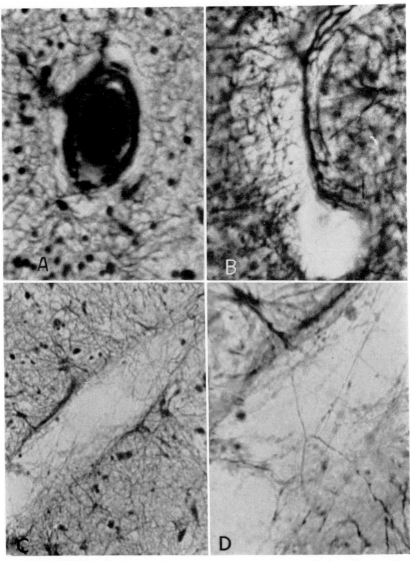

FIGURE 25. Glial membranes of the second portion of the perivascular space. A. Arteriole of the corpus striatum of a 34 year old man; note the thin glial sheath; Hortega method; magnification, 500 ×. B. Visible fibrillar glial membrane surrounding an arteriole of the inferior olivary nucleus in a one year old child. Hortega method; magnification, 500 ×. C. Held's glial membrane of a perivascular space in the mesencephalon of a one year old child. Hortega method; magnification, 350 ×. D. Detail of the same membrane as C, at a higher magnification of 700 ×.

dense interlacing gliofibrils (Fig. 25A, B). The thickness of the glial layer varies; it is constantly thicker in aged individuals than in young. It can be mistaken for collagenous structures, due to its fibrillar appearance but in this case polarized light shows sharply the glial nature of this layer.

(b) Around arterioles and venules of the white and gray matter of the spinal cord and brain-stem, ranging from 30 to 50μ in diameter, we see a thin perivascular space limited by a thin lamina, the glial membrane of Held. The structure of this membrane is as follows: Neuroglia cells neighboring the vessels send their processes to the vessel walls and build a thin interlaced sheath around them (Fig. 25C, D). The structural pattern of such a lamina bears some resemblance to that of basement membranes of epithelia, though the latter are made of collagenous fibers. It may be considered as a variant of the glial layer which surrounds the larger vessels.

(c) In arterioles and venules of smaller size the space is not visible or, more frequently, it appears to be incomplete and irregular. In certain sections of the vessel it seems to be adherent to the neuroglia, whereas at other points a thin space is found with a surface glial covering. It is not possible to affirm whether in these cases a thin persistent space disappears because of the adherence of the neuroglia to the vessels or whether the small perivascular spaces are technical artifacts. Occasionally many neuroglia cell processes encircle the vessel, but often they get fixed to the adventitia of the latter. These pictures correspond to the well-known patterns that have been described by several authors, who depicted the relationship of the footlike processes of neuroglia cells with the vessel walls (Fig. 26A, B, C, D). However, it is hard to state whether in these regions a true glial membrane does exist; in the cross sections of the vessel walls it is difficult, even under polarized light, to make a distinction between a connective tissue and a glial sheath.

The structures described above are apparent in regions in which the fibrous astrocytes are numerous. In contrast to this, the cerebral cortex and, especially, the cerebellar cortex are regions where fibrous astrocytes are scarce or missing and glial membranes are never found. In these regions the structure is that

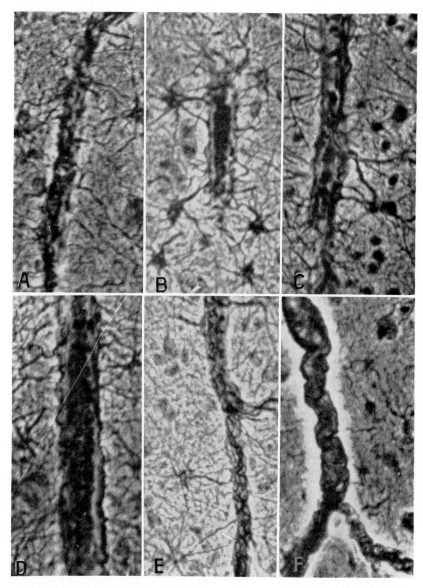

FIGURE 26A, B, C, D. Arterioles with many glial end-feet, from the white matter of the telencephalon of a 38 year old man. The perivascular space is not always visible. Hortega method; magnification, 500 ×. E, F. Comparison of arterioles of the white (in E) and the gray matter (in F) of the brain. Shrinkage of the nervous tissue from the vessel is apparent in F. Hortega method; magnification, 450 ×.

of a thin amorphous layer in which few short and protoplasmic processes of neuroglia cells are embedded. In silver stained preparations the vessel wall often appears surrounded by a poorly stained transparent layer which is crossed by the processes of neuroglia cells. In these regions we can often see a detachment of the nervous tissue from the vessel wall (Fig. 26E, F). Consequently, from the comparison between these pictures and the above mentioned structures of the white matter, it is possible to conclude that, where numerous feet of neuroglia cells actually touch the vascular wall the technique can scarcely break these connections and, where the end-feet are scarce or missing, such a detachment due to shrinkage is easly produced.

I am of the opinion that, at the level of arterioles and venules of the human nervous system, one can find almost constantly between the vessel walls and nervous tissue a *locus minoris resistentiae* which, in the histological preparations, looks like a perivascular space. It shows variations and irregularities according to the vessel calibers and is interrupted when glial feet make stable contact with the vascular wall. This space cannot be mistaken for the subglial and perineuronal spaces described by His and others and that nowadays are taken to be artifacts. This *locus minoris resistentiae* can either be due to a layer lacking glial structures but having amorphous cementing substance or can be due to the presence of a true perivascular space. It is my opinion that this second interpretation is more likely to be correct. However, it is very hard to define its extension around the small vessels and determine its morphological attributes with the ordinary techniques. The surfaces of these spaces are formed by the connective tissue of adventitia and by the neuroglia. This conception seems to be supported by some electron microscopical pictures of Van Bremen and Clemente ('55). It would seem that around the small vessels there is a true space limited by the vascular adventitia and by glial structures.

The living structure of human perivascular spaces shows three main structures related to caliber of the blood vessels and to regions; the fibrous astrocyte, the glial membrane and an almost amorphous layer. The characteristics depend on the peculiarities of the neuroglia in various locations. Fibrous astrocytes predom-

Biology of Neuroglia

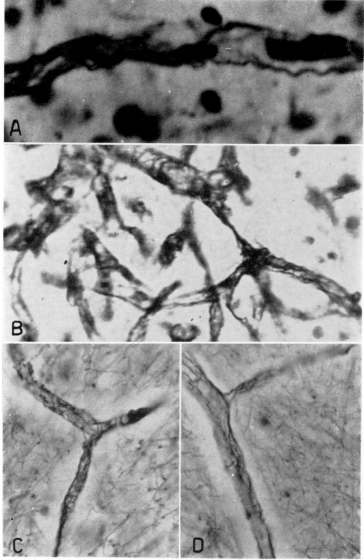

FIGURE 27. Capillaries in the brain of a 41 year old man. A. A little vessel of the cerebral cortex in which the reticulated adventitia of the precapillary seems to get lost in the true capillary; magnification, 1000 ×. B. Peculiar capillary vessels with thick adventitia from the paraventricular nucleus of hypothalamus. Magnification, 500 ×. C, D. Typical reticulated adventitia of capillaries of the mesencephalon. All were stained by Urechia-Nagy's method; magnification, 500 ×.

inate in white matter and in the gray of spinal cord and brain stem and, correlatively, fibrous glial membranes occur there. On the contrary, in the supra-axial centers, especially the cerebral cortex, where fibrous astrocytes are absent or scarce, simple amorphous layers almost totally lack neuroglia cell processes.

MORPHOLOGICAL BASIS OF THE BLOOD-BRAIN BARRIER

According to Patek ('44) the structure of the capillary endothelium is the same in nervous centers as it is in connective tissue of all the other organs. Therefore, capillary structure cannot help to explain the behavior of the hematoencephalic barrier. On the other hand, knowledge of the mechanism which checks the permeability of the capillaries in tissues—according to the view of Angevine ('50) on the hematoconnective barrier—indicates that the morphological basis of capillary permeability lies in the submicroscopic structure or even in molecular organization. This explains why the microscopical structure does not offer directly the morphological basis for the study of the hematoencephalic barrier. Only the use of the electron microscope and of histochemical methods made such an approach possible. Assuming the absence of a perivascular space at the capillary level, the following problems can be analyzed by the morphologist: structure of the capillaries of the central nervous system and relationship between capillaries and neuroglia cell processes.

Mainly for technical reasons, it remains undecided whether the capillaries of the central nervous system are enveloped by an adventitial reticular layer. The data now available on the basis of modifications of the silver staining methods, according to the suggestions of Lhotka and Myhre ('53), Massari ('54), Catolla-Cavalcanti ('49), Clara ('55) and my own studies under polarized light, may be summarized as follows: The endothelial lining of the encephalic vessels is not different from that of other territories. The existence of an adventitial reticular layer similar to that enveloping the capillaries of the other organs seems to have been verified for the white matter and for the brain stem in man (Fig. 27C, D). In the cerebral and cerebellar cortex, reticular fibers which surround the wall of precapillaries seem to get lost in true capillaries (Fig. 27A). In these regions, therefore, a collagenous fibrillary adventitia is lacking; this was found to be true by Dempsey and Wislocki ('55) by means of the electron micro- scope. In some regions of the brain, as for instance in the nuclei of chiasmatic-infundibular region of the hypothalamus and in the area postrema, special capillaries have been found which react well to the silver staining methods and reveal complicated fibril-

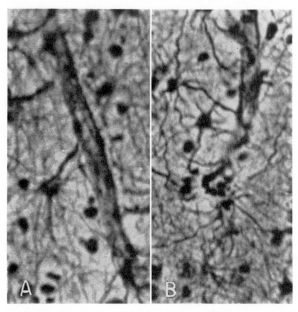

FIGURE 28. Many end-feet of fibrous astrocytes on capillaries of the mesencephalon of a 44 year old man. Hortega method; magnification, 500 ×.

lar structures (Fig. 27B). These capillaries have recently formed the object of electron microscopial studies by Dempsey and Wislocki ('55).

Relationship between capillaries and neuroglia cells have been discussed since Golgi, Ramon y Cajal and del Río Hortega. Fur- ther researches confirm their data (Fig. 28). The shape of these glial expansions is variable: membranous, spiral, funnel-like end- feet. As a matter of fact, the intimate adhesion of these end-feet to the vessel wall was beautifully shown by Wyckoff and Young ('54) by means of the electron miscroscope. The only point under discussion is whether all the expansions of the end-feet come into mutual contact to form another glial membrane on the endothelium, or whether the end-feet are discontinuous and scattered, to cover only parts of the capillary surface.

The researches of Dempsey and Wislocki ('55) revealed the existence of tiny intervals between the end-feet of the neuroglia cells. Furthermore, these authors have shown a thin layer lying between endothelium and end-feet.

A substance, apparently amorphous and moderately opaque to electrons, seems to fill these intervals. The behavior of this material in regard to its ability for silver reduction seems to be slightly different in nervous and connective tissues. However, in nervous tissue it seems to be continuous with other, more scarce, material lying in between the nervous elements.

CONCLUDING REMARKS

On the basis of morphological data, some interpretations may be given. An hypothesis may be advanced on the functional significance of the membranous glial structure which envelops the perivascular space. It may play some role in the circulation of the fluids. This seems more obvious if one takes into account the demonstration of the contractile capacity of the neuroglia cells, as recently shown by Pomerat ('53b). On the other hand, it is possible that the limiting membranes may check filtration of interstitial fluid flowing from the nervous tissue toward the cerebrospinal fluid spaces or vice versa, as was suggested by Weed ('23) on the basis of experimental researches and maintained by Patek ('44). However, this deserves further histophysiological investigation. In regard to the problem of the morphological basis of the hematoencephalic barrier, it may be said that analysis with the electron microscope has summoned data for interpretation of the mechanism. Glees ('55) previously held the view that the barrier may depend on the interaction of the physiological peculiarities of the capillaries and glial structures. Hess ('55c) focused the attention on the characters of the amorphous substance, showing experimentally that changes in the latter affect permeability of the blood-brain barrier. In this regard the researches of Dempsey and Wislocki ('55) are of great importance, insofar as they point out clear-cut differences between the capillaries of connective

Biology of Neuroglia

tissue and those of the nervous centers. In the former, direct relationships occur between the structureless endothelial substance and the ground substance of connective tissue. A unique filtrating membrane is thus formed by endothelium and by its subendothelial layer. On the contrary, in cerebral capillaries the membrane is further complicated by the existence of glial end-feet and of cementing material whose nature is different from that of ground substance of the connective tissues. It has been rightly pointed out that the existence of a stratification composed of two successive layers may be the morphological basis of the great selectivity of the hematoencephalic barrier.

Chapter 7

Fine Structure of the Neuropil in Relation To Neuroglia Cells*

EDWARD W. DEMPSEY AND SARAH LUSE

THE NEUROPIL may be defined as the material occupying the territory between the elements of the central nervous system which can be identified by light microscopy. It is the *terra incognita* which remains when the neurons, fibers and neuroglia cells are subtracted. In sections stained with hematoxylin and eosin, it has a faintly granular or fibrillar appearance and takes a pale pink coloration. Because the neural and glial processes course through it, branching into smaller and smaller elements, the neuropil is often thought of as a meshwork of submicroscopic neural and glial fibers, possibly embedded in a hypothetical extracellular ground substance.

In recent years, electron microscopy has progressed to such a point that its higher resolution can be applied to sections of the central nervous system. Methods have been devised permitting fixation, embedding and thin sectioning adequate for the high magnifications possible with the instrument. When such high resolution micrographs of the neuropil became available, it was immediately noted that the meshwork of fibers was extraordinarily extensive and that the individual processes were everywhere fitted together so accurately that little extracellular space was present. Figures 29, 30 and 31 illustrate representative areas of the neuropil. In them, profiles of the neural and glial processes approximate each other so closely that spaces of only 100 to 200 Å width separate the contiguous plasma membranes. Such dimen-

* This investigation was supported by a grant (B-425) from the National Institute of Neurological Diseases and Blindness.

99

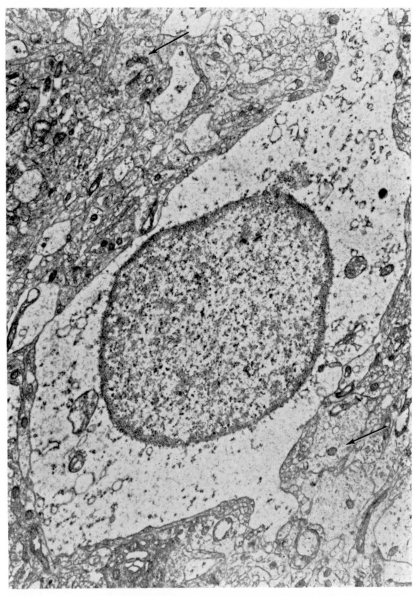

FIGURE 29. Section through an oligodendrocyte and its surrounding neuropil from the spinal cord of a 5 day old mouse. The pale cytoplasm, spheroidal nucleus and sparse, stubby processes of the oligodendrocyte are well illustrated. Further criteria for identifying this cell type are its occurrence in rows in white matter, its satellite location near neurons and its

sions are similar to those of the spaces separating the two elements of synapses and to those between adjacent epithelial cells. They are infinitesimal when compared to the extracellular territory in connective tissues.

The question arises as to the cells of origin of the various processes which collectively make up the neuropil. Some, by their characteristic fine structure, can be recognized as neural and identified as either axons or dendrons. Another type, illustrated in Figure 29, is pale and relatively infrequent. These can be traced into continuity with the cell body of a pale cell with a round or ovoid nucleus which, by its distribution, morphology and satellite relationship to neurons, we have identified as the oligodendrocyte. A remaining type of process is smaller in diameter, denser and ubiquitous in occurrence. This type is associated with cells which have a dense cytoplasm and irregular nuclei. From their distribution and other relationships we infer that they are astrocytes. They occur in two forms, the protoplasmic and fibrous varieties. In the latter, fascicles of delicate intracellular fibrillae are common. The margins of the astrocytes are extraordinarily complex; they are extensively refolded upon themselves so that the territory occupied by astrocytic cytoplasm proves to contain a multitude of processes or projections which apparently press into and occupy all of the available space between the other structures of the neuropil (Fig. 30). Myelinated axons, unmyelinated dendrons and oligodendrocyte processes are ordinarily surrounded by a feltwork of these pleated processes. They frequently establish contact with neurons on the one hand and with capillary walls on the other. The latter relationship leaves little doubt that they are the elements responsible for the

---

← ⫶

prevailing occurrence in an oligodendroglioma, which we have studied. The surrounding neuropil illustrates the dense meshwork of fibers of which it is comprised. Some of the processes are pale and resemble the oligodendrocyte cytoplasm. Others *(arrows)* are moderately dense and contain granules and mitochondria similar to those of neurons. A remainder of quite small, dense processes resemble the cytoplasm of astrocytes. These processes are tightly packed together, so that little extracellular space is demonstrable. Dalton's osmium-bichromate fixative; magnification, 10,000 ×.

Biology of Neuroglia

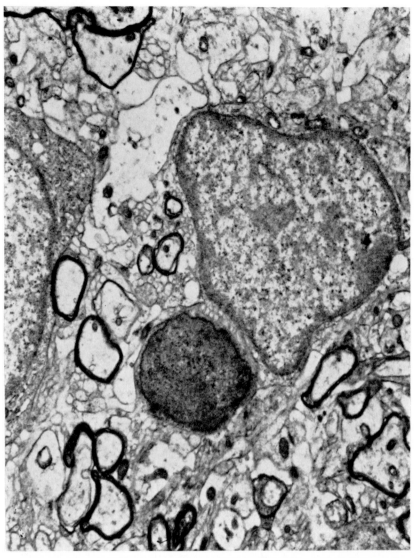

FIGURE 30. Sections through an astrocyte, microglia cell and part of a neuron from the cerebral cortex of a rat 25 weeks old. The astrocyte is the cell with the large nucleus in the center of the field. Near the nucleus, its cytoplasm is dense and granular. Farther away, the cytoplasm is divided into processes by extensive folding or pleating of the plasma membranes. In the meshwork of processes so formed, myelinated fibers, oligodendrocyte processes and a microglia cell are embedded. These glial processes also invest closely the margin of the neuron, as illustrated along the left of the

astrocytic end-feet which are apparent in silver stained preparations (Fig. 32A). The glial processes are closely applied to the capillary basement membrane, so that no perivascular space is visible. The capillary Virchow-Robin space seen in ordinary microscopical sections must therefore be regarded as a shrinkage artifact.

The relationship of the neuropil to the capillary wall, illustrated in Figure 32A, is not the only one encountered in the nervous system. Although in most locations the glial feltwork is closely applied to the capillary wall, it is well to remember that certain regions have an unusual kind of vascularization. Dempsey and Wislocki ('55) examined several of the areas of the nervous system which are unusual in that they are capable of storing vitally administered dyes. These regions, which include the pineal body, the infundibular process of the pituitary gland, the choroid plexus, the area postrema and the intercolumnar tubercle, become blackened when silver salts are administered to produce an experimental argyria. In these regions, the glial processes do not reach the basement membrane of the capillary but, instead, invest a second membrane which surrounds the capillary at some distance from its wall. Between this membrane and the endothelium is a space or sheath filled with collagenous fibers and connective tissue cells. Thus, these regions which are known to store vital dyes are characterized by a perivascular connective tissue sheath in which storage of silver particles can be demonstrated (Fig. 32C). Within this sheath, the elements of loose connective tissue, including its extracellular ground substance, fibrils and basement membranes are present and it is this area which contains most of the stored silver salts.

Another aspect of the neuropil concerns its relationship to the myelinated fibers which course through it. We have already indicated that such fibers are frequently surrounded by the processes of neuroglia cells, especially those of astrocytes (Fig. 30). Upon examination with higher magnification, the myelin sheath

---

← ◄◄◄

figure. Note that here, as in the preceding figure, little extracellular space is evident. Dalton's osmium-bichromate fixative; magnification, 10,000 ×.

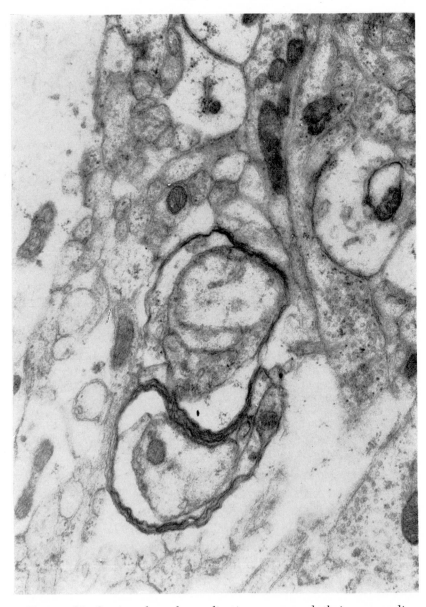

FIGURE 31. Section through myelinating axons and their surrounding neuropil from the spinal cord of a mouse 5 days old. In the lower center part of the figure is an axon with only a few lamellae of myelin. These lamellae are continuous with the plasma membranes surrounding contiguous glial processes, one of which exhibits a mitochondrion. In the neuropil,

becomes resolved into a system of concentric lamellae, similar to the structure of myelin as it has been observed in peripheral nerves (Geren, '54). Since in peripheral nerve, the lamellae are continuous with the plasma membrane of the investing Schwann cell, it was thought of interest to examine the brains of young animals during myelination to determine the possible relationship between myelin and the neuroglia cell membranes.

The axons of the brain and spinal cord are unmyelinated at birth in rats and mice. Myelin puts in its appearance during the first few days of postnatal life. For early stages of myelination, it is necessary only to examine sections made from animals killed during the first week after birth. In such preparations, we have frequently observed axons surrounded by a few lamellae of myelin. These lamellae, in high resolution micrographs, can be traced from their location in the myelin sheath through continuations which comprise the plasma membranes of contiguous glial processes (Fig. 31). Although absolute identification has not yet been accomplished, these processes appear to be terminal extensions derived ultimately from oligodendrocytes. In any event, the myelin sheath would appear to be a modified derivative of the plasma membrane of neuroglia cells. Such sheaths, once formed, may be isolated from one another by the secondary penetration of astrocytic processes between adjacent myelinated axons.

The structure of the neuropil, as described in the preceding paragraphs, requires some modification of the concepts of a ground substance of the central nervous system and of the blood-brain barrier. With respect to the ground substance, Hess ('53) observed a delicate pink reaction with the periodic-acid Schiff reagents which was localized within the neuropil and which was absent in the formed elements of the nervous system. Since the PAS reaction is characteristic of mucopolysaccharides, and since

---

many neural processes can be identified by their characteristic mitochondria and small vesicles. Relatively few astrocytic processes are apparent, but several of the large, pale processes of oligodendrocytes are present. The fibers of the neuropil are closely packed with little intervening space. Dalton's osmium-bichromate fixative; magnification, 35,000 ×. (From Luse ('56b); courtesy, *Journal of Biophysical and Biochemical Cytology.*)

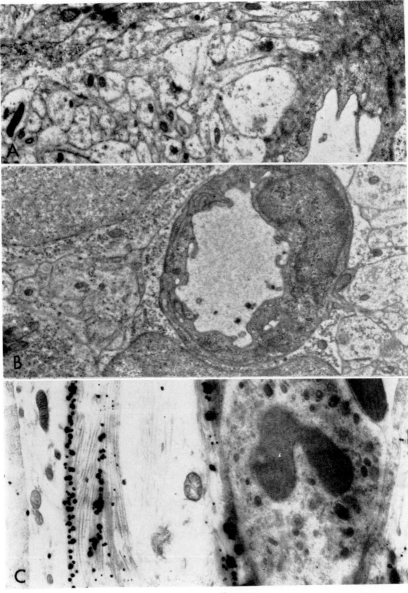

FIGURE 32. A. Section through the wall of a capillary from the spinal cord of a neonatal mouse. The wall of the capillary is in contact with glial processes without any perivascular space. Both the pale oligodendrocyte processes and the denser, smaller astrocyte end-feet (upper right) established contact with the capillary wall. B. Section through a capillary from

the reaction was abolished after acetylation of the sections, Hess regarded this as presumptive evidence for the presence of a ground substance, probably interstitial in location. In subsequent papers, he showed that the PAS reaction was absent at birth in rats and mice, and that it appeared coincidentally with the development of the blood-brain barrier (Hess, '55a, b). He found also that the PAS reaction was abolished together with the blood-brain barrier at the margins of surgical lesions (Hess, 55c). It appeared, therefore, that a substance, presumably a mucopolysaccharide, occupied the spaces between the cellular processes of the nervous system and that this substance was important for hydration and fluid transfer in the brain.

The observations cited above were made before it was known that interstitial spaces in the neuropil are extraordinarily small. An extracellular ground substance, as envisioned by Hess, now appears improbable since there seems not to be an adequate space for it. Yet, it is necessary to account for the PAS reaction of the neuropil. The areas exhibiting a positive PAS reaction are the same as those in which there is an extensive meshwork of fine glial fibrils. Hypertrophic astrocytes, in astrocytomas, are known to react with the PAS reagents. Moreover, myelin sheaths, here shown to be composed of layers of glial plasma membranes, also exhibit a PAS reaction. These considerations permit the speculation that the glial membranes are reactive. Because of their thin-

---

← ⫷⫷

the cerebral cortex of a neonatal mouse. To the right of the capillary, a glial investment is present. Along the lower and left-hand margins of the vessel, the cytoplasm of two neurons is contiguous to the vessel wall. The glial investment of capillaries is therefore incomplete in the brain of this neonatal animal. C. Section through the wall of a capillary from the area postrema of an adult rat. Filling the capillary lumen is a polymorphonuclear leukocyte. This rat had been given a dilute solution of silver nitrate to drink for 12 months prior to the removal of the tissue. The deposited silver, in this part of the brain, is localized in the basement membrane of the endothelium, in the perivascular connective tissue sheath and in an amorphous basement membrane at the margin of the neuroglia cell shown at the extreme left. A, B. Dalton's osmium-bichromate fixative; magnification, 100,000 ×. C. Palade's buffered osmium fixative; magnification, 20,000 ×. (A, from Luse ('56a); C, from Dempsey and Wislocki ('55); courtesy, *Journal of Biophysical and Biochemical Cytology.*)

ness, their reactivity is not ordinarily apparent with the light microscope; but it becomes so whenever the refolding process is so extensive as to build up many layers of membranes in the optical path. Such replication of the membranes occurs in myelin and on the refolded surfaces of mature astrocytes. This concept provides an alternative explanation for the localization of the PAS reaction in the neuropil.

A problem still remains concerning the coincidental appearance of the PAS reaction and the blood-brain barrier in the developing nervous system. We have observed, in our examination of the brains from neonatal animals, that the astrocyte processes are neither so numerous nor so ubiquitous in young animals as in older ones. Indeed, in neonatal animals, neurons have been seen to touch directly the walls of adjacent capillaries (Fig. 32B). On the contrary, in adults, capillaries are invariably ensheathed completely by glial processes so that a layer of glial tissue is interposed between the neuron and its neighboring blood vessel. The completion of the glial perivascular sheath occurs, therefore, at approximately the time at which the blood-brain barrier develops, and also at the time the PAS reaction puts in its appearance.

The exact location of the so-called blood-brain barrier has been extensively debated. Wislocki and Leduc ('52) have shown that different substances are stored selectively in the parenchyma and stroma in regions such as the area postrema and choroid plexus. Dempsey and Wislocki ('55) showed that silver deposits occur extensively in the connective tissues but not in the glial or neural tissues. Thus, the site beyond which the vital dyes are absent would seem to be the glial capillary margin. The fact that the glial investment of this margin is incomplete in neonatal rats and mice would seem to offer an explanation for the passage of vital dyes into the brain in these animals.

ROUND TABLE DISCUSSION

Dr. Windle: We have heard two excellent papers on these relationships and are left to wonder where the extracellular fluid of the brain, if such there be, is located.

DR. POPE: I would like to ask Dr. Dempsey: What constitutes the extracellular fluid or chloride space in the brain?

DR. DEMPSEY: I would like to ask whether you are sure there is an extracellular space in the brain.

DR. POPE: There certainly is something which operationally can be defined as a chloride or inulin or thiocyanate space, a space ordinarily equated with the extracellular fluid phase of the brain. Of course it is true that the figures for the volume of this space have varied greatly, depending upon the method used for its estimation. I believe that, based on the classical assumption that chloride is an extracellular ion, Lowry and others have calculated the extracellular fluid space to be of the order of 30 to 35 per cent of the total tissue volume.

DR. DEMPSEY: This is an assumption, however, that it must be extracellular, is it not? A space has not been demonstrated directly in the brain. It has been demonstrated in tissue other than nervous.

DR. POPE: That is correct, of course, and it is just because of this that I want to bring the question up for discussion. I wonder if you can elaborate on where you think the brain chloride might be, if it is not in the hypothetical extracellular fluid compartment.

DR. DEMPSEY: I don't know. There are many very baffling problems related to this that are to me great mysteries. One of them is the problem of cerebral edema. What happens in cerebral edema? Do neuroglia cell processes, which we see, enlarge because the fluid goes inside the neuroglia cells, or, under conditions of cerebral edema, is there a separation of the cells with the accumulation of an interstitial fluid? I don't know.

DR. ELLIOTT: I would like to see how things can be reconciled. We have been studying spaces in cerebral cortex from rat and man by a very simple technique. All we have are slices, 0.5 mm thick, in an isotonic medium with glucose and oxygen. By putting low concentrations of thiocyanate and sucrose in the medium and measuring the amounts of these that get into the slices, we find clearly defined intracellular and extracellular spaces. The intracellular space, which is the space not occupied by the marker substance, is the same with either sucrose or thiocyanate. Though I haven't done the calculations very recently, I think they are just about the same as the intracellular

Biology of Neuroglia

spaces found by chloride determinations. So to my mind there is a clear extracellular space.

When we put a slice like that in a medium and leave it, it swells nearly 50 per cent quite rapidly. This swelling fluid, under optimal conditions, does not seem to be in the intracellular space as judged by thiocyanide and sucrose; but it does not seem to be in the ordinary extracellular space either. When we use inulin as the marker, the inulin seems to occupy just a little more than the volume of the swelling fluid and not the whole extracellular space. As the swelling increases the inulin space increases. So the inulin occupies only a little bit more than the fluid of swelling. I don't know what this "swelling space" is. The fact that potassium does not escape at a great rate from the slice makes one think that swelling cannot be uptake of fluid through big holes opened in the cut processes. But swelling does seem, to some extent, to be connected with the extent of damage done to the tissue. If we cut thicker slices, in which the proportion of damaged cells must be less, we get less swelling. We don't get anything like as great swelling with tissues like kidney cortex or liver. But we get just as big swelling with nerve. So there is big swelling which seems to be in what we call the third space; sometimes we speak of it as "extraneous" fluid. The fluid that is taken up seems to have the same composition as the suspending medium.

There is another type of swelling. The simplest way of producing it, though we can produce it in two other ways, is to have the slice anaerobic. That swelling now happens clearly in the intracellular space. We get quite an increase in the intracellular space besides the extraneous or third space swelling. When metabolism is interfered with, by lack of oxygen, the intracellular space definitely swells as shown by both sucrose and inulin. A change in the membrane allows thiocyanate to penetrate slowly into the intracellular space, so you can't mark the space so well with thiocyanate anaerobically.

In order to prevent the swelling, we made the medium twice isotonic by putting in 10 per cent sucrose. After the usual period of incubation, the slice looked fine and it had not gained in weight but we found that the extraneous fluid, the swelling fluid, was still there as judged by an expanded inulin space. What had happened was that the intracellular space had shrunk. The increased osmotic pressure outside had shrunk the intracellular space to about one-third or less of what it was originally. The slice looked the same and had not apparently swollen, but it had swollen in one respect and had been shrunken in another respect, in the intracellular space. Now that is with medium made twice isotonic with sucrose. We have not done much with other solutes but, because we wanted to do some experiments with steroids dissolved in alcohol, we tested the effect of one per cent alcohol. This makes the medium nearly twice isotonic and also causes the intracellular space to shrink. I am quite sure that formalin or anything else you use as fixative is going to change the intracellular space drastically. So when one takes a tissue or a tissue culture and changes the situation one must expect the intracellular and extracellular spaces to be greatly altered from the original condition.

I would like to know how that fits in with what has been told us here. First of all, how the tissue can be packed full of cells and processes so that there is obviously no room for an extracellular space, and yet other studies indicate that there is a definite extracellular space, and a third or extraneous space, as well as an intracellular space which can expand and change under anaerobic conditions. How can you examine your tissues and get good pictures without changing the natural condition by fixation processes? I believe every word and picture that I have heard and seen here but I cannot believe them at the same time as I am thinking of our own experiments (Elliott, '55a; Pappius and Elliott, '56a).

DR. CAMMERMEYER: The effect of mutilation, as illustrated by differences in swelling of thin and thick brain slices submerged in a fluid, is also readily demonstrated over the spinal cord with even the smallest tear of the pia-glia membranes through which white matter bulges. Such a change may be erroneously interpreted as a tumor or duplication of the spinal cord, pseudoheterotopia (Weil, '46). A similar swelling of the spinal cord is obtained after submersion in distilled water. This reaction varies with the region and species. The area of greatest swelling for man is the lower cervical and upper thoracic segments (Cammermeyer, '53);

for cat it is the lower thoracic segments, for rabbit the lumbar segments and, for opossum the cervical segments moderately only. The speed with which swelling takes place in cats is apparently regulated by factors which are correlated with weight of the animals. The volume of successive spinal cord regions was determined according to a technique developed here (Cammermeyer, '55b), immediately after removal and again after submersion in distilled water for 0.5, 1, 2, 3 and 4 hours. The smaller cat cords increased in volume more rapidly than the bigger ones.

DR. POMERAT: One of the areas of study that those of us who work with living cells, particularly with time lapse cinematography, are always concerned with is the matter of cell drinking or pinocytosis. This was described initially by Warren Lewis ('31) who was able to demonstrate that a cell might take in a third of its volume of fluid in one hour. Pinocytosis has not only been seen in tissue culture but also in the work that Glenn Algire has done with chambers in the mouse skin. This would seem to be an important phenomenon with regard to the movements of large quantities of fluid.

DR. DEMPSEY: I am not quite clear as to whether I am supposed to clarify all the things that have come up in this discussion, but if so I would certainly like to do it before the situation gets any more obscure. There is a point I would like to make in answer to Dr. Elliott's comments. It is necessary at the present, I think, to expand the simple concept of an intracellular and an extracellular space. The cell can no longer be regarded as a sphere suspended in a solution. It ingests fluid by surrounding a droplet which it segregates within itself as a vacuole, by the process of pinocytosis. Hence, inside itself the cell has an intracellular space made up of vacuoles of extracellular material. Now this idea is by no means an invention of mine or of Dr. Pomerat. This process has been extensively studied by light microscopists. The tissue culture people and the people who record by motion picture techniques have studied this process extensively for many years. The electron microscopists have recently become interested in it. At the recent Tissue Fine Structure Conference held at Arden House, I thought a great deal of attention was paid to the fact that an extensive intracellular canalicular system exists in many cells, particularly those cells having an extensive endoplasmic reticulum which is continuous with the extracellular phase. That is, the canals inside the cell communicate by means of pores with the outside of the cell. Now they are neither-nor; they are not quite extracellular and they are not quite intracellular. One can regard them as being partially segregated within the cell. Those that are closed off completely as vacuoles, I would think, might well exhibit electromotive differences between themselves and the outside of the cell. They do create, it seems to me, a new category of space for the chemist to concern himself with and worry about.

DR. FLEXNER: Where is Hess' PAS-positive substance?

DR. DEMPSEY: Well, I wish I knew the answer. I think the best guess, since you are forcing me to speculate, is that there is a material which is PAS-positive. There appears to be no extracellular space sufficient in size to account for it. It is, however, known now—it was not known to Hess at the time—that hypertrophic astrocytes in tumors are faintly PAS-positive. It is also known that the substances commonly thought to be associated with cellular membranes are lipoidal in nature and many of the lipoidal materials give a PAS reaction. We have to consider now that the neuropil contains the most excessively refolded cell membranes you can imagine. The region is just full of membranes, which in microscopic sections 10μ thick must comprise many, many layers. These, if faintly PAS-positive, individually would add up to a perceptible reaction. So, forcing me to speculate, my best guess is that the PAS-positive material of Hess represents the margins of the excessively folded neuroglia cell processes.

DR. FLEXNER: Have you electron microscopists evidence that fixation and embedding, as carried out, does not produce shrinkage—a differential shrinkage of an extracellular space—or is that something that is impossible to answer?

DR. PALAY: I think most of the artifacts that we see are increases rather than decreases in the intracellular spaces. Elements of tissues are pulled away from one another. That is most commonly what you see when the method has failed as compared to what you would expect. The elements of cytoplasm within a cell simply seem to be pulled apart because if you carefully match the clots of the tissue with neighboring clots when there is a space between them, you can see that when you push them together they would exactly fit, and this is an indication that the spaces represent cracks.

Dr. Clemente: One of the primary points brought out in Hess' ('55a, b) articles was the close correlation between the time he observed PAS-positive material staining in the newborn rat brain (4-5 days) and the reported time of onset of the blood-brain

FIGURE 33. A median sagittal view of a 15 day old embryo which had been injected intravascularly with trypan blue and delivered 6 hours after injection.

barrier to trypan blue (Behnsen, '27). Grazer and I ('57) have recently reported some experiments in which rat fetuses were injected with trypan blue. Our findings do not confirm those of Behnsen and are inconsistent in time relationship with the appearance of Hess' PAS-positive material. Figure 33 shows a rat fetus of 15 days which had been injected with 0.5 per cent trypan blue 6 hours prior to delivery of the fetuses. Notice the entire nervous system remained uncolored while all other organs stained deeply with the dye. We have observed similar results in fetal and newborn kittens. The blood-brain barrier to trypan blue is a phenomenon which is observable in very early fetuses (in rats as early as the eleventh day of gestation). Therefore, we cannot see any relationship between the onset of the PAS-positive staining reaction and the blood-brain barrier formation, in any event with respect to trypan blue.

Dr. Dempsey: How long a time were you able to have the trypan blue in the animal before its death?

Dr. Clemente: The embryos were alive when they were delivered 6 to 24 hours after injection.

Dr. Dempsey: I believe it has been shown that leakage of trypan blue into the central nervous system is slow as compared with that in other tissues. The brain, even at the time when it has been claimed that the blood-brain barrier has not yet formed in the newborn rat and mouse, is still not as permeable to the dye as the connective tissue. So it could well be that the apparent discrepancy can be explained largely on the technical grounds of the length of time it would take an appreciable quantity of the dye to escape into the nervous system.

Dr. Clemente: This might be true but, if an adult rat is injected with one milliliter of a 0.5 per cent solution of trypan blue for several weeks, there is some staining of the nervous system beyond the capillary. Dye granules can be seen away from the ependyma all along the ventricular system. The degree of staining seems to increase with an increasing amount of dye in the circulatory system.

Dr. Dempsey: If you examine those tissues microscopically you will find that the granules of dye are located in the periventricular gray matter in what appear to be macrophages—microglia cells. Indeed, they can be found occasionally elsewhere in the brain as well. On long staining with vital dyes, some dye can be found here and there in almost any location of the nervous system but to a greater degree in the macrophages of the periventricular gray matter than anywhere else. This has been studied by Wislocki, among others. There is fairly extensive literature on this topic. It has been suggested that the phenomenon is caused by the wanderings of perivascular connective tissue elements from the large vessels into the brain. In other words, these cells enter the brain in the same way that microglia cells normally do. I don't think the observation necessarily bears on the blood-brain barrier concept.

Dr. Leonhardt: The following structural characteristics in my opinion are essential for the establishment of permeability of the cerebral vessels to acid semicolloidal dyes, such as trypan blue.

The absence of the perivascular limiting glial membrane explains the permeability to trypan blue which is exhibited by such vessels as those of the pars intermedia of the hypophysis and the epiphysis. The perforation of the basal plate by protoplasmic connections between epithelial cells and underlying adventitia accounts for the continuous permeability to trypan blue in the choroid plexus. The basal plate acts as a poor substitute for the perivascular limiting glial membrane. The preservation of protoplasmic connections between cerebral tissue and adventitia in acutely pathological conditions with disintegration of the superficial and perivascular limiting glial membranes allows for transport of the dye. Temporary permeability occurs after subarachnoid injection of trypan blue, meningitis due to staphylococci and exposure of the brain to ultrasound.

Guinea pigs were given trypan blue intravenously and subsequently the skull was exposed to ultrasound (24 watts per ml, frequency of 900 kilohertz). Numerous punctate and polyhedral extravasations of trypan blue appeared along the surface of the brain and continued in a cone-shaped fashion into the depth of the brain. The diffusion of trypan blue took place along the vasculated border of the necrotized tissue and extended for a short distance into adjacent normal brain tissue. The central part of the necrosis was free of trypan blue. This peculiar distribution of dye may be explained as follows: Trypan blue is bound to protein in the blood (Bennhold, '32; '53) and its diffusion is fundamentally related to the transport of the dye-protein complex via preformed pathways of the neuroglia. No transport occurs at sites of destroyed glial structures. Along the marginal zone of necrosis the protoplasmic connections survived sufficiently to help transport the dye from the vessel wall into the tissue. The basis for permeability at the level of the vascular wall is omitted in this brief review.

A model experiment may help to visualize how diffusion of colloidal dyes may be arrested or promoted at the border between connective tissue and brain tissue. This model consists of the use of a glycerine gelatin gel and an agar gel. Trypan blue is unable to diffuse from the one gel to the other unless the gel borders are liquified by adding caustic soda.

DR. CLEMENTE: Dr. Leonhardt's observations on ultrasound remind me of some experiments Holst and I (Clemente and Holst, '54) performed on monkeys. These animals had been injected intraperitoneally with trypan blue and, rather than ultrasound, we traumatized the nervous system with ionizing irradiation. We observed that certain regions in the brain stem showed marked trypan blue coloration following irradiation of the head. These areas were dorsal medulla oblongata and hypothalamus. Histologically, degeneration of the membranes surrounding the blood vessels and neuronal degeneration in the medulla oblongata and hypothalamus correlated precisely to the regions which showed trypan blue penetration.

DR. GLEES: Will Dr. Dempsey once more define ground substance of the brain? Nowhere have I seen extracellular substance; everything seems to be either glial or neural processes. Have we to understand that ground substance is entirely intracellular or is it something in between cells?

DR. DEMPSEY: I can only say again that I am pinch hitting for other people to some degree, Dr. Glees. The term ground substance, I personally believe, is an unfortunate one—an unfortunate term for even the connective tissue ground substance. I don't like the term. It has, however, come to mean an interstitial material. As applied in the central nervous system by Hess, it meant to him, I think, an interstitial material comparable in its staining reaction with the interstitial jellylike material present in the connective tissues elsewhere. It is specifically this interstitial material that I was addressing myself to when useing the term.

DR. GLEES: I am not quite clear yet. Where might I envisage this material to be deposited. Is it in what we call neuropil, to some extent at least?

DR. DEMPSEY: In microscopical terms, neuropil is vaguely defined. It is the area still remaining in the nervous system after one has subtracted all the formed structures one can recognize. One can recognize cells, myelinated fibers, capillaries, and so on. Consequently these objects do not constitute the neuropil. It is what remains, occupying the space between all the recognizable elements. Now, with the electron microscope, this territory can be more sharply defined and it appears to be filled with processes of unmyelinated nerve fibers and glial processes packed tightly together. The location, I would think, of an extracellular substance must be between the plasma membranes of these various cellular processes and there simply does not seem to be room for such a substance.

DR. CAMMERMEYER: In sections of the area postrema, Dr. Bairati demonstrated some vessels with large diameters, thin walls and conspicuous perivascular reticulum, conforming with structural qualities of the sinusoids of the liver. What do you propose to call these vessels of the area postrema—capillaries or sinusoids?

DR. BAIRATI: These vascular spaces have a different structure than the capillaries of the brain; also the astrocytes in the area postrema do vary inasmuch as they have no feet attaching to the wall of the vessel. Whether one should call the vessels sinusoids or capillaries may be a matter of choice. There is no particular reason to make such a distinction. I would not like to compare them with those of the liver but rather with the sinusoids of the pituitary.

DR. CAMMERMEYER: Although vascular permeability is fundamental for maintenance of metabolism, the limit of permeability varies from area-to-area and the blood-brain barrier is not absolute but relative (Himwich, '51; '54). The cerebral vessels exhibit permeability less readily than the vessels of other organs; trypan blue represents the limit of molecular size of substances to which it is impermeable. Dr. Dempsey has briefly pointed out the complex factors concerned with permeability. Of interest is the significance ascribed to the presence of collagen. For normal tissue, the area postrema is typical (Wislocki and Putnam, '20); for pathological material, Dr. Dempsey mentioned the example of a stab wound which exhibits permanent permeability because of the profuse formation of collagen. In support of this view is the observation by Broman ('40; '41) that other lesions with only minimal collagen formation, such as those produced by emboli, display changed permeability for a short period only. There are regions of the brain, namely the pallidum, substantia nigra, dentate nucleus and cerebellar cortex, where the vessels appear to be more permeable than elsewhere in the brain, as evidenced by an unusual deposition of iron (Guizzetti, '15; Spatz, '22a). Nevertheless, these vessels have not the same striking collagen coating encountered in the area postrema or in stab wounds.

The selective nature of vascular permeability is also illustrated by some other observations, such as the considerable amount of fat laid down as free fat in the normal pallidum of man (Wenderowiĉ and Nikitin, '13; Spatz, '22b; Wenderowiĉ, '25; Kodama, '26) and monkey (Scherer, '44), and the distribution of bilirubin in Rh-incompatibility. Neither of these is encountered in the area postrema.

The discussion on metachromasia of the neuropil brings up the problem of specificity of reaction, the effect of fixatives and staining. Holmgren ('38; '39; '40) and Sylvén ('41; '45) described metachromasia after staining with toluidine blue in all tissue with growth potential, as in the white matter of newborn, the umbilical cord, the papillae of the skin, hair follicles, malignant neoplasms, the capsule of abscesses and wound healing. How are these results to be understood in the light of present concepts about metachromasia?

DR. DEMPSEY: With respect to your comment about the metachromasia of the nervous system, Wislocki and Singer have described that myelin is metachromatic when stained with toluidine blue. I would suggest that the metachromasia described by Holmgren might be that of myelinated fibers and not of a mucopolysaccharide. Perhaps, therefore, it is unrelated to this general problem.

DR. LUMSDEN: I have some pictures to show tomorrow on the formation of PAS-positive granules and inclusions in normal adult astrocytes in culture and, also, on Saturday, on tumor astrocytes. There an interesting point arises which indicates in the case of the tumors that the amount of this material seems to increase with the more dedifferentiated varieties of astrocytes and this makes me wonder whether one of the curious features which was noticed by Hess ('53), and to which a good deal of importance was attached, might be explained hereby. He showed that most of this ground substance was in the gray matter and not in the white and I wonder whether, if it were related to the astrocyte, the difference might simply be due to the preponderance in the cortex of protoplasmic over fibrous astrocytes.

DR. KLÜVER: The intravital deposition of silver seems to be a rather time consuming affair. In case of intracerebral hemorrhages all three types of neuroglia cells participate in the resorption of the erythrocytes (Diezel, '55). I wonder whether there have been electron microscopic studies of neuroglia or of other cells with iron deposits.

DR. DEMPSEY: In our experiments, silver was the only metallic compound used.

DR. KLÜVER: In one of their papers on "silvered" rats, Wislocki and Leduc ('54) also refer to a golden yellow fluorescence in peri-ventricular neuroglia cells and to yellowish granular material in the cytoplasm of such cells when examined in unstained sections under the light field microscope. This makes me wonder whether possible differences between the neuroglia cells of young as compared with those of adult rats have been explored by electron microscopy.

DR. DEMPSEY: I believe that Wislocki and Leduc described a golden brownish fluorescence which occurs in the neuroglia cells of old animals. This, I think, has been interpreted as an accumulation of pigment in these cells. Such pigment has been seen in a variety of cells, also with the electron microscope, but it has no special features making it pertinent to this discussion.

DR. KOREY: Have tissue cultured neuroglia cells ever been stained with PAS? I should think the resolution of whether they can be stained in the central nervous system would be helped if tissue cultures were to be stained in this manner.

DR. LUMSDEN: I propose to put that in tomorrow's talk. I have a number of preparations to show. They do stain.

DR. WOODBURY: Precise definition of the extracellular space in brain is an essential prerequisite to the study of the ionic composition of cells in this organ. Such definition is hampered by the fact that the extracellular space in brain, unlike that in muscle, is markedly heterogeneous, as evidenced by numerous studies showing pharmacological actions of substances that are present in remarkably low concentrations. Although measurement of the volume of homogeneous fluid spaces is a well-defined procedure, relatively little work has been done in organs where the extracellular space is heterogeneous, as in brain.

Cotlove ('54) has demonstrated that the chloride space in muscle is a measure of the total extracellular volume and that this consists in a rapidly equilibrating space and a connective tissue or slowly equilibrating space. On short-term infusion, inulin and sucrose measure the rapidly equilibrating space in muscle, which constitutes about 80 per cent of the chloride space. However, on long-term infusion, the inulin space becomes equal to the chloride space and thus measures the total extracellular volume. Walser, Seldin and Grollman ('54) have shown that radiosulfate is also a

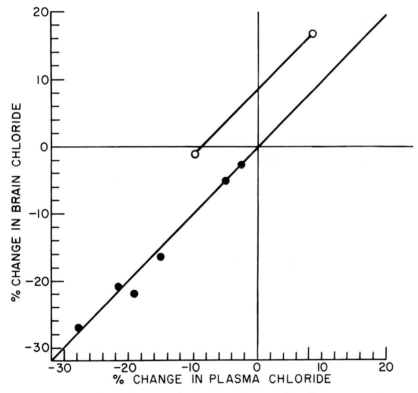

FIGURE 34. Effect of acute changes in plasma chloride concentration on brain chloride concentration under various experimental conditions. The ordinate shows per cent change in brain chloride concentration; the abscissa, per cent change in plasma chloride concentration. The *closed circles* represent effect of intraperitoneal injection of isosmolar glucose (5.5%) on plasma and brain chloride concentrations. The *open circles* represent effect of intraperitoneal injection of hypertonic sodium chloride (20 mEq/kg; upper point) and of hypertonic sodium nitrate (20 mEq/kg; lower point) on plasma and brain chloride concentration.

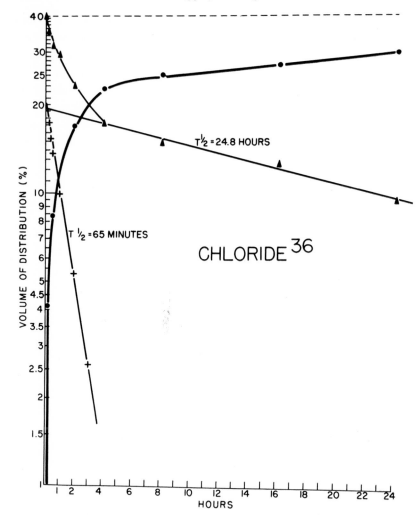

FIGURE 35. Uptake of radiochloride (Cl[36]) by the cerebral cortex of the rat at various times after intraperitoneal injection. The ordinate shows volume of distribution of chloride (chloride space) in per cent

$$\frac{\% \text{ injected dose in brain/g wet tissue}}{\% \text{ injected dose in extracellular fluid/ml}};$$

the abscissa, time in hours. The curve of *closed circles* can be resolved into two half-life components, indicated by *plus signs* and *triangles*, by the method described by Solomon ('49).

measure of the rapidly equilibrating extracellular space in muscle. Since chloride is probably distributed only in extracellular fluid, the chloride space would be expected to be an adequate measure of the total extracellular volume in brain. This is so only if tissue chloride is in complete equilibrium with plasma. In order to test this hypothesis, rats were given intraperitoneal injections of isosmolar glucose solutions and the concentration of chloride in brain was determined as the plasma chloride concentration fell. If chloride in brain is in complete equilibrium with that in plasma, the per cent change in brain chloride will equal the per cent change in plasma chloride and the points will fall along a line

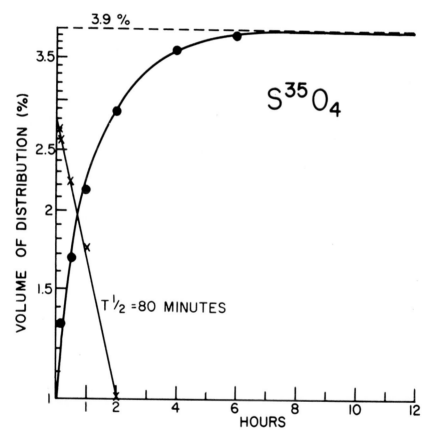

FIGURE 36. Uptake of radiosulfate ($S^{35}O_4$) by the cerebral cortex of the rat at various times after intraperitoneal injection. The ordinate shows volume of distribution of sulfate (sulfate space) in per cent; the abscissa, time in hours. The curve of *closed circles* can be resolved into one half-life component, indicated by *times signs*.

having a slope of one. The results, depicted in Figure 34, show this is the case. As a further test, the effects of equimolar injections of sodium chloride and sodium nitrate on brain and plasma chloride have been measured; 20 mEq/kg of NaCl or NaNO$_3$ were injected into rats by the intraperitoneal route, and 3 hours later plasma and brain samples were taken for chloride analysis. The results of this experiment, also plotted in Figure 34, show that NO$_3$ caused a decrease in plasma and brain chloride concentrations whereas Cl caused an increase. These two points lie on a line which has a slope of one but which lies above that of the curve for intraperitoneal glucose. This is due both to expansion of the extracellular space and to incomplete equilibration of the added solute in brain tissue (see below).

The uptake of radiochloride by the brain of rats as a function of time is shown in Figure 35. This curve can be resolved into two components (Solomon, '49). One component has a half-life of 65 minutes whereas the other has a half-life of 25 hours. The uptake of radiosulfate by the brain of rats is shown in Figure 36. At 6 hours, the curve approaches its asymptote of 3.9 per cent (16% of the chloride space) and remains at this level until 16 hours. Subsequently, sulfate appears to be bound to tissue and the sulfate space rises progressively. Before binding occurs, the uptake of sulfate can be resolved into a single component with a half-life of 80 minutes. This corresponds to the rapid component of chloride uptake. The uptake of radiosodium by the brain is shown in Figure 37. The curve was found to resolve into three components. Two of these correspond to the two components of the chloride curve, and the faster corresponds to the single component of the sulfate curve. The third component has a half-life of 13 minutes and is postulated to represent cellular uptake since it corresponds to a similar fast component in the uptake of the predominantly intracellular cation, potassium.

In Figure 38 is presented a summary of our concept of the various spaces of the brain. Plasma is in equilibrium with a so-called rapid phase which is still relatively slow compared with other tissues; this indicates a blood-brain barrier even for entrance into this rapid phase. Once a substance enters the rapid phase (sulfate space), it can then enter the slow phase if permeable or enter cells and cerebrospinal fluid, with which most ions are in rapid equilibrium. It has been shown by many investigators, and most recently by Olson and Rudolph ('55), that substances

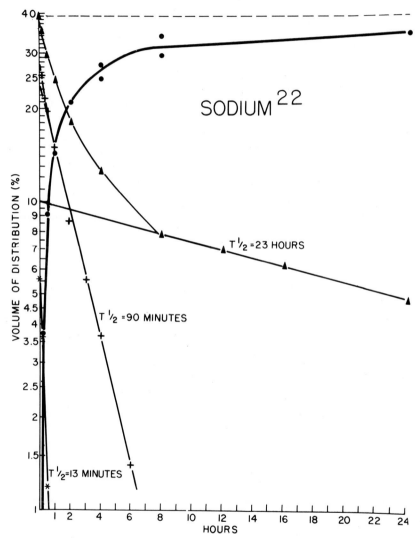

FIGURE 37. Uptake of radiosodium (Na[22]) by the cerebral cortex of the rat at various times after intraperitoneal injection. The ordinate shows volume of distribution of sodium (sodium space) in per cent; the abscissa, time in hours. The curve of *closed circles* can be resolved into three half-life components, indicated by *asterisks, plus signs* and *triangles*.

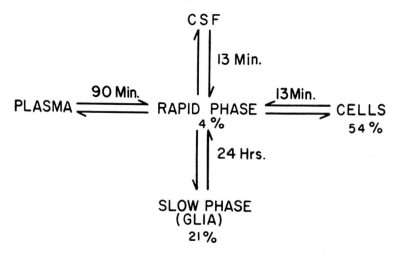

Wet – Dry wt. measures total H_2O

Cl space measures total E.C.W.

Total H_2O – total E.C.W. measures cell H_2O

$S^{35}O_4$ space measures rapid phase of E.C.W.

Total E.C.W. – Rapid Phase measures slow phase of E.C.W.

FIGURE 38. Concept of the various spaces in the cerebral cortex as derived from the experimental data. Time indicated on the arrows is the half-life for equilibration of a solute across that particular phase boundary. The figure under each phase is the percentage of total water in that phase. Abbreviations are: *E.C.W.*, extracellular water; *CSF*, cerebrospinal fluid. A possible route of transfer of materials from plasma directly to cerebrospinal fluid is not indicated on this diagram. The half-time figure for exchange between the rapid phase and the cerebrospinal fluid is obtained from the data of Olson and Rudolph ('55).

such as Na and Br are in rapid equilibrium with brain substance when injected into the cerebrospinal fluid. The half-life of exchange of Na^{24}, for example, is 13 minutes. Substances such as Br, I, sulfate and inulin (in very young animals) distribute only in the rapidly equilibrating phase of brain; even though their concentration in this phase may be the same as that in plasma, the resulting concentration in total brain is very low. Thus, the so-called blood-brain barrier is related more to the small volume in which substances distribute rather than to an active extrusion process.

DR. LUMSDEN: Do these measurements entail the use of slices of tissue?

DR. WOODBURY: No, these were in vivo experiments. The radioisotope under investigation was injected and at various times after administration, the rats were killed and blood and cerebral cortex removed for determination of radioactivity, electrolytes and water.

DR. LUMSDEN: Is it possible, in technical work of this sort, to empty the perivascular spaces of fluid? If not, this would be included in your extracellular fluid.

DR. WOODBURY: Since, according to our postulate, the cerebrospinal fluid is in rapid equilibrium with the rapid phase (sulfate space), cerebrospinal fluid is considered to be extracellular fluid. Therefore, it makes little difference whether all of the cerbrospinal fluid is removed from the brain tissue at the time it is removed from the animal.

DR. LUMSDEN: The existence of a reservoir of cerebral spinal fluid in the depths of the perivascular spaces around the capillary vessels would not invalidate in any way these observations?

DR. WOODBURY: No.

DR. WINDLE: Dr. Tschirgi, how much extracellular space, anatomically speaking, do you think has to exist to fulfill physiological criteria?

DR. TSCHIRGI: That is a difficult question. Unfortunately there is no way of determining with certainty the degree to which any given solute enters the intracellular fluid compartment. Even such substances as thiocyanate, bromide, sulfate and other solutes thought to remain largely extracellular may, and indeed certainly do, penetrate into cells to a greater or lesser extent. Furthermore, there is reason to suspect from analyses of cerebrospinal fluid that the concentration of many solutes in the central nervous system interstitial fluid may not represent a Donnan distribution with the plasma under steady state conditions. As Dr. Woodbury has indicated, if chloride in the central nervous system were entirely extracellular—a highly unlikely state of affairs—and were in the same concentration as it is in the plasma—which it most probably is not—then the extracellular volume, as calculated from the total chloride space, would be 25 to 30 per cent of the central nervous system volume. Other experimental studies using the volume distribution of inulin in slices of central nervous tissue in vitro indicate about 16 per cent of the total tissue volume available to the inulin. If the inulin remains extracellular, as is the case for most cells, then 16 per cent of the central nervous system volume must be outside of cell membranes and represents, in some sense, an "interstitial" space. If, on the other hand, the inulin has diffused into some intracellular compartment, then the cells involved are endowed with membranes of a most unique and peculiar sort.

I would like to ask Dr. Woodbury if his T-1/2 times for chloride and sulfate are about 90 minutes for the fast stage compared to about 13 minutes for sodium?

DR. WOODBURY: That is correct for chloride and sulfate but the corresponding component for sodium is also 90 minutes. The 13 minute half-life component for sodium is interpreted as penetration into neurons which occurs very rapidly once the sodium has entered the sulfate space.

DR. TSCHIRGI: How do you account for the volume of blood which may be in your sample?

DR. WOODBURY: We remove most of the blood by blotting the brain tissue on filter paper. This procedure leaves less than 0.1 per cent of the wet brain weight as blood. Normally, 1.0 per cent of wet brain weight consists of blood.

DR. ELLIOTT: All that Dr. Woodbury has said helps to solve the question that I asked originally. But there is something odd about even what I would call the boundary to the intracellular space. I mentioned that we can shrink this space by making the medium that the slices are in twice isotonic with sucrose—and very clearly that space shrinks. But when we measure the potassium in the slice we find that it hasn't gotten away (Pappius and Elliott, '56b). We always think of potassium as being in the intracellular space. The intracellular space has become very small, and yet the potassium is still there. It has either become very concentrated in the intracellular space or it is held in some space or form which is not limited by what, in our operation, appears to be the cell membrane.

Dr. Glees: In Dr. Dempsey's pictures we have seen that the neuroglia fills most of the spaces between capillaries and neurons. I would like to ask again—in the naivete of a morphologist—have we now to assume that the neuroglia contributes to metabolic transportation from capillary wall to neuron or can it all be explained by these hypothetical extracellular spaces? Can we somehow come closer to our basic problem—what does the neuroglia cell do besides filling up empty spaces?

Dr. Windle: I believe Dr. Tschirgi made a point that neuroglia cells may regulate the exchange of ions.

Chapter 8

The Blood-Brain Barrier

Robert D. Tschirgi[*]

CONSIDERATION of the phenomenon of the blood-brain barrier is unavoidable in any discussion of neuroglial function. Spatz ('33), in his comprehensive review of central nervous system dye penetration studies, clearly outlines the two most probable sites subserving this permeability peculiarity—the capillary endothelium and the perivascular astrocytic membrane. Numerous experiments utilizing dyes and other solutes, to which the blood-brain barrier is relatively impermeable, have been performed in an attempt to clarify this elusive problem (Bakay, '56; Broman, '49; Rodriguez, '55) but as yet no final agreement exists concerning which of these two structures represents the primary impediment. Dr. Daniel Pease recently informed me that his electron micrographs demonstrate a uniquely thick and solid arrangement of the endothelial cells in brain capillaries which might make them more "leak proof" than capillaries elsewhere. However, he also observes a pericapillary structure approximately 0.5μ thick which appears to be composed largely of astrocyte end-feet applied directly to the capillary wall without the intervention of a Virchow-Robin space. I shall attempt to harmonize these divergent views by suggesting the possibility that both endothelium and astrocytic membrane perform a role in regulating the transfer of solutes between plasma and central nervous system interstitial fluid.

With respect to vital dyes, most of which combine strongly with plasma proteins, a primary impermeability to protein molecules would appear to be involved. This is further evidenced by extremely low protein concentration normally present in the

[*] Drs. J. Langdon Taylor and R. W. Frost participated in these investigations.

130

cerebrospinal fluid. Since capillaries of other tissues, for the most part, are significantly less permeable to protein than to other plasma solutes, it is readily conceivable that the capillaries of the central nervous system have developed an endothelial structure which, like the kidney glomerulus, excludes plasma protein transfer almost completely. This would, I believe, suffice to account for much of the absence of vital staining of the central nervous system following the parenteral administration of dyes.

With the introduction of radio tracer techniques, it was discovered that most inorganic ions also penetrate into the central nervous system much more slowly than into other tissues (Bakay, '56). In this respect, the analogy to the permeability of the kidney glomerulus is inadequate, since inorganic salts appear to pass through this membrane unimpeded. We must therefore attribute to the central nervous system capillary endothelium a very exceptional structure with a uniquely impermeable intercellular cement, or impose a further barrier between the plasma and the central nervous system interstitial compartment. The adherents of the endothelial hypothesis base their conclusions largely on observations utilizing vital dyes, and have marshalled impressive though not entirely conclusive evidence in favor of this barrier locus (Broman, '49; Rodriguez, '55; Grontoft, '54). However, with respect to inorganic ion impermeability, little evidence is available to implicate directly either the endothelium or the pericapillary astrocytic membrane. It has been generally assumed that whatever structure prevents the passage of the protein-dye complex is also responsible for the retarded exchange of inorganic ions. This parsimonious belief is, in our opinion, somewhat unsatisfactory if one examines in more detail the nature of the inorganic electrolyte and some organic solute exchange between plasma and central nervous system.

As long as the blood-brain barrier is conceived to be a completely passive phenomenon, a static wall through which diffusion of many solutes is much slower than through water, then a tightly "calked" endothelium might suffice. Under these circumstances, one would conclude that for solutes to penetrate from plasma to central nervous system interstitial space, they must pass through and not between the endothelial cells, and the phenomenon of the blood-brain barrier would thus represent simply a special case of endothelial cell permeability. If one considers the factors which appear to influence the rate of migration of substances into the central nervous system from the plasma—lipoid solubility, particle size, charge, hydration, etc.—they are, indeed, identical to the factors known to be involved in cell permeability generally (Tschirgi, '52). However, it is necessary to inquire further into the solute distribution between plasma and central nervous system interstitial space in order to determine whether the cellular barrier separating these compartments imposes any unique configuration on the composition of the interstitial fluid. For this purpose, we must accept the belief that cerebrospinal fluid represents the average composition of the interstitial fluid of the central nervous system, insofar as no direct quantitative analytical data are available on samples of interstitial fluid. In view of the rapid solute equilibration between cerebrospinal fluid and central nervous tissue (Bakay, '56; Davson, '55) and the abundant evidence to indicate a continuous centrifugal flow of interstitial fluid from the brain surface (Manery, '54), there is general agreement that the cerebrospinal fluid does represent the interstitial fluid more nearly than does blood plasma. A rapid outflow of central nervous system interstitial fluid through the pia mater into the subarachnoid space is required to account for the simultaneous appearance of intravenous radio tracers in the ventricular and subarachnoid fluids when all direct communication between these fluid compartments is blocked (Sweet and Locksley, '53). This outflow of interstitial fluid is also indicated by the more rapid equilibration between plasma and intracisternal fluid than between plasma and ventricular fluid following intravenous injection of D_2O in normal humans (Sweet, Selverstone, Soloway and Stetten, '50; Bering, '52).

Chemical analyses of cerebrospinal fluid (Flexner, '34; Wallace and Brodie, '39) as well as radio tracer studies (Greenberg, Aird, Boelter, Campbell, Cohn and Murayama, '43) have led to the conclusion that thermodynamic energy in excess of filtration pressure is required to form cerebrospinal fluid from blood plasma, especially to account for the higher concentration of Na^+ and Cl^- in the cerebrospinal fluid. If, as seems likely, this same situation pertains for the formation of interstitial fluid directly from the central nervous system capillaries, then we must endow the blood-brain barrier with the ability to perform thermodynamic work, and to produce an interstitial fluid of unique composition, significantly different from an ultra-filtrate of plasma. What sort of metabolic machinery might we envision residing within the barrier cells which could accomplish this task? A

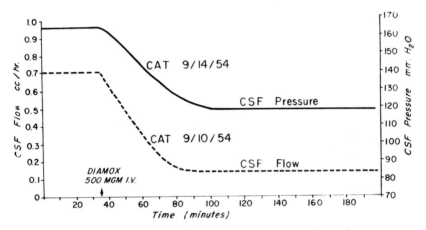

FIGURE 39. Representative curves illustrating the effect of intravenous Diamox on cerebrospinal fluid formation and intracranial pressure. (From Tschirgi, Frost and Taylor ('54); courtesy, *Proceedings of the Society of Experimental Biology and Medicine.*)

multitude of possibilities present themselves but I shall describe an hypothesis which we have developed as a result of our recent studies on Diamox.

Diamox (2-acetyl-amino-1, 3, 4-thiadiazole-5-sulfonamide)* has been reported to specifically inhibit the enzyme carbonic anhydrase, which catalyzes the reaction $CO_2 + H_2O \rightleftharpoons H_2CO_3$ (Miller, Dessert and Roblin, '50). Carbonic anhydrase occurs in a variety of secretory tissues, including stomach, pancreas, kidney and ciliary body of the eye (Davenport, '46) and is known to be present in appreciable amounts throughout the central nervous system (Ashby, Garzoli and Schuster, '52). Diamox alters

---

* Supplied through the courtesy of Dr. James D. Gallagher of Lederle Laboratories, Pearl River, New York.

secretory activity in those tissues where carbonic anhydrase occurs and which are known to possess a secretory function (Hunter and Lowry, '56) and was therefore investigated to determine its effect on cerebrospinal fluid formation and intracranial pressure. In a series of cats and rabbits, at least a threefold reduction in rate of cerebrospinal fluid flow, or a decline of approximately 30 per cent in intracranial pressure, was observed following intravenous administration of 150 mg/kg soluble Diamox (Fig. 39).* This effect was found to be unrelated to altered blood CO_2 tension, blood pH, altered renal excretion or circulatory hemodynamics and is apparently due to inhibition of the intrinsic carbonic anhydrase of the central nervous system. The mechanism hypothesized to account for this phenomenon is diagrammed in Figure 40. It is proposed that a fraction of the CO_2 produced by central nervous cellular metabolism does not diffuse into the blood as molecular CO_2, but is rapidly hydrated to carbonic acid in the presence of carbonic anhydrase. This reaction could most reasonably occur within a cellular structure immediately adjacent to the capillary separating the blood from the extravascular compartments and, for this reason, is proposed to exist within the neuroglial perivascular membrane. A further mechanism is suggested as residing within this membrane, which can selectively exchange the H^+ and HCO_3^- ions thus formed for other electrolytes, largely sodium and chloride from the plasma. The Na^+ and Cl^- ions thus obtained would be then introduced into the interstitial fluid of the nervous system. The view that H^+ and HCO_3^- ions do not rapidly diffuse in any simple fashion between plasma and cerebrospinal fluid or central nervous system interstitial fluid is indicated by the observation that intravenous injection of $NaHCO_3$ solutions markedly increases the alkali reserve of the plasma while changes in cerebrospinal fluid alkali reserve are slight and retarded (Collip and Backus, '20) and our observation that depression of arterial pH to 6.9 by intravenous infusion of HCl produces little change in cerebral cortical pH (Fig. 41). The inability of sodium and chloride to diffuse readily between plasma and central nervous system extravascular fluids has been verified by several investigators utilizing a variety of techniques

---

* For preliminary article see: Tschirgi, Frost and Taylor ('54).

(Tschirgi, '52). Because of this barrier to free diffusion of electrolytes, a net increase of two osmols of NaCl in the central nervous
system interstitial fluid will result from each mol of CO_2 thus
hydrated and exchanged. Water, which moves freely among all

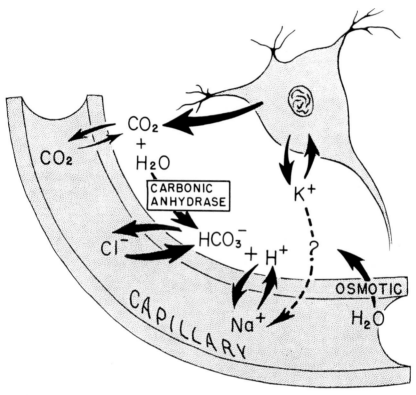

FIGURE 40. Diagram illustrating proposed mechanism for converting central nervous system metabolically produced CO_2 into carbonic acid with
subsequent exchange for plasma Na^+ and Cl^-.

the intracranial compartments (Bering, '52) enters from the plasma
to establish osmotic equilibrium. Insofar as Na^+ and Cl^- are thus
transferred into the interstitial fluid and cerebrospinal fluid from
the plasma preferentially, at a rate greater in proportion to their
plasma concentration than other electrolytes, then the cerebrospinal fluid and interstitial fluid will have a higher NaCl concentration than plasma, but maintain isotonicity.

This mechanism is hypothesized to exist throughout the entire

Biology of Neuroglia

parenchymal perivascular membrane of the central nervous system, including the choroid plexus, with the exception of the arachnoid villi in the dural sinuses, thus providing a hydrostatic pressure gradient to drive interstitial fluid outward through the pial surface of the nervous system into the subarachnoid space,

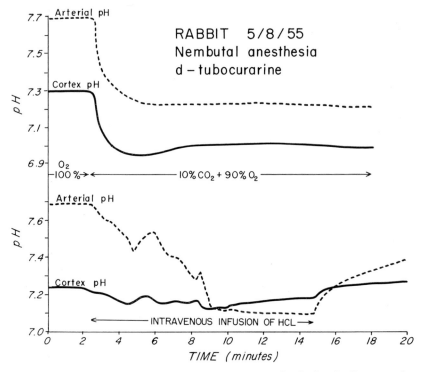

FIGURE 41. Representative curves contrasting the lack of effect on the brain pH of intravenous HCl with the depression of brain pH resulting from CO_2 inhalation. The initial blood alkalosis was produced by artificial hyperventilation.

and cerebrospinal fluid through the ventricular system into the cisterna magna and thence over the convexity of the brain. The net influx of intracranial extravascular electrolytes and water is envisioned as moving into the subarachnoid space and back into the blood stream, largely through the arachnoid villi, at a rate determined by, among other factors, the CO_2 production of the central nervous system.

The maximum rate of extravascular fluid production predicted by this hypothesis can be calculated for man on the assumption that all the CO_2 produced by the central nervous system is hydrated and exchanged for NaCl and that the blood-brain barrier is otherwise completely impermeable to NaCl. Since it is highly unlikely that either of these conditions is actually achieved, the calculated results would be expected to be high. Accepting a CO_2 production of 46 ml/min by the human brain (Kety, '52), 13.5 ml/min of isotonic NaCl could be moved from the plasma into the extravascular compartments. This figure greatly exceeds the generally accepted values for rate of cerebrospinal fluid production (Masserman, '34) and the proposed mechanism is therefore theoretically capable of producing the observed water movement.

On the basis of this hypothesis, it is possible to account for the decrease in intracranial fluid formation after Diamox administration in the following manner. Carbonic anhydrase inhibition in the central nervous system allows essentially all of the metabolic CO_2 produced by the cells to diffuse freely into the blood plasma before any appreciable hydration to H^+ and HCO^-_3 has occurred. Such rapid equilibration of molecular CO_2 between plasma and extravascular fluids of the central nervous system is indicated by Figure 40, which shows that cerebral cortical pH decreases when arterial pH is depressed by inhalation of CO_2 rich gas mixtures. Therefore, after Diamox inhibition of the carbonic anhydrase, the H^+ and HCO^-_3 available for exchange with plasma Na^+ and Cl^- diminishes and, since this represents a decreased rate of production of osmotically active particles in the extravascular fluids, the net movement of water from the plasma is proportionately reduced.

This mechanism for the transfer of Na^+ across a cellular membrane by exchange for metabolically produced H^+ with the accompaniment of osmotically obligate water is essentially identical to that proposed by Pitts ('50) for kidney tubular reabsorption of sodium. Furthermore, interference by Diamox with this kidney tubular mechanism in a manner entirely analogous to that proposed for intracranial fluid formation is thought to be responsible for the lack of water reabsorption and consequent diuresis produced by this compound (Berliner, Kennedy and Orloff, '51). Since tubular secretion of K^+ in exchange for Na^+ can occur in the kidney, the possibility of such a transfer across the blood-brain barrier must be considered, in addition to the H^+-Na^+ exchange.

We have thus, essentially, transplanted a kidney into the central nervous system, hypothesizing a protein impermeable glomerularlike endothelium for the central nervous system capillaries and a tubular cell transport function for the astrocytes. Such an active transport mechanism would appear to be involved in movement of organic molecules as well as inorganic electrolytes from plasma to central nervous interstitial fluid. Geiger, Magnes, Taylor and Veralli ('54) have shown that glucose does not enter the cat brain from an artificial vascular perfusate unless the liver is included in the perfusion system. Without the liver, the glucose content of the cerebral cortex diminished progressively during perfusion, despite high glucose concentrations in the perfusate, unless liver extract, muscle extract or whole fresh blood was added. They conclude that the uptake of glucose by the brain is an active process, dependent upon and regulated by certain "activators" normally present in the circulating blood. Here, again, an analogy may be drawn to kidney tubular activity, where a glucose transport system apparently functions to return the filtered glucose to the blood. In this manner we envision the astrocytes providing a milieu for the neurons, more suitable for their normal functioning than a simple ultrafiltrate of plasma would be. As the kidney performs a vital role in maintaining an optimum environment for most cells, so the central nervous system endothelial-glial barrier is proposed to further impose a unique homeostatic regulation on the neuronal atmosphere. We suggest, therefore, that investigative efforts be directed toward discovering whether or not the astrocytes contain the metabolic machinery and the functional capacity to regulate solute transfer as proposed and, if so, what may be the significance of this mechanism to neuronal function.

SECTION III

Structure and Function of
Neuroglia Cells In Vitro

Chapter 9

Histological and Histochemical Aspects of Normal Neuroglia Cells

CHARLES E. LUMSDEN°

MY REPORT deals with morphological and histochemical aspects of normal neuroglia cells in culture. This study was begun over four years ago with two purposes: to provide control material for our studies on the problem of differentiation and de-differentiation in gliomas in culture in regard to grading of malignancy and to attempt to isolate normal neuroglia cells away from neuronal and connective tissue elements of the brain, with a view to metabolic and biochemical studies. As you will learn, this second objective has not yet been realized owing to various difficulties which, however, have been most instructive in themselves on some of the biological properties of astrocytes.

Normal adult human neuroglia cells have been grown from surgical biopsies of cerebral subcortical white matter taken during the exposure of nongliomatous tumors, as for instance in explorations in tumor cases proving subsequently to be secondary carcinomas; and from nontumoral cases, such as dementias of the Alzheimer type, focal epilepsies and similar processes calling for surgical investigation. In a few instances, these latter have included children with diffuse cerebral disease such as cerebral diplegias and one with cerebral lipidosis which will be the sub-

° I have pleasure in recording my debts to Mr. Valentine Logue, F.R.C.S., Neurosurgeon, The Institute of Neurology, University of London, for the provision of human surgical biopsy material over the past four years; to Miss Rosemary Piper, for her technical skill in the microdissection of cell suspension cultures for electron microscopy and for the technical work on the histochemical methods on cultured glia; to Miss S. F. Jackson, of the Biophysics Research Unit, King's College, London, for her kindness in taking electron micrographs of our preparations.

141

ject of a separate report. This adult type of material is thus all of pathological origin but we have controlled our culture studies with histological sections from residues of the biopsy sample and, as far as can be seen in this way, all of the samples which we have categorized as normal for the purposes of our tissue cultures either show no histopathological lesion at all or, at most, some degree of reactive astrocytosis. Indeed, it has been found that the occurrence of some degree of reactive astrocytosis favors the chances of migration of astrocytes, since these are normally sedentary in our experience. The enhancement of cell migration by prestimulation appears to involve a biological principle which we have found useful with other types of tissue, e.g., allergic encephalitis (Lumsden, '56a), and which I think also explains the quantitative difference in the outgrowth of mesenchyme from gliomas and from normal brain tissue (Lumsden, '55a).

The human fetal or embryonic material has been obtained from therapeutic abortion cases. Twenty-four brains from embryos, usually about the tenth to sixteenth weeks of pregnancy, have been used for cultures, though two of 4.5 months and one of a 6 month embryo have also been studied. There is some technical difficulty in deciding where to separate the white from the gray matter in these immature brains. Our procedure is to strip off the vascular membrane adhering to the parietal region of the cerebrum (this is easy in very young embryos and cultures can in consequence often be obtained entirely free of mesenchymal cells), then remove the whole thickness of the hemisphere from the ependyma outwards, cut away a shaving comprising the ependymal wall and subependyma to a depth of 1.0 to 1.5 mm. The remainder is then bisected sagittally so that two main plates of tissue are obtained, one predominantly cortical, and the other predominantly deep substance corresponding eventually to the white matter. Whereas explants from the former yield rich outgrowths of nerve fibers with a certain proportion of free nerve cell bodies (Fig. 42A), the explants from the deep substance, in from 10 to 50 per cent of explants, yield neurite-free outgrowths of cell bodies which we have come with experience to identify with the neuroglia cells, since they are morphologically distinct both from neuroblasts and from the mesenchymal cells of the vessels and meninges which can of course be cultured separately as controls.

STRUCTURAL FEATURES OF ASTROCYTES IN CULTURES

ADULT NEUROGLIA CELLS. The first, and highly disappointing, feature of the normal astrocytes, unlike the neoplastic variants, is that they are almost entirely nonmigratory. The fragments of normal adult subcortex are very inert and may appear completely dead for the first week in roller-tube cultures, or show only a few outwandering macrophages. Then slowly, and in fact almost invariably, there has followed an outgrowth of mesodermal cells, both fibroblasts—slender argyrophilic cells growing in columns—and endotheliumlike mesenchymal cells of undifferentiated type (Fig. 42B). I use the word mesenchymal even for this adult tissue deliberately, since it accords with Maximow's view that undifferentiated, pluripotent, mesenchymal cells persist in the vascular adventitia in the adult organ. In the cultures, the outgrowth of this mesenchymal element accelerates from day to day, owing to the increasing number of cell divisions which occur during this phase of the culture growth. Soon such outgrowths are dense and several cell layers thick. By the end of the third week, this mesodermal outgrowth is so thick that one is apt at first to discard these cultures as devoid of further interest. If, however, they are patched and fed regularly they can be kept going for a few weeks more until the explant has thinned a little. At this stage small numbers of astrocytes will be found to have migrated, or to have been extruded, just beyond the margin of the explant and restricted to a zone here of 1.0 to 1.5 mm width (Fig. 42C). Very characteristically they lie deep to the sheet of mesodermal cells so that they are easily missed, since they are on a much deeper plane of focus, not only in the fresh preparation under phase contrast but even after fixation and staining. Since they are obscured in this way and since only a small proportion of the cultures shows these astrocytes, it is better to fix and stain all likely preparations. While the overlying sheet of mesodermal cells tends to obscure the astrocytes, also for the purpose of photography it provides excellent facility for comparing the morphology of the astrocytes and the mesodermal elements. The differences are most striking.

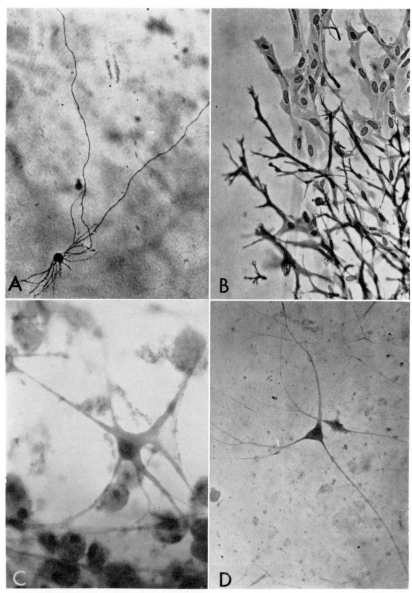

FIGURE 42. Photomicrographs of cells in tissue cultures after fixation in formalin-Ringer solution and staining in A and B by the Bodian technique and in C and D with hematoxylin and eosin. A. Nerve cell from a culture of human embryo brain. B. Mesodermal cells from a brain culture. C, D. Astrocytes from a culture of adult human brain tissue. Magnifications, A, B, 336 ×; C, D, 84 ×.

These astrocytes are stellate or angulated cells with processes of very great length, usually 0.5 mm or more (Fig. 42C, D). In several instances processes of 1.2 to 1.25 mm length have been measured, and such require to be photographed at especially low magnifications (Fig. 43A). These processes arise fairly sharply from the perikaryon and are slender throughout. They branch and anastomose freely, as though somewhat sticky, and often look tightly stretched, as though somewhat elastic. In this free anastomosis and appearance of stickiness and slight elasticity they seem to differ quite distinctly from nerve fibers which, though they may branch, do not anastomose at their tips and, indeed, behave in moving films as though mutually repellent. These physical characters of the cytoplasm of the astrocytes in culture suggest a mucinoid quality which is of interest in view of the histochemical features to be described later and in view of current ideas on the nature of ground substance to which I shall refer later.

In Figures 42C, D and 43A, a shadowy background is present due to the overlying sheet of mesodermal cells at the surface of the plasma clot. Why the astrocytes always occur at a deeper plane is not yet clear but I believe it to be a highly characteristic feature of these normal astrocytes from adult material. The astrocytes appear to be completely buried within the plasma clot but they do not seem to come in direct contact with the surface of the glass. In their behavior in this respect there is a suggestion of an analogy with that of facultative anaerobic bacteria in a deep agar tube which might be worth further investigation.

The cell bodies of these astrocytes, too, have a characteristic brightly eosinophilic and highly granular cytoplasm which contrasts with the somewhat basophilic cytoplasm of the overlying mesodermal cells. But even more characteristic are the lateralized, rather polymorphic nuclei. Many are bi-nucleated and sometimes the nuclei show amitotic features, though these cells are not pyknotic nor evidently degenerating (Fig. 43B, C). The appearance of the two cells in this last figure suggests that a recent division may have occurred. So far, however, I have not witnessed an actual cell division among these presumably normal astrocytes which appear in the outgrowth only in very small numbers and then apparently solely by migration. In the normal embryonic

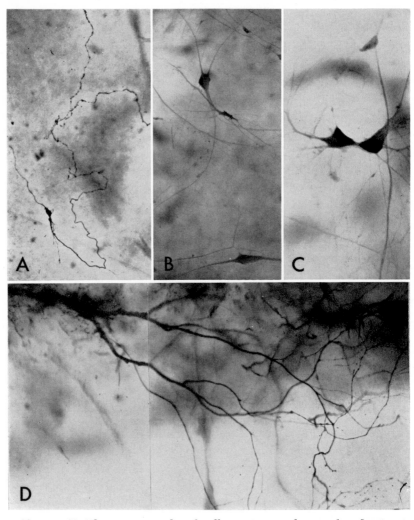

FIGURE 43. Photomicrographs of cells in tissue cultures after fixation in formalin-Ringer solution and staining (A, D) by the Bodian technique and (B, C) with hematoxylin and eosin. A. Astrocyte whose longest dimension, if stretched out, would be 1.048 mm. B. C. Astrocytes, one (B) with a lateralized nucleus and one (C) with two nuclei, as though recently undergoing cell division. D. A cell which may be either an astrocyte or a neuron. Magnification, B, C, D, 336 ×.

and fetal neuroglia cells, both human and animal, there is no doubt at all that multiplication is mitotic, as likewise in all the grades of astrocytomas. The statement made by Penfield ('32b) that astrocytes multiply by amitosis can be traced back to Ramon y Cajal ('13) but I have never been able to find the evidence for this and it seems to me, on the basis of current knowledge of cell division (Hughes, '52), extremely improbable that this can be so.

When eosin is used as a counterstain, apart from the granulation, the extremely delicate cytoplasmic quality of the processes is revealed. But this cytoplasm, or the cell surface (since in all of these preparations we are dealing with unsectioned cells), like that of the neuron, reduces silver proteinate very strongly. Silver impregnation emphasizes strikingly the similarity of these astrocytes to neurons. Indeed, the problem is rarely to distinguish the astrocyte from the connective tissue elements but from neurons. Though the brains of human adults usually fail to yield any outgrowth of nerve fibers, these latter are occasionally seen, even from quite elderly subjects (I have seen this in brain biopsy material from a 65 year old man). By taking material for this study only from white matter, the risk of confusion from this source has, I think, been avoided; but it is not possible to exclude absolutely the possibility that a small group of nerve cells either from a deep layer of the cortex or from basal ganglia might have been present in the sample. Figure 43D shows one of these problematical cells which may be either neuron or astrocyte. All that can be said meantime about this is that such cells are frequently seen in cultures from astrocytic gliomas corresponding to Kernohan's histological grades 1 or 2 and in such numbers that there can be no doubt of their astrocytic origin.

Culture thus stresses the similarity between the neuron and the neuroglia cell and the complete dissimilarity of the latter from connective tissue cells. Perhaps this affinity between the neuron and the neuroglia cell suggests a basically similar ultrastructural organization, which in turn might be expressed in certain similar biochemical properties (one of which may be the strong reducing properties for silver solutions). Thus it might be of value to scrutinize the neuroglia cell as well as the neuron in regard to enzymes like choline esterase and choline acetylase (adenosinetriphosphatase).

EMBRYONIC NEUROGLIA CELLS. Embryonic and fetal neuroglia

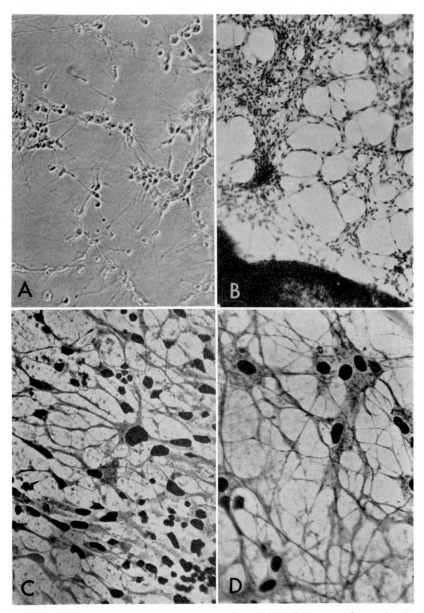

FIGURE 44. Neuroglia cells in tissue cultures from human embryos (A, B, C) and a newborn guinea pig (D), fixed in formalin-Ringer solution. A. Human embryonic neuroglia cells, unstained, as seen with phase contrast. B. Fenestrated or microcytic pattern of human embryonic neuroglia cells stained with hematoxylin and eosin. C. Human embryonic neuroglia cells

cells are much more plastic but, even in cultures from 10 week human embryo brain, neuroglia cells already appear as a characteristic race, distinct from the cells that form nerve fibers. Figure 44A shows these immature neuroglia cells in a living preparation by phase contrast. The cell bodies migrate quite rapidly, within 4 or 5 days, and in profuse numbers. The cell bodies are small and spherical and show marked refractility suggesting contractility rather like oligodendrocytes, though we have not yet tried to make motion picture films of these. The processes are fine, short and anastomose richly. I feel confident that these are not neuroblasts, for the reason that adjacent cultures in the same plasma clot, and sometimes the other half of the same explant, give a profuse outgrowth of typical long processes without cell bodies; the distinction between the two varieties of outgrowth is very sharp. To those familiar with astrocytomas in culture, a glance at Figure 44A will at once suggest the behavior of a moderately well differentiated astrocytoma (corresponding to Kernohan's histological grade 2). This resemblance is even stronger in the case of neuroglia cells from slightly older human embryos—say 14 to 16 weeks, when this tissue in culture often tends to form fenestrated patterns strongly reminiscent of the behavior, both in vivo and in vitro, of microcytic gliomas (Fig. 44B).

I have persisted in calling these cells neuroglia and, of course, it will be pointed out that the majority of such cells in normal white matter, especially in the fetus, are likely to be oligodendrocytes. But I confess I cannot distinguish primitive oligodendrocytes and astrocytes in culture and, conversely, in many astrocytomas in culture I find cells that look and behave like oligodendrocytes, even to the point of showing twitching movements of the cytoplasm in motion picture films which we have made of tumors in culture, which are indubitably astrocytoma. I think one of the most immediate problems in neurogliology is to revise and further our knowledge of the histogenesis of these two cell races, astrocyte and oligodendrocyte. But this may be an

---

stained by the Bodian technique. D. Neuroglia cells cultured from the brain of a newborn guinea pig and stained by the Bodian technique. Magnifications, A, B, 84 ×; C, D, 336 ×.

extremely tricky problem since, in our own experience with the Hortega methods, the results are unsatisfactory with fetal and embryonic material.

Figure 44C shows a culture of human embryonic centrum ovale stained with the Bodian silver proteinate. It reveals the character of the cytoplasm of these still primitive spider cells and illustrates the problem of deciding whether the cells seen are oligodendrocytes or astrocytes. It shows, incidentally, how pure such cultures may be, there being no nerve fibers here at all—and in young human embryos it is usually easy to avoid mesenchyme if one takes tissue before vascularization of the deep tissues of the brain. The anastomotic or syncytial character of the glial protoplasm is also well seen—a feature that recurs with dedifferentiation in the gliomas. The outgrowth of cell bodies is profuse in these normal embryos, as a result both of migration and of cell multiplication which, as has been said earlier, is mitotic. Another detail of interest is that even at this early stage, and despite the rapidity of migration and multiplication, these cells early develop cytoplasmic acidophilia and granulation unlike the neuroblasts or the mesenchyme.

As we progress towards the more mature fetus the processes of these neuroglia cells become more fibrillary, more densely argyrophilic and longer; but they still anastomose freely. Neuroglia cells cultured from fetal guinea pigs near term show the highly characteristic appearance of the tissue when it is obtained independent of mesoderm. The astrocytic features are now more clearly pronounced. Figure 44D shows such a culture from the cerebral white matter of a newborn guinea pig. At this stage, the neuroglia cells in culture are clearly distinct both from neurons and from the mesodermal cells. However, only occasional explants of the white matter yield such outgrowths of neuroglia cells—but when they do so, often in almost pure form—as though it arose from nests or foci scattered at relatively rare intervals throughout the white matter. It is very striking when one obtains these cultures which are so unlike the majority from the same piece of brain; and it is a pity that they cannot so far, in our hands, be obtained "to order" since they are often quite pure in type and would provide rich material for quantitative cytochemical approaches. This problem calls for further work with different media and with more carefully selected sources of material, on lines which we hope to follow up.

CYTOPLASMIC ACTIVITIES OF NEUROGLIA CELLS IN CULTURE

FIBER TIPS. Reference has been made earlier to the mutual repulsion that appears to exist between the tips or growth cones of nerve fibers in culture and to the difference in behavior, in this respect, of the tips of neuroglia cell processes which exhibit mutual adhesiveness so that they anastomose to form syncytial networks. It is perhaps worth repeating that this applies not only to the embryonic astrocytes in culture but also to astrocytes from adult material. Since the latter are only obtained in reasonable numbers, as in Figures 42D and 44A when they have already been activated by some sort of pathological stimulus in the parent tissue, it might be contended that this property is one only of immature or reactive neuroglia cells and that syncytial networks are not a feature of the quiescent astrocytes in the normal adult histology, a point which Ramon y Cajal ('13) made many years ago to bring the neuroglia cell into line with the neuron at the time of the now historic controversy on Held's syncytial doctrine of nervous tissue structure. But, whatever the implications of our own observations to histology, it is an interesting fact that, in the conditions of tissue culture, the tips of astrocytic processes show a distinct property of adhesiveness which is unlike that of the nerve fiber tips.

When free, the tip of the astrocyte process in culture is not unlike that of a nerve fiber, with an ameboid terminal expansion. This is usually of smaller area and less highly mobile in the normal astrocyte than in the nerve fiber but it is much more elaborate and highly active in the neoplastic astrocyte in culture (Lumsden, '55a). In cultures of normal human embryo neuroglia cells, at the free edge of the outgrowth, one occasionally sees impressive cell processes like that shown in Figure 45 in which the analogy with the vascular attachment of the adult astrocyte in histology is evident. It also shows how, in the conditions of culture where the whole cell is seen throughout, there exists a broad veil of very delicate protoplasm extending out beyond the denser part which alone would probably be visible in histological sections. The marked vacuolation of this expansion can also be seen and, from the analogy of the similar activity at the tip of nerve fibers, I am tempted to assume that this is evidence of active pinocytosis.

ULTRASTRUCTURE OF THE CYTOPLASM OF ASTROCYTOMA CELLS. In the relative restriction (or polarity) of ameboid activity to parts only of the cell membrane where processes form and to the tips

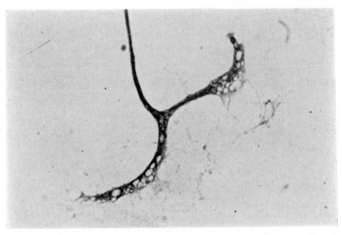

FIGURE 45. Tips of a process of a young astrocyte, showing the thin veil of cytoplasm peripherally. Fixation in formalin-Ringer solution; staining by the Bodian method; magnification, 800 ×.

of these processes when they have formed, a basic ultrastructural similarity of nuron and neuroglia cell protoplasm is suggested. In the case of normal adult astrocytes in culture, the presence of an overlying layer of mesodermal cells entails ultra-thin sectioning and the consequent problem of accurate identification of the cell type. Thus we have not so far succeeded in making electron micrographs of the normal astrocyte.

But the astrocytes of well-differentiated astrocytomas can frequently be grown directly on glass, without plasma, from cell suspensions prepared either by careful instrumental dissociation or by the method of partial tryptic digestion. After a few days in culture, traumatic effects are recovered from, and healthy cultures are obtained of nicely dispersed tumor astrocytes which, in the absence of any plasma clot, reveal very delicate detail within the cells (for illustrations, see Lumsden, '55a). We have grown such cell suspensions similarly on Formvar-coated cover glasses and later, after fixation, have dissected off, under direct micro-

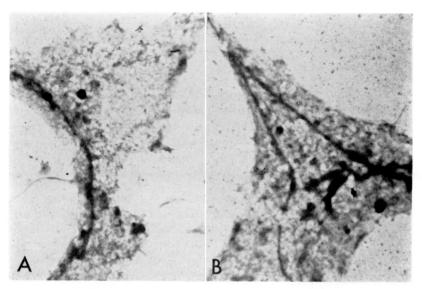

Figure 46. Electron micrographs of the tips of processes of astrocytes (explanation in text). Magnification, 5,900 ×.

scopic vision, selected portions of the Formvar strip containing suitable cells for direct examination as whole cells, under the electron microscope. While the nucleus, perikaryon and main portions of the cell processes are usually too thick for study, the extremities of the fibers are often transparent enough to the electron beam. In this way, as seen in Figure 46, we have found evidence of the existence of intracytoplasmic longitudinal fibers of high electron density, apparently rather similar to those in nerve fibers in tissue culture as reported by De Robertis and Sotelo ('52). No cross-banding such as that reported by Bairati ('47) on ultra-thin sections of histological material with fibers from glial plaques (in multiple sclerosis) was observed in our cultures with fibers formed by these astrocytes from well-differentiated astrocytomas. But it is possible that the resolution is insufficient in our unsectioned material for this degree of detail and we consider that ultra-thin sectioning will be necessary with cultures also, though this might be to the prejudice of accurate cell identification.

MUCOPROTEIN OR MUCOPOLYSACCHARIDE PRODUCTION BY ASTRO-CYTES. I would like to mention briefly the peculiar eosinophilic material which adult astrocytes tend to accumulate in the perikaryon. This has been seen, too, to migrate along the cell processes in the living cells, to appear in their terminal expansions and even to be discharged from these almost in the manner of a secretory product.

Cells of all types in culture are prone to a variety of granules and inclusions, e.g., the giant centrospheres of Warren Lewis ('20), but I do not refer to these. Astrocytes in culture are peculiar, in my experience, in the frequency with which the normal, healthy looking cells show their nuclei lateralized or displaced by a mass of brightly eosinophilic material in the cytoplasm.

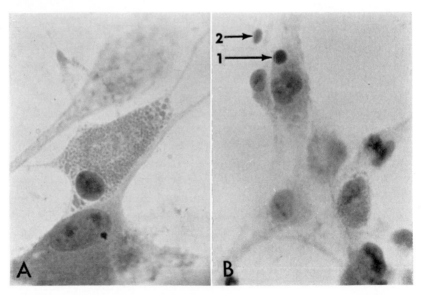

FIGURE 47. Photomicrographs (A) of normal and (B) tumor astrocytes in tissue culture fixed in formalin-Ringer solution. A. Marked eosinophilic granulations in the cytoplasm are seen after fixation in formalin-Ringer solution and staining with hematoxylin and eosin. B. Intracytoplasmic eosinophilic body *(1)* and an extracellular body which is similar *(2)* in a culture fixed with Os_3O_4 solution and stained with hematoxylin and eosin. Magnifications, approximately 600 ×.

Close inspection shows how frequently this nuclear displacement occurs. The astrocytes from normal adult human white matter are usually rich in these eosinophilic granules (Fig. 47A). The granules are often accompanied by larger inclusions (Fig. 48C, D) which probably develop from aggregations of the granules; I have seen the reverse process occurring once in a preparation set up for ciné-filming, when a large inclusion disintegrated suddenly into 4 or 5 small inclusions of somewhat larger size than the granules. These were then seen to migrate along the astrocytic process towards its tip. Frequently at the terminal expansions of such normal adult astrocytes at the edges of the explants of the normal human white matter we have found large eosinophilic spherical bodies. There is no doubt from our evidence on tumor astrocytes that such bodies escape from the cell and lie about freely, undissolved, in the medium; they may even be taken up by phagocytes in the culture (Fig. 47B).

I regret that I was slow to appreciate the interest of these

TABLE I

HISTOCHEMICAL REACTION OF CYTOPLASMIC INCLUSION MATERIAL IN TUMOR
ASTROCYTES

Group	*Tests Applied*°	*Result*
Polysaccharides	Glycogen	Negative
Mucoproteins, mucopolysaccharides	a. Periodic acid-Schiff	Strongly positive in most astrocytes, even in mitotic cells
	b. Performic acid-Schiff	Negative
	c. Brominated PFAS	Negative
Phosphatides	a. Baker's acid hematin	Negative
	b. Feyrter's thionin "enclosure" method	Negative
	c. Sudan Black	Negative
Lipoids	a. Sudan IV in propylene glycol	Negative
	b. Osmium tetroxide	Negative
Lipofuscins	a. Long Ziehl-Nielsen	Negative
	b. Schmorl method	Negative
	c. Lillie's ammoniacal silver	Negative
Nucleoproteins	Jacobson's modified Giemsa. Ribonuclease tests not applied.	Granules and inclusions stain dark blue-black, perhaps due to presence of ribonucleic acid

° From Pearse ('53).

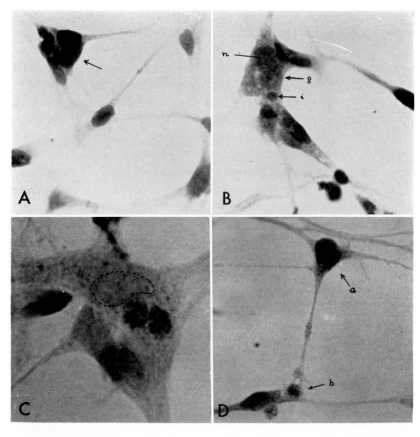

FIGURE 48. Astrocytes from tumor tissues in culture, fixed in formalin and stained by the PAS technique. Magnifications, A, B, D, 600 ×; C, approximately 1100 ×. A. The cell indicated by the *arrow* shows the dark mass of the PAS-positive material in the cytoplasm. B. PAS-positive granulation of cytoplasm is shown at *(g)* with aggregation at *(i)* to form spherical body which also gives a positive PAS reaction. The nucleus is at *(n)*. C. In this instance there are two spherical collections of granules of PAS-positive material in the cytoplasm in the juxtanuclear region of the cell on the left. The outline of the nucleus has had to be traced in, since this was not reproduced clearly in the black and white print made from the original color transparency. D. Shows a mass of PAS-positive substance in juxtanuclear region at *(a)*, and at the tip of a process at *(b)*.

bodies; but with increasing experience of the astrocytomas in culture it became clear that the production of this eosinophilic substance was even more marked in the astrocytes in the neoplastic state and that it was not a degenerative feature, since it was frequently observed even in tumor astrocytes in mitosis. In order to investigate some of the histochemical reactions of this material more thoroughly we have resorted to our technique of cell suspensions from astrocytomas grown directly on glass without plasma, the avoidance of the plasma being a great advantage for chemical studies. The material referred to has been found to be strongly positive with the Hotchkiss periodic acid-Schiff (PAS) technique and negative for phospholipids and lipoids. The results of the histochemical tests applied are listed in Table I; the findings refer to the normally abundant cytoplasmic material in these astrocytes and not, of course, to the occasional presence of other substances like traces of fat, slightly positive phospholipid reactions in mitochondria, lipochromes and even traces of iron, all of which are occasionally found as separate constituents apparently independent of the PAS-positive material. Figure 48A shows the intense PAS reaction of the granules and Figure 48B both granules and an inclusion giving the same reaction. In Figures 48C the apparent aggregation of granules into inclusions is shown; and in Figure 48D PAS-positive material is seen partly in the juxtanuclear cytoplasm and partly at the tip of its process.

It is evident from the data in the table that the material is not phosphatide (i.e., cerebroside or lecithin, etc.), as we at first postulated might be the case, but is either a mucoprotein or mucopolysaccharide. Our few observations on the normal adult astrocytes indicate that the eosinophilic substance referred to earlier is of the same nature. We hope now to take up this study more thoroughly on embryonic and fetal neuroglia cells in culture.

Though most of the PAS-positive material of the astrocytes in our cultures is intracellular we have clear evidence that it can escape and lie free between the cells and even be taken up by the phagocytes in the cultures. It seems possible that it might be taken up by other types of cells in vivo, and this suggests a possible link with the fascinating demonstration of exchange of material between cells in culture in one of the moving picture films which Dr. Pomerat has shown.

I have ventured, too, to present my own observations, preliminary as I regard them, on the production of mucoprotein or mucopolysaccharide by healthy living astrocytes in view of the interest that Hess' ('53) report on the PAS-positive ground substance has aroused; this will lead me, after a slight recapitulation, to my final comment on what I consider to be the important role of the neuroglia in relation to the blood-brain barrier.

RECAPITULATION AND COMMENT ON THE RELATIONSHIP OF NEUROGLIA CELLS TO THE BLOOD-BRAIN BARRIER

The first point I should like to stress again is that the similarity of the neuroglia cells (astrocytes and oligodendrocytes) to neurons should be investigated further along the lines suggested earlier. I exclude microglia cells. These are phagocytes (histiocytes) and we could well afford to drop the special name of microglia.

The second point, not yet stressed adequately here, is that in tissue culture we see cells, to some extent under an abnormal stimulus which causes them to react. The nonneoplastic neuroglia cells of our cultures are, like nerve cells, sedentary; when they react in culture they exhibit the same behavior as in pathological processes in vivo. Thus, we witness the regression towards increased plasticity of the cytoplasm; and it becomes evident that all the pathological reactions of the astrocyte are mediated through this very highly reactive cytoplasm. Astrocytes from adult brain do not undergo cell divisions in culture but merely cytoplasmic hypertrophy and migration. Likewise in vivo, in pathological material, true mitoses hardly ever occur and the nuclear response is restricted to budding and to reduplication of nuclei without cell cleavage. Thus, nuclear reduplication may well be amitotic, occurring in response to the tremendous cytoplasmic hypertrophy; but I am skeptical about the occurrence of actual increase in the numbers of astrocytes even in such classical instances as multiple sclerosis, where the astrocyte reaction is so intense.

Reaction in the astrocyte takes the form of great increase in cytoplasmic volume and in number and length of processes; nuclear hypertrophy and budding are probably secondary to this. Associated with the increased plasticity of the cytoplasm, I presume, there are corresponding increases in mitochondria. Quite obviously, these are important principles when attempts are made to correlate quantitatively biochemistry and morphology in neuroglia (Lumsden, '56b).

The third point is the evidence that astrocytes in culture form mucoprotein or mucopolysaccharide. The studies on astrocytes from differentiated astrocytomas suggest that the more highly plastic—or the more highly reactive—the cell, the greater is the production of this material. This led me to suggest in the round-table discussion yesterday that the quantitative differences that Hess ('53) reported in the PAS-positive ground substance between cortex and white matter might be related to the more protoplasmic character of the astrocytes in the former.

Fourth, and finally, though I have shown that the PAS-positive material can escape from the astrocytes and remain as free intercellular substance, I am skeptical about the intercellular nature of much of the so-called ground substance reported on studies based on microtome sections.

In emphasizing the great lengths of astrocyte processes, the complexity of their connections, the extremely delicate character of their ultimate cytoplasmic expansions (Fig. 45) and the production by astrocytes of mucoprotein and mucopolysaccharide, I have in mind the idea that that which has been reported by others as ground substance is nothing more than glial cytoplasm.

The relationship of the blood-brain barrier to neuroglia cells was the subject of an earlier communication (Lumsden, '55b) and I should like here to repeat only a few of the points. The permeability properties of the blood-brain barrier are those of a cell membrane and the chemical facts can only be explained by active transport which is a slow process relatively to passive transport of fluid. Thus, bromides, iodides, phosphates, chlorides and thiocyanates which, in extracellular spaces outside the central nervous system, are equalized with the blood in a few minutes, are not even approximately equalized in the central nervous system in three hours. These are well-established facts. Now, in physiology generally, total extracellular fluid in the body is measured by the intravenous injection of sodium thiocyanate which passes quickly out of the bloodstream and is soon distributed evenly between plasma and tissue fluid but it does not enter living cells nor is it quickly eliminated. The fall of thiocyanate thus resulting in the plasma is consequently an index of the total volume of fluid outside cells. This volume—the thiocyanate space —minus the plasma volume (measured, e.g., by the Evans Blue dye method) is then a measure of tissue fluid. It is the special peculiarity of brain as contrasted with other organs that thiocyanate, *inter alia*, does not leave brain capillaries except very slowly. I therefore suggested in 1955 that the explanation may be that there is little or no tissue fluid in the normal brain comparable to that in other organs, apart from the cerebrospinal fluid system which is normally closed at the pre-capillary level. This does not overlook the fact that, in the work of Wallace and Brodie ('39) and Wallace, Brodie, Friedman and Brand ('37; '39), bromide and thiocyanate measurements were related in the case of the brain tissue to the chlorides. But even the passage of chlorides through brain capillaries—as in the cerebrospinal fluid—has been shown to be much slower than elsewhere in the rest of the body.

In view, therefore, of these foregoing aspects of the anionic exchange process between blood and brain, it was suggested that interstitial fluid channels are normally absent in the depths of the parenchyma and also that the ground substance is in fact the neuroglia cell cytoplasm. Brain tissue approximates much more than other organs to the homogeneous gel structure which living tissue generally is said to possess. The characteristic physical consistency of brain is a result of this; and, experimentally, the ready demonstration in brain of artificial Liesegang diffusion patterns, compared, for instance, with liver (unpublished observations), may be cited to support this. Thus, in the brain, the transport of water and other molecules may rely more on true diffusion through the cytoplasm of the neuroglia cells, aided by protoplasmic streaming and molecular exchange at the cell interfaces, than upon intercellular percolation. In this sense the blood-brain barrier is not a specific membrane or architectural layer but the whole width of the gel-like matrix which extends from the capillary endothelium right up to the nerve cell and its processes.

As a corollary to this it might be added also that if in the brain so much exchange of water and dissolved substances has to be done at the molecular level, a special problem then arises in the need for provision for transport of insoluble materials. It may be in this that we can now see the special significance of the rich development of the macrophage system as a special tissue—the microglia cells—in the brain.

Chapter 10

Functional Concepts Based on Tissue Culture Studies of Neuroglia Cells[*]

CHARLES M. POMERAT

NEUROGLIA cells may be readily observed in the outgrowth resulting from the explantation of nervous tissue. In contrast to the difficulties encountered in the staining of elements of this series in sectioned material, the bodies and processes of neuroglia and microglia cells are easily demonstrated in tissue culture preparations even with nonmetallic techniques. An examination of the entries in the comprehensive bibliography of tissue culture prepared by Murray and Kopech ('53) covering the literature to 1950 reveals a comparatively small number of this important group of nervous tissue constituents. It appears evident, therefore, that excepting their importance in neoplasia, neuroglia cells have attracted proportionately as little attention from investigators employing in vitro culture methods as has been invested in the analysis of their possible dynamic role with the classic methods of histology.

Figure 49 illustrates cellular constituents in a 45-day roller tube culture of thalamus from a 4 month human fetus. The cultures were made in our laboratory, while the staining with variants of the method of del Río Hortega and the photography were done by Professor Costero. In terms of morphology and functional reactions, the identity of the various cell species can be established with data obtained from the analysis of sectioned tissue blocks.

At the risk of engendering hostility by the statement that much of our present knowledge rests on what may be called "silver-

* This investigation was supported by a research grant (B-364) from the National Institute of Neurological Diseases and Blindness.

162

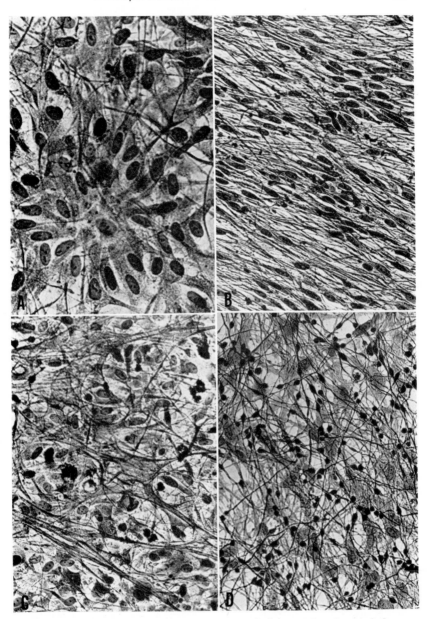

FIGURE 49. Roller tube culture from the thalamus of a 4 month human fetus after 45 days' incubation. Variations of the Hortega method have been used to demonstrate neuroblasts (A) spongioblasts (B) astrocytes (C) and oligodendrocytes (D). Magnifications, 192.5 ×.

plated" neurocytology, it is nonetheless very probable that neuro-anatomy stands to gain even more than most divisions of mor-phology from emerging newer knowledge regarding cell architec-ture, as revealed by phase contrast microscopy of living cells, and from the rapid advances in the description of fine structure with current techniques of electron microscopy.

RE-INTERPRETATION OF THE FIXED PREPARATION

One of the fundamental problems which faces all students of cell differentiation when in vitro culture methods are employed is the reconciliation of information obtained on living elements with that already well established in textbooks.

As in the case of results accumulated with the aid of modern electron microscopy, the most serious initial barrier to the inte-gration of knowledge is being removed with an increased appre-ciation that routine methods employed in histopathology greatly alter the attributes of cells as they probably appear in situ. Of special importance is the destruction of very delicate sheets of ectoplasm which may exercise an extraordinarily important role in the living organism.

Figure 50 shows characteristic blister formation resulting from the slow fixation of astrocytes from the diencephalon in a tissue culture. The selected film frames were taken from a record made by Borghese ('54). The cells were in a perfusion chamber so that neutral 10 per cent formalin could be made to replace the nu-trient fluid while photographs were made at 17 frames per min-ute. Blisters on cells after formalin fixation have been observed by many workers. Data of this type are being accumulated in relation to several kinds of fixatives over a range of concentra-tions introduced at various rates. Numerous artifacts are pro-duced but the most pertinent object to this discussion is the shrinkage of delicate extensions of the plasma membrane, espe-cially following harsh fixatives slowly introduced or following an ascending series of concentrations designed to imitate their pene-tration into blocks of tissue. These often result in the production of nubbins of coagulated protein which may subsequently serve as the focal points for deposition of metallic substances. As would be expected, immediate flooding of a monolayer of cells in tissue

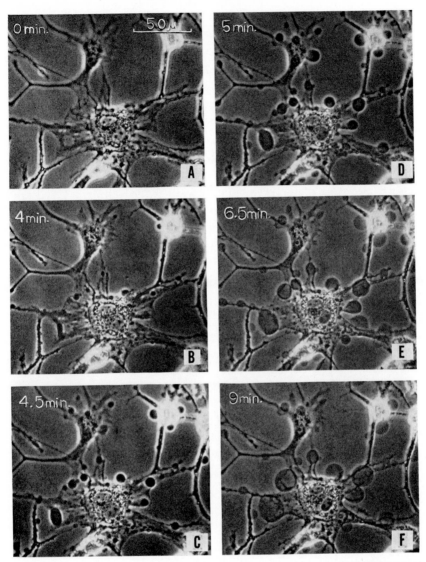

FIGURE 50. Culture of diencephalic tissue in a perfusion chamber showing blister formation resulting from slow fixation with 10% neutral formalin. Time intervals in selected film sequences are indicated on the upper left area. Magnifications, 600 ×.

cultures wtih 2 per cent buffered osmic acid yields very faithful fixation of neuroglia cells, especially when these are in sites where

clot liquefaction has occurred. However, the margins of ectoplasmic extensions as paucimolecular layers bind so little osmic acid
or dyes, such as Azure II, that little more can be seen of their outline with the phase contrast microscope than with ordinary light
microscopy. Electron micrographs of such material are urgently
needed.

As a preliminary statement, results of these investigations were
outlined in a lecture (Pomerat, '52), in which an attempt was
made to reconstruct the probable appearances in life of structures described from silver preparations. With what might be
called a degree of impertinence, drawings by Ramon y Cajal and
del Río Hortega were reconstructed in the light of accumulated
experience in studying living preparations of neuroglia cells (Figs.
51-53). The legends for these figures include speculation re-

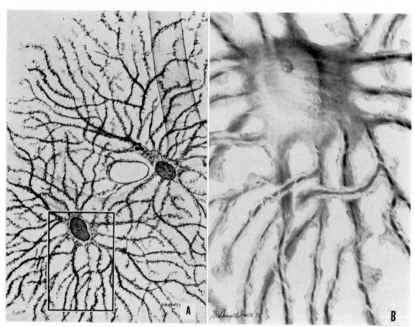

FIGURE 51. A reconstruction of the probable appearance of a living astrocyte from a classical drawing derived from fixed metallic preparations. The
portion indicated by the inset in A, taken from del Río Hortega's ('49)
drawing, was reconstructed in B on the basis of the study of living neuroglia
cells and with the direct evidence of fixation injury effects. (From Pomerat
('52); courtesy, Texas Reports on Biology and Medicine.)

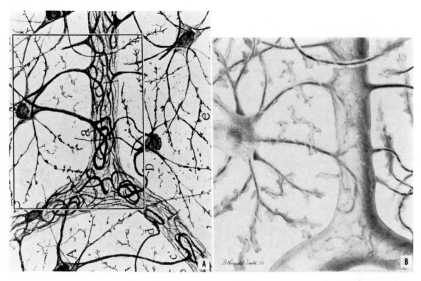

FIGURE 52. A reconstruction of the appearance of living astrocytes, particularly of their foot processes. A classical metallic preparation, drawn by Ramon y Cajal ('13), is shown in A; and, with the premises given in the description of Figure 51, the probable appearance of various structures within the inset is shown in a reconstructed drawing B. Stringy and straplike components of the foot processes have been expanded as they might have been in the living state, which suggests an almost complete encasement of the blood vessel. (From Pomerat ('52); courtesy, *Texas Reports on Biology and Medicine.*)

garding the structure of neuroglia cells in the organism. Recent agreement among students of fine structure, that brain tissue is practically devoid of ground substance and that it is almost solidly packed with cellular material, gives new meaning to the observations made with the aid of tissue cultures that neuroglia cells, especially astrocytes, are characterized by extraordinarily well-developed systems of membranes which are interlaced in complicated systems when occurring in dense outgrowths. If they can be carried over from the in vitro to the in situ situation, reports that the membranes along the course of neuroglial processes exhibit constant movement may have notable physiological importance. Such considerations may lead to the description of a more dynamic role for glial elements in the metabolic well-being of neurons.

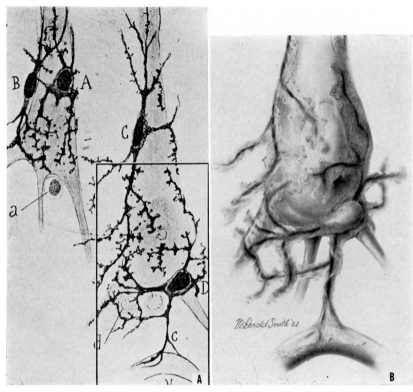

FIGURE 53. The area of the inset in a drawing A, by Ramon y Cajal ('13), has been reconstructed in B to show the probable structure of glial elements intimately associated with the perikaryon of nerve cells, as they might appear in the living state. Twiglets and nubbins typical of fixed metallic preparations have been redrawn as foliose processes with extremely thin margins. Without exaggerating this technique of interpretation, it becomes obvious that the cell bodies of neurons might be held in the extensive clasp of satellite cells. Should such glial elements have an inherent rhythmic contractile activity a "massaging" action might be exerted on the neuroplasm. The presence of a foot process extending from the neuroglia cell is of special interest to the speculation presented in this thesis. (From Pomerat ('52); courtesy, *Texas Reports on Biology and Medicine.*)

ASTROCYTES

New information accumulated by our group regarding astrocytes in vitro, as revealed by phase cinematography, has been

→→→→

FIGURE 54. Mitosis in an astrocyte from a 6 day culture of the spinal cord of a normal adult cat. Magnification, 600 ×.

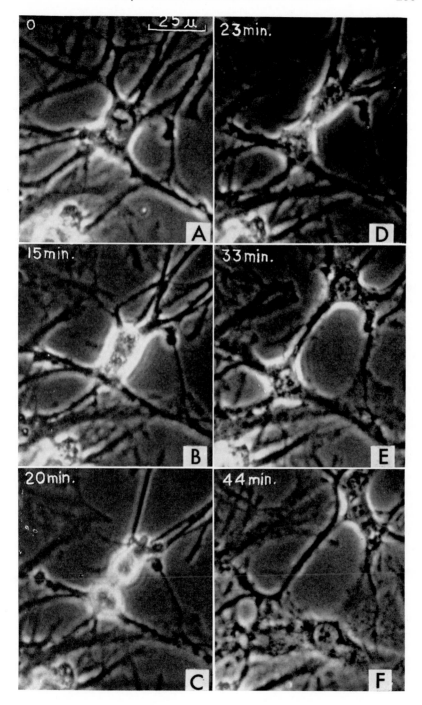

assembled in the course of studying human neoplastic tissue. Publications have included descriptions of the characteristics of normal and pathological neuroglia cells, especially in relation to the problem of fibrogenesis (Costero and Pomerat, '51, '52; Costero, *et al.*, '54a, b; '55a, b).

Descriptions of normal living and stained preparations, including an illustration of a possible modulation in the form of an astrocyte observed in a film sequence, were reported in a study of the hypothalamohypophysial system in vitro by Hild ('54a, b). He found that, in early stages of cultivation, astrocytes from different parts of the brain formed a three-dimensional network of various densities. The cells were connected with one another by their processes. Ciné records showed a characteristic shaking movement of the cell bodies. This movement differed somewhat from the pulsatile activity of oligodendrocytes. Mitoses were frequently seen during which the astrocytes withdrew their processes and thus lost their close contact with neighboring cells. After the completion of the cell divisions, new processes were sent out by which daughter cells re-established contact within the network. As the cultures grew older, astrocytes at the periphery sometimes lost their contact with other cells and thereby gradually withdrew their processes. At the same time they tended to flatten out and become attached closely to the smooth glass surface. In extreme cases the astrocytes, by this process, could transform into completely flat cells without processes. The evidence that one was still dealing with astrocytes could be established only by following one particular cell and observing its transformation from a multibranched into a flat, unbranched form. This behavior might be interpreted as a phenomenon of adaptation or a modulation in relation to the particular conditions in vitro.

The appearance of various neuroglia cells which are found in easily reproducible cultures of the cerebellum of newborn kittens has recently been described with the aid of ciné techniques (Pomerat and Costero, '56). Astrocytes in a thin zone of outgrowth present a typical network of stellate processes but at the periphery a gradual transformation of astrocytes is regularly encoun-

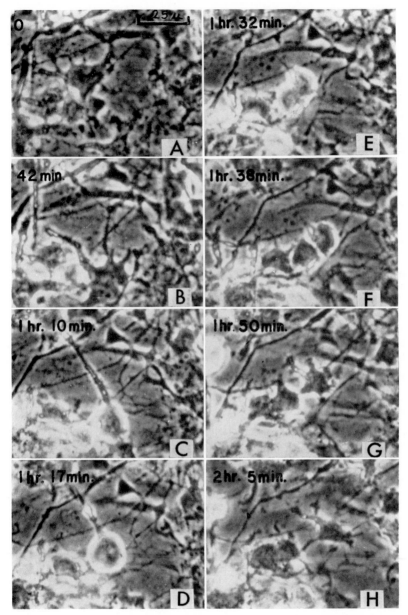

FIGURE 55. Mitosis of an astrocyte from a tissue culture of the posterior pituitary gland of a normal cat. Magnification, 600 ×.

Biology of Neuroglia

tered; their appearance can become similar to cells described as ependyma.

There has been considerable disagreement among pathologists regarding the capacity of astrocytes to show mitotic activity. Many years ago, Canti, Bland and Russell ('37) made a record with ordinary light microscopy of a dividing tumor astrocyte. Divisions of malignant astroblasts are regularly encountered in our films of the behavior of human brain tumors in vitro. Figure 54 of selected film frames from a record of a 6 day culture of a fragment of normal adult cat spinal cord and Figure 55 from the posterior pituitary of a normal cat (record made by Dr. Hild) are presented showing that at least in vitro nonmalignant astrocytes are capable of division. Nuclear rotation (Pomerat, '53a) which has been found in cultures of regenerating neurons from the dorsal root ganglia of chicks (Nakai, '56) has also been observed for astrocytes in a few film sequences.

OLIGODENDROCYTES

Oligodendrocytes in vitro are characterized as being small cells with globose, vase-shaped or rounded perinuclear zones rich in highly refractile granules and droplets which tend to obscure the nucleus. A small number of processes arise abruptly, i.e., without a cone-shaped base, from the perinuclear cytoplasm. An idealized common form for cells of this type would be described as resembling the egg case of a skate with four long processes extending from a fusiform cell body. However, there is a considerable range of variation probably in part resulting from physiological responses to environmental conditions.

Oligodendrocytes usually are among the first elements to migrate from explanted brain tissue. In view of their emigration on the second or third day of culture, their high sensitivity to illumination and the fact that they are soon overrun by larger and more vigorous outwandering cells, they easily may be overlooked. While they are obtained from various brain tissues, the corpus

---

Figure 56. Mitosis of an oligodendrocyte from a tissue culture of the hypothalamus of a newborn kitten. Magnification, 600 ×.

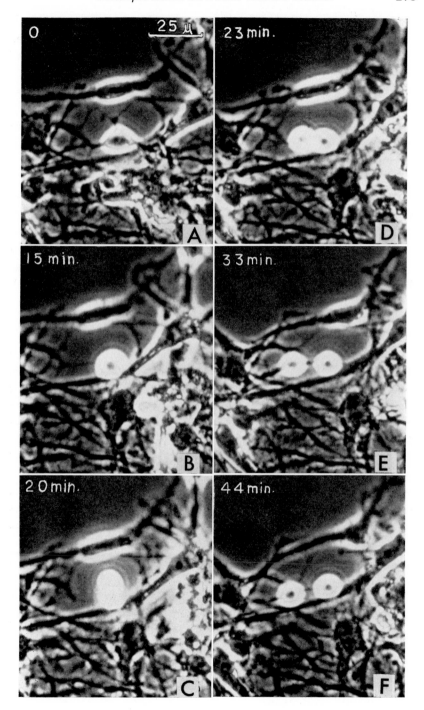

callosum has served as a favorite source of material even though clot liquefaction of such explants is troublesome.

Figure 56 shows their bright glowing appearance with phase optics and proves that they are capable of mitosis. The illustrations were prepared from a ciné record of tissue from hypothalamus of a newborn kitten.

Results obtained from cinematographic records of the rhythmic contractility of oligodendrocytes from the corpus callosum of normal adult rats were reported by Lumsden and Pomerat ('51). These findings were extended to include cells from presumably normal human brain tissue obtained in the course of the removal of intracranial tumors and from tissue obtained in lobotomies performed for intractable pain (Pomerat, '51). Cultures of an oligodendroglioma provided an opportunity to confirm the original observation by Canti, Bland and Russell ('37) of rhythmic pulsatile activity of oligodendrocytes of neoplastic origin (Pomerat, '55).

The contraction-expansion cycle of oligodendrocytes generally was found to be approximately 5 minutes. Rhythmic activity was not always found for all cells of the same form. This is also true for other cell activities observed with time-lapse cinematography such as nuclear rotation, pinocytosis and translocation of mitochondria. Much work remains to be done to define the conditions under which these modalities are expressed and their relation to underlying biochemical events. Of special significance are the inroads being made by Benitez, Murray and Woolley ('55) on the effect of serotonin and other chemicals on the contractility of oligodendrocytes.

Another important field of investigation which may clarify the role of the oligodendrocytes emerges from the report by Hild that myelin formation easily can be obtained in vitro from neurons of the central nervous system.

Phase contrast, time-lapse cinematographic techniques offer special opportunity for studies on the dynamic properties of neuroglia cells. The rate of cell emigration, the development of patterns of outgrowth, rhythmic contractility, nuclear rotation, mitotic activity and the behavior of various organoids can be analyzed under conditions in which exact temporal relations are available. With the use of perfusion chambers, ciné records can be made of the effects of imposing a wide variety of physicochemical variables on the cellular environment. Like the kymograph record, the film strip may serve for quantitative analyses of cellular phenomena. This method of investigating cell physiology has been discussed in several reviews (Pomerat, '53b, '54; Pomerat, Lefeber and Smith, '54).

Chapter 11

Response of Oligodendrocytes to Serotonin*

Margaret R. Murray*

IT HAS BEEN shown that the vaso-constrictor serotonin will
act directly upon the smooth muscle of blood vessel walls,
uterus and intestine when rings of these organs are suspended
in dilute solutions (0.1 µg/ml) of the drug. Cardiac muscle also
responds to it. Serotonin, as 5-hydroxytryptamine, was identified
by Rapport in mammalian serum at time of clotting. It is found
in quantity also in other situations, as in intestinal mucosa and in
brain, where it appears to be synthesized (Amin, Crawford and
Gaddum, '53). There are indications that its presence in suitable
quantities contributes to the normal functioning of the brain.
Among these is the proficiency of some of its structural anologues
and antagonists to cause mental disturbance (Shaw and Woolley,
'54; Woolley and Shaw, '54a, b, '57). The question at issue for us
was: how do serotonin and its congeners act upon the central
nervous system? The demonstration that oligodendrocytes are
contractile cells, having a function reminiscent of that of involun-
tary muscle, offered a clue that we couldn't resist following up to
see whether they might also show a similarity in pharmacological response.

This sort of experiment, i.e., direct exposure of cells to drug, is
fraught with difficulties in both execution and interpretation and
our methods to date are very crude. However, it is a crucial and
necessary type of experiment, results of which indicate that serotonin in a concentration of about 5 µg/ml will induce prolonged
tonic or spasmodic contraction of oligodendrocytes in vitro. This

---

* The work which I shall briefly describe was done in our laboratory by Mrs.
Helena Benitez in collaboration with Dr. D. W. Woolley of the Rockefeller Institute.

response can be prevented or reversed by the serotonin antagonists medmain and 1-methyl medmain. Lysergic acid diethyl-
amine (LSD) is antagonized by serotonin but does not itself an-
tagonize serotonin; LSD administered simultaneously intensifies
or prolongs the action of serotonin, probably because it inactivates

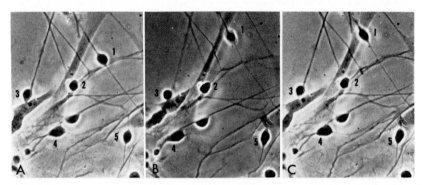

FIGURE 57. Serial photographs of a control culture of human fetal oligodendrocytes showing normally pulsating cells. Note the changes in outline
of cells 1-5. In B, cell 1 contracted during an exposure time of 2 minutes,
producing the recorded blurred outline. Magnifications, 600 ×.

amine oxidase and thus spares serotonin. Thus, it appears that
oligodendrocytes are capable of making a direct physiological
response to the vaso-constrictor and that their response is basically similar to that of smooth muscle.

Though the concentration of serotonin in these experiments
appears high, its effects are in all cases reversible and are not to
be confused with a general toxic action. The effect becomes apparent a few minutes after drug administration, reaches its peak
in 40 to 60 minutes and then gradually subsides. The culture, being embedded in a plasma clot, is probably less accessible to the
experimental medium than are the cells of tissue rings suspended
in saline solutions; in the culture the ratio of volume of medium
to tissue weight is also less than in ring preparations, since the
culture is dipped twice (a total of 2 minutes) in the serotonin
saline solution, then removed and mounted for observation, retaining only the amount of experimental solution adhering to culture and clot. These circumstances may account in some degree
for the 50-fold concentration found effective in the bath for this

material (5 µg/ml). In the bath, 2 µg/ml is sub-liminal for oligodendrocytes under these conditions. Controls were exposed to the
same treatment, using a bath of balanced saline solution only. In
this work it should be possible to employ a perfusion chamber
such as Dr. Pomerat uses but, as yet, we have not been able to
get the perfusing arrangement to work.

In the first experiments (Benitez, Murray and Woolley, '55)
observations were made on human fetal material by means of
serial still photographs over periods of about 3 hours. Later, time-
lapse movies were made from newborn rat brain, the same material used by Lumsden and Pomerat ('51) in their original demonstration of pulsation in normal oligodendrocytes. Figure 57,
three photograhs selected from a longer series, shows the changing outline of normally pulsating oligodendrocytes and which
serve as controls. The individual cells have been numbered. In
A, relaxation is seen in cells 1, 3 and 4, contractions in cell 2. An
intermediate stage, beginning contraction, may be noted in cell 5.

In B, attention is directed to cell 1, which appears particularly
active. Since the photograph was arranged for a 2 minute exposure time and the systole may be as short as 1.5 minutes,
changes in cell shape are recorded in the single film. Cell 2 is
relaxed but cells 3, 4 and 5 are contracted.

In C, cells 1, 2 and 5 are contracted; cells 3 and 4 have begun
to relax. As indicated by this control series, the normal pulsation
of this type of brain cell is very easily recognized. It is not syn-
chronized but the individual cells seem to command their own
rhythm. Any interference with the normal pulsation can therefore
be picked up, and the simultaneous appearance of all or a high
percentage of the observed oligodendrocytes in any given phase
of the pulsating process is significant.

Figure 58A and B shows effects of immersion in serotonin at
5 µg/ml. On the left is the culture before serotonin was applied;
on the right, 35 minutes later. Here the cell groups are identified
by numbers. Before the application of serotonin (A) some cells
are in contraction, some are rather extended. After serotinin (B)
contraction is general; groups of cells have drawn together and
pulled away farther from other groups. Note also the contracted,
often lobate, outline of individual cells.

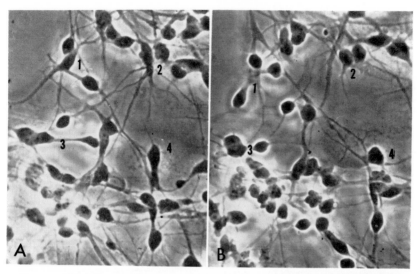

FIGURE 58. Effects of serotonin (5 μg/ml) on human fetal oligodendrocytes. A shows the culture before administration of the drugs; B shows the same culture 35 minutes after serotonin was introduced into the medium. Note particularly the behavior of cells 1-4; following exposure to serotonin the individual cells enter into a tetanic contraction and this may result in groups of cells drawing together, as shown in the vicinity of cells 1, 2, 3 and 4. Magnifications, 600 ×.

The moving pictures were taken at no more than 8 frames per minute in order to avoid light damage to the cultures. Since they are shown at 16 frames per second, movements are accelerated 120 times. This means that after treatment with serotonin the greatest effect of the compound appears within the first 20 to 30 seconds of a film sequence. The film first shows typical cell outlines and some rhythmic movements of the oligodendrocytes. The cells do not all pulsate at any one time; nor do they pulsate continuously; nor do these cells, mounted in balanced saline, pulsate as enthusiastically as Dr. Pomerat's did. We omitted the serum that ordinarily is a component of our medium, in order not to introduce any serotonin into the environment of the controls.

The second half of the film is composed of 4 short serotonin sequences, each representing an experimental run of about 3 hours. The effects of serotonin on the cell may be described as a suddenly adopted spasmodic or tetanic contraction; a tight constriction of the cell body which, like a synaeresis, squeezes small granules and vacuoles out into the cell processes where they shuttle actively back and forth. The processes also exhibit some peculiar membrane movements. I would like to emphasize that these effects are reversible; towards the end of the sequence the cell relaxes and may begin to pulsate rhythmically.

This exploration of serotonin effects on oligodendrocytes is still incomplete and obviously there is much more to be done. The reason for introducing these preliminary results at this time is that they indicate the possibility of a direct physiological action of certain drugs upon the brain. We suggest that the capacity which oligodendrocytes possess to respond to serotonin may enter into the mechanism by which this hormone and its analogues bring about mental disturbance.

ROUND TABLE DISCUSSION

DR. KLÜVER: Mast cells and enterochromaffin cells appear to contain relatively large amounts of serotonin. Instead of applying serotonin directly to the experimental cultures, would it not be possible to introduce serotonin-containing cells, such as the mast cells, and let them live together with the oligodendrocytes?

DR. MURRAY: It certainly would be possible if you could get a large amount of mast cells to work with.

DR. KLÜVER: Benditt, and his collaborators (Benditt, Wong, Arase and Roeper, '55) isolated mast cells and obtained a concentration of 0.7 milligram of serotonin per milliliter of subcutaneous mast cells. It is my understanding (Benditt personal communication) that serotonin has been demonstrated to have biological effects in concentrations as low as 0.0001 µg/ml in vitro and 0.25 µg/ml in vivo. Would it not be possible to obtain sufficiently large amounts of mast cells to do the experiment?

DR. MURRAY: In tumors, yes. But how can you get them in quantity in the normal state? It might be worthwhile to try the tumor cells; however, the question in my mind is whether the mast cell would give up its serotonin in large amounts.

Dr. KLÜVER: If I recall correctly, various agents capable of releasing serotonin from mast cells are being specified at the present time (Rowley and Benditt, '56).

Dr. MURRAY: There must be a relatively large quantity of serotonin available. We hit these cells rather hard. Nevertheless, your approach would be interesting to try.

Dr. ALBERS: Have you used marsalid which is an antagonist of amine oxydase?

Dr. MURRAY: That is something we would like to do but have not done.

Dr. WINDLE: Perhaps the most primitive glial element is the ependyma cell. In some of the lowest forms of animals, the only type of neuroglia cell present is supposed to be ependyma. I understand that Dr. Hild has some observations on it.

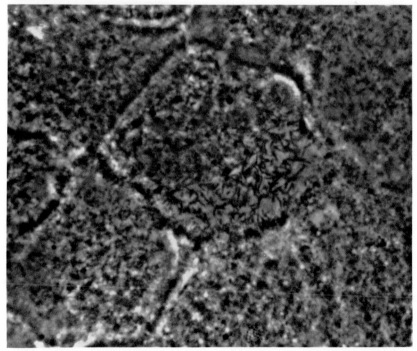

FIGURE 59. Outgrowth of ependyma cells as an epithelial sheet in a living 26 day old roller tube culture of cat choroid plexus, photographed under phase contrast in the plane of the apical cell pole bearing the cilia. Magnification, 2250 ×.

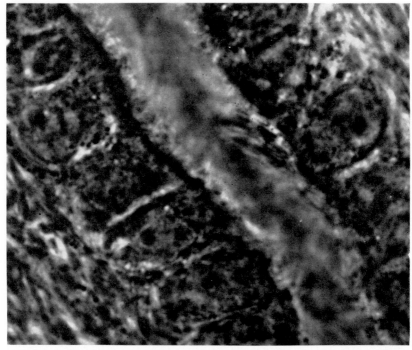

182 Biology of Neuroglia

FIGURE 60. Typical area from an ependymal "pool" seen under phase contrast, in a living 76 day old roller tube culture from the floor of the fourth ventricle of a kitten. The cilia are blurred due to their rapid movement during exposure time. Magnification 2250 ×.

DR. HILD: I have some preliminary results concerning the ciliary activity of ependyma cells of the ventricular linings and the choroid plexus from brains of kittens, adult cats, adult rhesus monkeys and one human fetus of 7 months. Such cells were maintained in vitro for periods up to 3.5 months, during which they did not show any regressive changes.

Ependyma cells were observed to establish two types of outgrowth patterns, the first being in the form of an epithelial sheet (Fig. 59) in which the cells became flattened to a considerable degree, attaching to the surface of the cover slip with what seems to be their original basal end. The free surface bearing the cilia was directed toward the culture medium. The second manner in which ependyma cells established themselves in vitro was with the formation of pools or elongated parallel double rows. The apical parts of such elements in one row faced the apical parts of those on the opposite side. The cilia extended into the space between the two rows (Fig. 60). These could be seen to originate from blepharoplasts located near the free borders of the cells. The cilia were in constant motion which was apparently very well co-ordinated. If the cells established themselves in an epithelial sheet, the cilia caused the fluid nutrient medium to flow in an oriented direction, as indicated by floating particles of debris or of free rounded cells. In the ependymal pools, the motion of the cilia also seemed to be well co-ordinated. Frequently, within such pools, one could see free or clustered cells or debris being rotated in the whirls of fluid produced by the cilia. This ciliary motion also is known to take place in situ as observed by Purkinje (1836) and Valentin (1836) and, therefore, may have some significant effect on the movement of the cerebrospinal fluid within the brain ventricles. In this connection, it is of interest that explants of ependyma derived from the narrow portions of the ventricular system, i.e., the foramen of Monro, the aqueduct of Sylvius or the posterior recess of the third ventricle, yielded especially active cells. In addition, the cilia of ependyma derived from such regions seemed to be longer than those of other regions of the ventricular walls.

Besides being of intrinsic interest, ependymal cultures explanted with tissue of other parts of the brain proved to be valuable in determining the general condition of the medium, because this influences ciliary activity. In tissue cultures, lack of oxygen or marked changes in pH retarded ciliary motion, thus indicating that the medium should be replenished.

Preliminary experiments on the reactivity of the cilia have been made in perfusion chambers with phase contrast microcinematographic recording. Changes in the electrolyte composition of the medium expressed themselves very clearly in the behavior of the cilia. For instance, when Gey's balanced salt solution was replaced by so-called physiological saline solution, the ciliary movement was regularly arrested after 28 to 32 minutes. The return to balanced salt solution or proteinaceous fluid nutrient caused the movement to resume without visible damage to the cells. However, if saline solution had been in contact with the cells for more than 40 minutes they were irreversibly damaged and ciliary movement was not restored even after prolonged and repeated washings with balanced salt solution or complete nutrient medium.

On the other hand, ependyma cells were found to be astonishingly resistant to the action of some other unphysiological conditions, such as ethyl alcohol or methyl alcohol added to the fluid nutrient. Whereas neurons are irreversibly damaged by an ethyl alcohol concentration of 0.5 per cent in the medium, ependyma cells tolerated ethyl alcohol up to 20 per cent and methyl alcohol up to 15 per cent in the fluid medium. Both alcohols stopped the ciliary movement completely but it recovered as soon as the alcohol was washed out. We have not yet determined the time after which damage due to alcohol is irreversible.

Dr. Scheibel: The ependyma cell is another type of neuroglia cell showing intimate contact with unmyelinated nerve fibers. In studying the periaqueductal gray matter of the kitten or puppy, we found that the mass of fibers wound closely around the bases of ependyma cells and were intricately woven around the long stems of these cells that sometimes extend several millimeters away from the central canal. Physical contacts are so close that it is very difficult to avoid thinking that some kind of activity, or impress of activity, may be transferred over to the ependyma cells themselves. Especially in primitive forms and in certain areas even in the higher vertibrate forms, the ependyma cells are likened to gland cells, and we know that gland cells in various parts of the body usually have some kind of innervation at their base or around the individual cells. Here again, we may have an example of this interesting phenomenon of axonal innervation of neuroglia cells.

Dr. Elliott: To what extent has Dr. Pomerat watched the effect of variations in the medium on the behavior of cells? I mean variations that may have physiological significance: anoxia, potassium, osmosis, pH, carbon dioxide?

Dr. Pomerat: We have not worked over those problems systematically, although we have some general information on the subject. There is one area that Dr. Hild has explored with respect to neurosecretion in which he varied the concentration of sodium chloride in the perfusion fluid.

Dr. Hild: I have investigated the reaction of hypothalamic

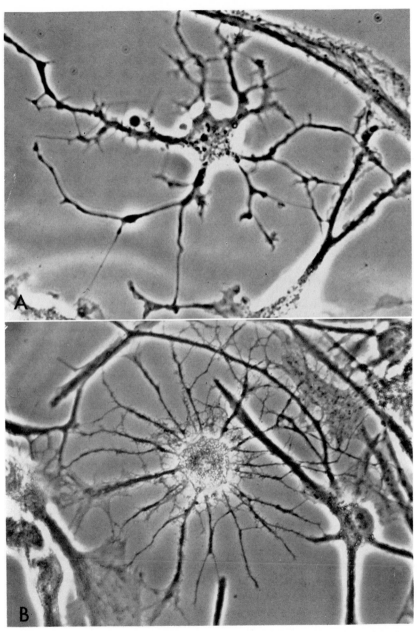

FIGURE 61. A. An oligodendrocyte from the corpus callosum of a 6 day old kitten, 6 days in culture. Magnification 1250 ×.

B. A fibrous astrocyte from the corpus callosum of a 3 day old kitten, 3 days in culture. Magnification, 750 ×.

neurosecretory neurons against hypertonic media in comparison to the reaction of Purkinje cells and various types of neuroglia cells. I have not investigated the effects of anoxia, increased or decreased levels of potassium or carbon dioxide. As far as the pH is concerned, we do not worry about slight changes and I do not even add pH-indicators, such as phenol red, to my cultures, now that we have established basic standard methods. As I have pointed out earlier, we check the condition of the medium by observing the mobility of the ependymal cilia when possible.

DR. ELLIOTT: What would happen if you deliberately change the pH?

DR. HILD: I have not investigated events following deliberate changes of the pH. However, increased or decreased tonicity of the nutrient medium as represented by NaCl at 0.96 per cent, versus that at 0.75 per cent, does not visibly influence the shape and motility of neuroglia cells, as observed with time lapse photography. Moreover, Purkinje cells adapt themselves very well to increased or decreased tonicity of the medium without any visible disturbance, whereas neurosecretory neurons react in a specific manner (Hild '54a, b).

DR. POMERAT: This reaction is observed only in certain neurons. It appears to be independent from the adjacent astrocytes and oligodendrocytes. This is the only area that we have fairly well documented but Dr. Hild has not published all his data because he wants to explore them further.

DR. ROSE: Dr. Elliott's question concerning the effects of change of pH on cultures prompts me to discuss tissue culture techniques in general. Dr. Frederick Wolfgram and I have been students of tissue culture for several years. Much of our inspiration and guidance have come from Dr. Pomerat and Dr. Murray. The aim in our laboratory has been to grow adult human oligodendrocytes. Thus far we have failed to reach this goal, primarily, we believe, because of the problems of the proper medium. We have struggled in an attempt to find a medium which could be sufficiently synthetic so that other workers could reproduce what we have attempted to do in our laboratory. I might say that, with natural media, experiments are very difficult to reproduce exactly. One cannot be certain that one experiment is similar to

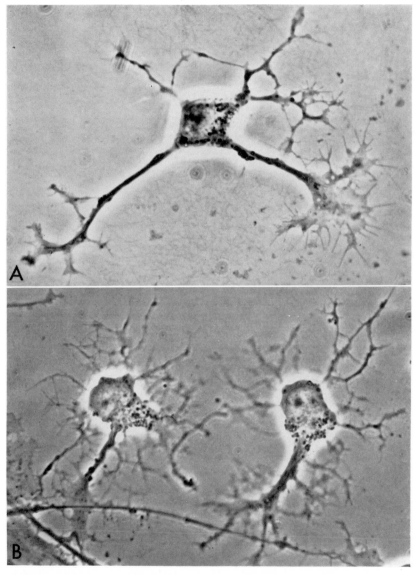

FIGURE 62. A. An oligodendrocyte from the corpus callosum of a 7 day old kitten, 4 days in culture. Magnification, 1500 ×.
B. Oligodendrocytes from the corpus callosum of a 3 week old kitten, 9 days in culture. Magnification, 1200 ×.

another experiment. Cells are different depending on the medium in which they are living. Dr. Lumsden called attention to the response of neuroglia cells to a change in their environment—as in pathology. The stimulus which brings about the cellular response is derived from the surrounding medium. A synthetic medium would be desirable. The medium which we have developed is not entirely satisfactory. It consists primarily of purified serum albumin, balanced salt solution, glucose, vitamins and co-enzymes. I will demonstrate several neuroglia cells cultured in this medium. We studied the morphology of individual cells and they appear to us to be more mature in form than when other media are used. An oligodendrocyte from kitten corpus callosum is shown in Figure 61A. Note the characteristic swellings (gliosomes) in the processes. A typical fibrous astrocyte showing the radiating processes bounded by fine filamentous membranes may be seen in Figure 61B. Figure 62A is an oligodendrocyte; I call attention to the structures within the processes and point out that its morphology is somewhat different from that of the oligodendrocyte demonstrated in Dr. Murray's motion pictures. In Figure 62B there are two cells with the typical cell bodies of oligodendrocytes but with more than the common number of processes. They suggest transitional forms. Figure 63A shows an oligodendrocyte with extremely long radiating processes. The cells in Figure 63B have long radiating processes containing many mitochondria; and we feel that in general these cells have many of the characteristics of fibrous astrocytes.

From our tedious experience in attempting to develop a synthetic medium for neuroglia, I wish to submit a word of caution with respect to coming to firm conclusions about adult, mature neuroglia cells from what is seen in cultures. It would appear that neuroglia cells differ in form and in reactions in dependence upon the medium in which they are living.

DR. GLEES: I ought to challenge the idea that some of these pictures are of neuroglia cells. They have a certain polarity which you very rarely see in neuroglia cells. You say that you took material from the corpus callosum and, therefore, it can contain only neuroglia cells? The corpus callosum of all animals, including man, is covered by gray matter. Therefore, to assume the corpus callosum free of nerve cells may be a fallacy.

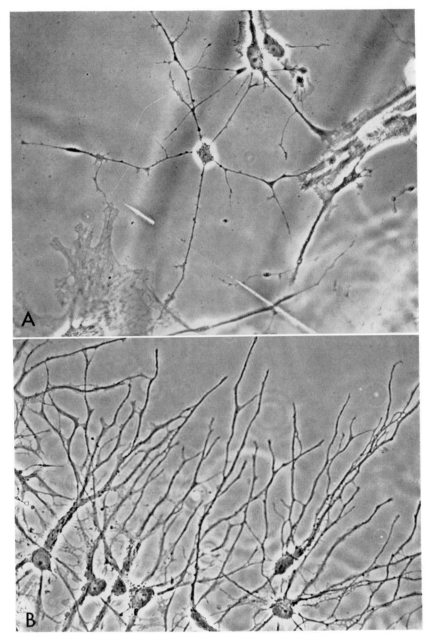

FIGURE 63. A. An oligodendrocyte from the corpus callosum of a 2 week old kitten, 5 days in culture. Magnification, 465 ×.

B. Fibrous astrocytes from the corpus callosum of a 6 week old kitten, 10 days in culture. Magnification, 450 ×.

Dr. Rose: However, we dissected out the corpus callosa with the aid of a dissecting microscope and made every reasonable effort to secure clean specimens of white matter. Furthermore, our semisynthetic medium is not satisfactory for neurons and will only support the growth of neuroglia cells. While we may have doubts about different neuroglia cell types in culture, we can exclude the possibility of neurons being present. However, the difficulties of identification have led us to hope that a study of cell behavior with use of time lapse movies—as a sort of third dimension—would bring further assistance.

Dr. Pomerat: With cinematography we begin to see something of the tremendous importance of what electron microscopists refer to as the ectoplasmic portion of the cell. This is of monumental value in considerations of the biochemistry of cells, since the extension of surface afforded by paucimolecular layers of cytoplasm increases the opportunity for reaction systems. There is a great need for exchanging information with electron microscopists with regard to the complications of infolded membranes.

SECTION IV

Biochemistry of the Neuroglia

Chapter 12

Direct Enumeration of Cells of the Brain*

John I. Nurnberger

A NUMBER of years ago I completed a cytochemical investigation of certain metabolic events occurring in the supraoptic nuclei of cold-stressed rats, using Caspersson's ultraviolet microabsorption technique. Subsequently, we used more conventional macro- and microchemical techniques to explore further the biochemical significance of some of the observations made by that technique. We encountered serious difficulty in attempting to translate conventional biochemical information into data interpretable at the cellular level. One source of this difficulty stemmed from the fact that we had no reliable and truly meaningful reference standard. Dr. Flexner and his associates (Flexner, Belknap and Flexner, '53) had calculated their biochemical data to unit wet mass of cellular phase, using chloride and radiosodium compartment values. Also, they had published a classical study of the volumetric fractions of various cellular components in guinea pig fetal cortex as determined by the Chalkley technique (Peters and Flexner, '50). Because serious questions had been raised concerning the interpretation of so-called tissue ionic compartments, and also because of the magnitude of volumetric contraction artifacts in histologic sections as compared to fresh tissue, we sought a more immediate biological referent. The technique which was finally used for determining this reference for biochemical data had much in common with a direct enumer-

* New observations recorded in this chapter were made with Dr. Malcolm Gordon and Mr. Walter Borden. The latter made most of the observations on chick embryo brains. The work was supported in part by the Medical Research and Development Board, Office of the Surgeon General, Department of the Army, under Contract No. DA-49-007-MD-204; and in part by the Jane Coffin Childs Memorial Fund for Medical Research.

193

ation technique described by Heller and Elliott ('54). Our technique permitted not only a direct enumeration of the total cells
within any bit of fresh tissue but also an approximate enumeration of nuerons as well as of nonneuronal cell populations. Differential counts were not attempted by Dr. Elliott and his group.
Semiquantitative data on the differential cell densities of whole
adult rat brain as well as various dissected portions of that brain
were obtained and will be reviewed. Subsequently, similar counts
were obtained for the developing chick embryo brain from the
seventh day of incubation to hatching. These observations have
not been published elsewhere.

A brief résumé of the technique will suffice for our purposes
here. Fresh brains or dissected parts of brain were removed in the
cold room and, when necessary, were pooled to provide a sample
sufficiently large to weigh accurately. The weighed fresh sample
was suspended in a measured volume of 0.2 molar potassium
chloride solution buffered to pH 6.5 with 0.2 per cent potassium
phosphates. Sufficient glass beads of 6 mm diameter were then
added to provide ball mill action during subsequent agitation in
the stoppered glass bottle in which the sample had originally
been weighed. Free tissue nuclei were progressively liberated
into the suspending medium with increasing time of agitation.
Aliquots of the resulting suspension, appropriately diluted with
0.1 per cent methylene blue chloride in buffered potassium chloride, were counted directly in a 0.2 mm hemocytometer chamber.
Differential counts were made under glycerine immersion in thin
layers of suspension covered with a No. 1 coverslip. During the
first 15 minutes of agitation, few nuclei were destroyed as estimated by direct microscopic control. After 15 minutes, however,
an increasing number of nuclear fragments could be identified
with continuing agitation especially in preparations of rat cortex
and in early embryo chick brain. This distintegration of isolated
nuclei made impossible the determination of maximal direct
counts, since total nuclear counts increased for a variable period
after the first identifiable nuclear fragments were noted. Liberated nuclei were counted and the values were plotted against
time of agitation through the early phase of blenderization and
well into the period during which disintegration of nuclei was

occurring. The rate of breakdown as well as liberation of nuclei could then be estimated from such curves and straight line tangents representing these two rates extrapolated to a theoretical maximum at their point of intersection.

This method was discussed in Chicago last summer (Nurnberger and Gordon, '57) and was criticized at that time from a theoretical standpoint. As already mentioned, the maximum nuclear count is impossible to determine directly by this technique. Dr. Gordon has derived mathematical expressions for the independent maximal rates of liberation and destruction of nuclei from our data and has calculated theoretical maxima for several

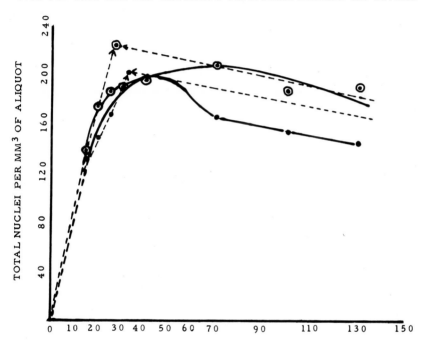

TIME OF AGITATION IN MINUTES

FIGURE 64. Rate of liberation and eventual destruction of free nuclei in 2 whole rat brains disintegrated by agitation in a modified ball mill (see text). Maximum rates of liberation and disintegration are indicated by broken lines. Observed counting curves are drawn in solid lines. Points of intersection for maximal liberation and destruction rates are indicated by arrows, the extrapolated maximum number of total nuclei being read from these points of intersection. (From Nurnberger and Gordon ('57); courtesy, P. B. Hoeber.)

Biology of Neuroglia

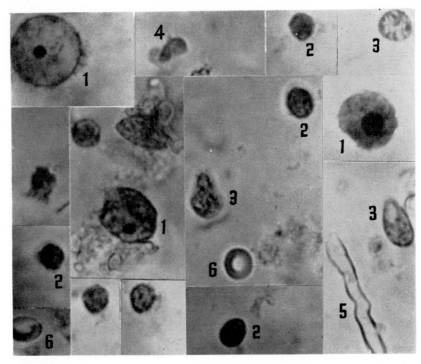

FIGURE 65. The appearance of free nuclei from rat brain liberated into buffered 0.2 M KCl by ball mill agitation. Nuclei are stained with the counting diluent, 0.1% methylene blue chloride in buffered 0.2 M KCl. 1. Nuclei of neurons of several types. Note the prominent heavily staining central nucleolus and pale chromatin network, except in the folded and partly disintegrating nucleus at left center. 2. Nuclei of neuroglia cells, probably oligodendrocytes; these nuclei are uniformly oval or round and are about the same size as erythrocytes. In this medium they stain brilliantly and have an iridescent sheen. Note the heavily staining dense chromatin mesh and multiple dark paracentral nucleoli. 3. Large pale oval to round nuclei with multiple paracentral nucleoli and diffuse chromatin mesh, presumably from astrocytes. 4. Small, crescentic nucleus which may be either from microglia cells or from vascular endothelium. Such nuclei are relatively common in samples from the cerebral cortex. 5. Myelin fragment. 6. Erythrocyte. All were recorded on Eastman ortho press plates at a magnification of 1250 ×. (From Nurnberger and Gordon ('57); courtesy of P. B. Hoeber.)

counting series from a number of samples of rat cerebral cortex and whole brain. Cortical nuclear counts decrease more rapidly than do those for whole brain following the observed maximum because of the relatively high proportion of delicate neuronal nuclei in the former. It is of interest that his calculated theoretical maxima agreed within 5 per cent with the extrapolated value obtained by the approximation noted above. This, of course, is not a mathematical proof of the method but is rather a demonstration that such treatment of the data, which makes possible a continuous correction for nuclear disintegration during the period of liberation, gives approximately the same values as does the extrapolation method.

Data from counting series in two whole rat brains are presented in Figure 64 and the method of extrapolation is demonstrated. The counting diluent used, 0.1 per cent methylene blue chloride in 0.2 molar potassium chloride solution, stained the nuclei quite distinctly, simplified total counts and permitted fairly clear differentiation of nuclear types in most instances. It was necessary, particularly with cortical samples, to obtain frequent counts during the early minutes of agitation so that the maximum could be bracketed. For each part of rat brain studied, the maximum was reached at a characteristic total time of agitation. In chick embryo brain, the maximum was encountered after somewhat longer periods of agitation in older than in younger brains.

Figure 65 is a composite photomicrograph of freshly liberated nuclei as they appear in the coverslip preparation used for differential counts. Nuclear types can be distinguished with reasonable certainty in such a preparation, though it was impossible to make such distinctions convincingly in chick embryo brain preparations before the twelfth day of incubation. Extraordinary difficulties were also encountered in distinguishing nuclei of various cell types in cerebellar samples from adult rat brain.

The distribution of neuronal and nonneuronal nuclei in unit wet mass of various parts of rat brain is diagrammed in Figure 66. Attention is directed especially to the lowermost of these three figures. Here we have charted the density of neuroglia cell nuclei and of all other nonneuronal elements in the various noted parts of adult rat brain. The only other nuclear elements which were encountered were, as a matter of fact, nuclei of endothelial cells. These are included in the total counts of the lowermost figure. Numerical counts are projected onto the particular region of brain from which the appropriate sample was taken, with the

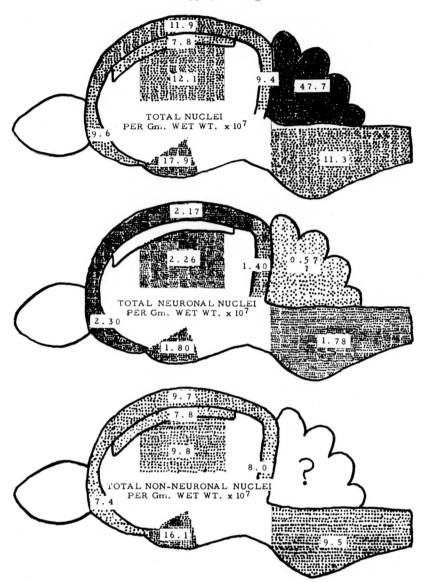

FIGURE 66. Nuclear densities of various regions of the rat's brain. Total nuclei per gram wet weight of the area indicated in upper diagram. Absolute values are obtained by multiplying the recorded figures by 10^7. Regions studied were: mixed parietofrontal cortex, striate cortex, pooled cortex from all areas (recorded in diagram at frontal pole), hypothalamic area, thalamic region, whole cerebellum and medulla plus pons. Density of stippling is directly proportional to nuclear densities. The middle diagram is similar ex-

exception of total counts recorded in the frontal polar region. These are counts of cortical samples pooled from all regions of the cerebrum. In cerebellar preparations it was possible to identify only a limited number of nuclei as unequivocally neuronal. Many nuclei of small neurons could not be distinguished from neuroglia cells and other nuclei in the cerebellum.

In general, the glial-endothelial matter, encountered in various parts of the adult rat brain, is remarkably uniform in density. The mean count for pooled cortex was 7.4×10^7 nuclei per gram wet tissue. The parasagittal cortex, on the other hand, 9.7×10^7 nuclei were glial-endothelial, whereas, in the subjacent white matter, 7.8×10^7 were counted as nonneuronal per unit wet mass; 8 or 9×10^7 nuclei per gram were counted in other parts of cortex. Why the total counts in the parasagittal region should have been greater than in other areas of cortex is not entirely clear. It is possible that the endothelial contribution in this region is unusually high. For purposes of calculation it was assumed that the number of endothelial nuclei per unit mass of vascular network is constant and that the vascularization of white matter is approximately one tenth as dense as that of the immediately overlying cortex in the parasagittal region. By solving two appropriate simultaneous equations derived from the counts of parasagittal cortex and subjacent white matter, we calculated that 22 per cent of the nonneuronal nuclei in this cortical region should be endothelial nuclei. A crude check on this estimate was made by enumerating both endothelial cells and neuroglia cells in measured areas of histologic preparations of rat cortex. Tissues were fixed in a mixture of acetic acid, formalin and alcohol and stained either with hematoxylin and eosin or with buffered thionine. Direct differential counts in the parasagittal cortex indicated that between 27 and 30 per cent of such nonneuronal nuclei are nuclei

---

←◀◀◀◀

cept that counts of neuron nuclei alone were made. The value for whole cerebellum is for nuclei of Purkinje cells and cells of the roof and dentate nuclei. Nuclei of granule and other cells could not be recognized as such. Total numbers of nonneural (neuroglial and endothelial) nuclei are shown in lower diagram. (From Nurnberger and Gordon ('57); courtesy of P. B. Hoeber.)

of endothelial cells. The Chalkley technique was not used in these counts, since only glial and endothelial nuclei were counted and all of these are of the same order of size.

The hypothalamic area and the cerebellum are relatively unique among the areas studied in the adult rat brain. To take the hypothalamic area as an example, if one assumes that the glial matter is about as dense here as in white matter, then the cell count data would indicate that there are approximately 4 times as many endothelial nuclei in unit wet mass of hypothalamus as in a comparable mass of fresh parasagittal cortex. Such a difference would speak for a fourfold more dense vascular network in the hypothalamus than in this cortical area. Though no quantitative data are available, the passing impression of those who have observed the vascular meshwork in these two portions of rat brain does not support such a marked disparity. The probability is that a great number of the free nuclei liberated from the hypothalamic area are nuclei of neurons which do not have sufficiently distinct morphological characteristics to permit their differentiation from neuroglia cell nuclei by this staining technique. It is rather difficult, as a matter of fact, to differentiate some of these cells in the best histological preparations. Whatever the interpretation may be, the hypothalamic area stood out as an unusual zone, not only from the standpoint of its total cellular density per unit wet weight, but also for its density of nuclei not clearly identified as neuronal in type. In these respects it was surpassed only by the cerebellum.

Nuclear counts of whole white leghorn chick embryo brains from the seventh day of incubation to hatching are plotted in Figure 67. It was impossible to differentiate neuronal from other nuclei by the methylene blue staining technique until the twelfth day of incubation; thus, for the interval 7 to 12 days, only total counts are recorded. During the early phases of incubation, counts vary within relatively narrow limits. The spread in individual counts is much greater in older embryos. Formation of new cells follows a remarkably regular course from the seventh to the twenty-first day and especially from the eleventh or twelfth day on. The rate of new cell formation seems to increase somewhat after the tenth or eleventh day of incubation. It is of particular

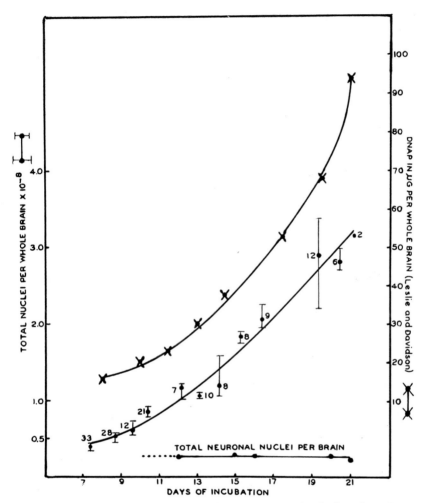

FIGURE 67. Total nuclei and neuron nuclei per whole chick embryo brain from the seventh day of incubation to hatching (21st day). Mean values are recorded as *black circles*, the extremes for each group of counts by vertical projections from the mean. Numerals adjacent to black circles indicate the total number of brains used. Six to 8 brains were pooled for individual determinations during the period from 7 to 11 days of incubation. Two or more brains were pooled for individual counts from the twelfth to nineteenth days. Plotted immediately above the total nuclear count data, are recalculated chemical determinations of desoxyribonucleic acid phosphorus (DNAP), as reported by Leslie and Davidson ('51) for whole white leghorn chick embryo brain. White leghorn chicks were also used for nuclear counts.

interest to note that, from the twelfth day on, the total number of neuronal nuclei remains quite constant within the experimental error of this technique. New cells which are formed in chick embryo brain after the twelfth day of incubation must be largely neuroglia and endothelial cells and not neurons. On the same graph with these total cell counts, are plotted values of total brain desoxyribonucleic acid phosphorus (DNAP) as determined in the same species of chick embryos during this phase of development. These data were published by Leslie and Davidson ('51) and provide an interesting comparison with cell count data. I was thinking especially of Dr. Elliott when I drew up this graph. He will be happy to see, as he must have suspected, that in this material the total nuclear counts parallel rather impressively the DNAP values. These observations do lend support to the now common practice of using DNA values as a chemical cell referent rather than counted total cells. Chemically determined DNA gives no information concerning cell types and it is obvious that differential counting data are still required where such information is needed for interpretation.

It is unfortunate that the counts reported here are too few to provide a clear answer to another question of interest; namely, is the mean DNA content of all cells in neural tissue identical? A close comparison of the course of the two curves in Figure 67 suggests, but does not confirm, that the total DNAP per nucleus is greater in neuronal nuclei than it is in neuroglia cell nuclei. Simple calculations indicate that the mean DNAP per nucleus in the early chick embryo brain is considerably higher than the calculated mean value per nucleus in the chick embryo brain at or near hatching. This may be because the relative proportion of neuronal nuclei is so much higher in chick brain during the earlier phases of incubation than at hatching. Whether this difference reflects the fact that there is a progressive dilution of DNA rich neuronal nuclei from the twelfth or thirteenth day onward or whether it results from low counts because of disintegration of more nuclei before they can be enumerated or corrected for in the younger chick embryo brains, cannot be resolved by these data. Many more counts must be made and the DNA data carefully rechecked before a final answer can be given to this question.

Chapter 13

Concentration of Neuroglia Cells*

SAUL R. KOREY

THE CELLULAR constitution of the central nervous system is structured in sheetlike dispersions and nuclear concentrations. The intragroup organization and the interrelations of these groups are the elements of the communication process. But beyond this common integrative aspect, experimental inquiry has established the individuality and distinctiveness of the participating cell types. Further, the nervous complex is woven into a fabric provided by nonneural cells, the neuroglia, whose activities are largely undisclosed and are probably multiple, e.g., supportive, myelinating, nutritive. Specificity of neuroglia cells in terms of physicochemical attributes and functional correlates likewise can be anticipated.

Viewed in these terms, a solely holistic approach to the study of the nervous system is experimentally inadequate and many means have been employed to minimize the heterogeneity of the units under investigation. A rather standard procedure consists in the fragmentation of a tissue followed by differential sedimentation to collect units of similar densities and physiology. This procedure when applied to isolation of neuroglia cells risks the occurrence of serious changes in them. Despite this evident consideration it still appears useful to obtain enriched fractions of neuroglia cells directly from white matter. These cells so secured may be used for metabolic and immunologic studies. The present discussion is concerned with the techniques of obtaining neuroglial cells from white matter and with some features of the chemical constitution of these cells.

*This work, conducted in co-operation with Mildred Orchen, has been supported by the National Institute of Neurological Diseases and Blindness (B-1006) and the National Multiple Sclerosis Society (85(1)).

203

METHODS OF CONCENTRATION OF NEUROGLIA CELLS

Lamb brains are obtained at the abbatoir some 20 minutes after slaughter. These are wrapped individually in aluminum foil and carefully iced for transport to the laboratory. The white matter of the centrum ovale is isolated by removing all overlying gray substance with suction. The centra of 10 brains, each weighing 100 grams, are homogenized in a Waring blendor. The blades of the blendor are flattened to remove their torque and the edges dulled. Homogenization occurs at low speeds; the variac is set at 45. Each cycle of homogenization lasts 7 to 10 seconds. The medium is 0.25 M sucrose, 0.003 M K_2HPO_4. The coarsely homogenized white matter is filtered with gentle suction through silk bolting of 400μ diameter and the residue returned for further homogenization. The entire cycle is repeated until almost all the white matter is filtrable. The collected filtrate is passed through silk bolting of 250μ diameter and usually through a grid of 100 to 150μ diameter. The latter passage may not be necessary. At this stage the concentration of the suspension is one gram of white matter per 15 ml of homogenizing medium.

Glass centrifuge cups of 250 ml capacity are prepared with 50 ml of 1.75 M sucrose, 0.003 M K_2HPO_4 overlayered with 0.5 M sucrose, 0.003 M K_2HPO_4. The suspension is carefully added to fill the remainder of the cup. Centrifugation is performed in the International PR-2 centrifuge at 1300 rpm, 0° C for 20 minutes.

At the conclusion of this phase, the layers of the centrifugate are constituted as follows (Fig. 68A). Layer 1 has subcellular particles and very small fragments of myelin. Larger myelin elements collect in layer 2, the interface between 0.25 M and 0.5 M sucrose. Layer 3 consists of cells in various states and a fine dispersion of myelin cutlets. Layer 4 is the main neuroglial layer contaminated with red blood corpuscles and some fragments of myelin. It represents the interface between 0.5 M and 1.75 M sucrose. Finally, layer 5 is found to be free of any constituents and is mainly a supporting vehicle. In some cases, sucrose solutions of 0.8 M may be substituted for the 1.75 M. In this event, the major purified cellular component is found in this layer.

All the material above layer 4 is removed by suction and then the contents of layer 4 are recovered and made up to 0.8 to 1.0 M sucrose, 0.003 M K₂HPO₄, and spun at 18,200 × g for 15 minutes in a Lourdes angle head centrifuge. At the conclusion of this centrifugation (Fig. 68B), a heavy concentration of myelin fragments with associated axoplasm but free of cells is seen to collect at the surface. A cell layer of neuroglia cells and some red blood cor-

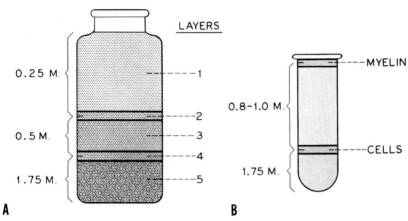

FIGURE 68. A. Schematic representation of the appearance of the first centrifugate. The figures on the left signify the increasing molarity of the sucrose solutions while those on the right refer to the layers visible following centrifugation (see text). B. After centrifugation at 18,200 × g for 15 minutes, the myelin and cells are separated, as seen in this diagram. The notations are the same as in A.

puscles are found at the surface of the 1.75 M sucrose. There is practically no free myelin in this layer but occasional clusters of cells may enmesh skeins of myelin in their partially intact processes. Further concentration of the conglutinated cells is accomplished by dilution in Krebs-Ringer phosphate solution and recentrifugation at 12,000 × g for 10 minutes. In the saline solution the formerly adherent cells are seen to disperse immediately. After centrifugation, the cells may be homogenized directly in the centrifuge tube for metabolic studies. All operations are performed at 0°-3°C. About 18 mg of cell protein are obtained from the white matter of 10 lamb brains. The entire preparation, from abbatoir to its termination, requires 5 hours.

The cells thus obtained are represented in Figure 69. Here

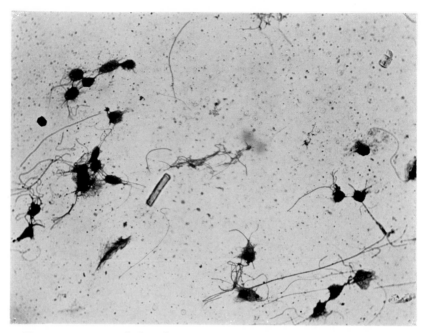

FIGURE 69. Neuroglial and contaminating elements in 0.8 M sucrose, as they appear when stained by the Holzer method. The preparation was spread directly on the slide and dried prior to staining. The background stippling is due to dye precipitation and occasional red blood cells (see text).

there is seen a variety of stages in the structural preservation of the cell state. Most of the cells are partially denuded of their fine processes but retain perinuclear cytoplasm and the general configuration of similar cells derived from usual preparations. In addition, there are occasional clumps of cells which appear to be attached to a fragmentary thread of myelinated nerve. Further histological study of these cells by heavy metal impregnation and other means is being carried out. The proportion of partially intact cells to bare nuclei and fiberless cells is likewise under investigation.

STUDIES ON NUCLEIC ACID AND LIPID CONTENT AND RESPIRATION

In order to estimate comparative rates of synthetic processes, reference standards of biological significance are required. Such

TABLE II

DISTRIBUTION OF NUCLEIC ACID AND PHOSPHORUS FRACTIONS IN SAMPLES OF
CEREBRAL CORTEX, WHITE MATTER AND NEUROGLIAL ELEMENTS

Constituent	Cerebral Cortex			White Matter			Neuroglial Fraction	
	per g WW	per mg N-total	per mg N-tca	per g WW	per mg N-total	per mg N-tca	per mg N-total	per mg N-tca
Nitrogen-total	1270	....	1.35	1274	....	1.19	....	1.09
Nitrogen-tca	940	0.74	....	1062	0.84	....	0.92	....
$\frac{\text{N-tca}}{\text{N-total}}$ (%)	74.2	....	....	83.7	....	....	92.0	....
Phosphorus-total	77.2	4.34	5.85	187.5	10.5	12.5	4.3	4.67
Acid Soluble-P	20.8	1.17	1.58	22.0	1.23	1.47	0.57	0.62
Lipid-P	47.2	2.66	3.58	152.0	8.54	10.2	1.95	2.12
Residual-P	7.23	0.41	0.55	21.6	1.21	1.45	1.98	2.15
Recovery (%)	98	....	....	104%	....	....	104%	....
$\frac{\text{N-total}}{\text{P-total}}$	16.5	....	....	6.8	....	....	16.5	....
$\frac{\text{N-tca}}{\text{P-total}}$	12.2	....	....	5.7	....	....	15.2	....
DNA-P	1.85	0.10	0.14	3.14	0.18	0.21	1.14	1.24
RNA-P	1.43	0.08	0.11	1.41	0.08	0.10	0.05	0.06
Total NA-P	3.27	0.18	0.25	4.55	0.27	0.31	1.20	1.31
Inorganic-P	0.76	0.04	0.06	1.34	0.08	0.09	0.04	0.04
"Inositol"-P	3.21	0.18	0.24	15.7	0.87	1.05	0.76	0.83
$\frac{\text{DNA}}{\text{RNA}}$	1.30	....	....	2.23	....	....	22.8	....

Reference is in terms of Moles per unit. Ratios are molar unless designated as percentages. N-total is the total nitrogen of sample; N-tca is the nitrogen precipitated by 10% trichloracetic acid; NA-P is total nucleic acid phosphorus; DNA-P is desoxyribonucleic acid phosphorus; RNA-P is ribose nucleic acid phosphorus; WW is wet weight of tissue.

standards as total nitrogen content, trichloracetic acid precipitable nitrogen, DNA content have been used. It is with this in mind that some analysis of the various constituents of the cellular preparation has been undertaken. In Table II a comparison of the distribution of the nitrogen content, nucleic acid, and phosporus fractions of cortex, white matter and the cellular material is given (Logan, Mannell and Rossiter, '52; Rossiter, '55).

It is evident that the patterns of the three tissues are different in that both the absolute quantities and the ratios of some of these are distinctive for each tissue. The proportion of trichloracetic acid precipitable nitrogen in relation to total nitrogen is much greater in the neuroglia cell fraction than in the others. This tentatively suggests that the procedure of isolation is attended by cellular changes in the soluble nitrogenous constituents which are washed out by the hyperosmotic homogenizing medium. It is for this reason that the various components are related not only to the total nitrogen but to the trichloracetic precipitable nitrogen content of the tissues. Of further interest is the greater amount of DNA and lesser amount of RNA found in the cell fraction than in the tissues. The possibilities in this instance include at least that the neuroglial RNA has been partially removed, that there is a high proportion of bare nuclei, or that the relatively dwarfed cytoplasmic component of the neuroglia cell is quantitatively insignificant in comparison with the nuclear component. Although these and other factors may be operative, the point has biochemical implications and will require additional attention.

The analysis of the lipid components of the cellular fraction is associated with some difficulty due to the persistent contamination of the chloroform-methanol extract of the cells by sucrose retained from the homogenizing medium. The procedure of Folch, Ascoli, Lees, Meath and Le Baron ('51) for obtaining lipids of tissues was used. Repeated dialysis and re-extraction of the lipid concentrate did not entirely free the extraction from sucrose. Lipid weights were somewhat uncertain and cerebroside determinations unreliable. In Table III, a preliminary survey of the relations of the lipid, phosphorus, nitrogen and cholesterol components to other references is given. A complete study of the lipids of the cellular fraction is in progress. The pattern of ratios obtained here appears rather specific for this type of preparation. It may be remarked that the amount of plasmal phosphatide in relation to the total lipid phosphorus is increased (Wittenberg, Korey and Swenson, '56). This suggests that this compound may be a significant component of the phosphatides of the neuroglial

TABLE III

THE RELATION OF LIPID NITROGEN, PHOSPHORUS AND
CHOLESTEROL TO REFERENCES

Nitrogen			Phosphorus			Cholesterol
N-tca mg	N-lipid mg	$\frac{N\text{-}tca}{N\text{-}lipid}$	Total mg	Lipid mg	$\frac{Lipid}{Total}$	Total mg
23.4	2.73	8.5	3.44	1.21	0.35	10.5

fraction. Whether or not the plasmalogen may interfere with the PAS reaction reported to be present in the neuroglia cells requires further study. Although these results represent the averages obtained in the preparation of over 100 brains, the constancy of the lipid constituents in relation to other cellular components is still being explored.

In the course of the present work which has been directed to provide neuroglia cells in as intact a state as possible and in sufficient amounts for investigation of the synthetic processes, it became apparent that the procedure of washing with hyperosmotic solutions resulted in cells respiring at a low rate. The loss of essential constituents and salts limited the metabolic capacities of the cells. When diphosphopyridene nucleotide, cytochrome-c and adenosine triphosphate are added to the homogenates of the cellular fractions in Krebs-Ringer phosphate buffer with glucose and α-ketoglutarate as substrates, a Qo_2 of 4-5 may be achieved. At the same time, the homogenized cortex of the lamb brain in this supplemented medium respires with a Qo_2 of 13.5. The presence of potassium is essential to the continued steady respiration over a period of 30 minutes at 37°C. The preferred substrates and the requirements of the homogenates are being investigated.

CONCLUSION

Although this study is in its initial stages, it is possible to say that a certain degree of success in the isolation of neuroglia cells and myelin free of cells can be expected. The possibility of using the cellular components as antigens to produce a specific neuroglialytic change is evident. It is likely that with changes in the contents of the homogenizing medium and further study of basic supplementary requirements, a suitable system to promote lipid synthesis by these glial extracts can be achieved. What is equally apparent is the difficulty of overcoming the sapping effects of the hyperosmotic media employed in this technique of isolation and of realizing the cellular potentialities present in their native state.

Chapter 14

Implication of Histochemical Studies for Metabolism of the Neuroglia

ALFRED POPE

I AM GLAD that the word "implication" rather than "accomplishment" was used in assigning this subject because, in spite of the fact that neuroglia cells must outnumber neurons by perhaps as much as 10 to 1, it must be admitted that no orderly knowledge exists concerning either their structural components or metabolic behavior.

This lack of knowledge is unfortunate for a number of reasons. It is unnecessary to stress to this group the importance of such information for understanding the nature and role of neuroglia cells in the nervous system, but other problems are also involved. For example, in evaluating comparative biochemical studies on diseased brain tissue it is essential to have suitable base lines as referents for pathological data. Thus, studies on the biochemistry of tumors of the glioma group can have but limited value until comparable information is available concerning their normal homologous cell types. Also, for those of us interested in the biochemistry of the normal brain it is a matter of great concern to know the proportional contribution made by the neuroglia, both to structural components and metabolic and enzymatic activity associated either with whole brain or with particular nuclear and tract regions.

The reason for this lack of knowledge upon biochemistry of the neuroglia is principally the difficulty of obtaining relatively pure samples of neuroglia cells for analysis without at the same time causing changes in the very elements we are interested in studying. As a consequence, most of what can be said about their

211

chemistry is the result of deductive inferences rather than direct observations.

There are a number of ways, of course, in which this problem may be approached. Advantage can be taken of differences in quantitative distributions of cellular components in different parts of the nervous system. The most obvious example is the difference in structural and metabolic properties of gray and white matter which alone provides a number of clues concerning the chemistry of the neuroglia. Obviously, the use of tissue cultures of neuroglia cells is a direct and, in many ways, particularly suitable way of obtaining pure samples of these cells. I will consider this point again later. Attempts have also been made to use areas of gliosis, either occurring naturally in the course of disease or in experimentally induced lesions. This is satisfactory for obtaining relatively pure cultures of fibrous astrocytes but will not do for protoplasmic astrocytes or oligodendrocytes. Analogous samples of activated microglia cells would provide information on the chemistry of macrophages, but that is not where our interest lies. A procedure such as the one Dr. Korey described has, I am sure, great promise but, even in this case, the final preparation will necessarily contain something of a mixture of elements. Moreover, as he was careful to point out, it is not possible to prepare systems of this kind without doing considerable physical violence to the cells in question. The use of tumor material as a means of getting at the biochemistry of normal neuroglia cells is in principle unsatisfactory. It is important not to be misled by the histological similarity that tumor cells may show to their normal homologues, for if they were otherwise biologically similar they would not constitute a tumor.

Surely, the best way to study glial biochemistry is by direct sampling and analysis, either with the use of microdissection methods or by direct in situ biochemistry, but these approaches have been greatly limited, at least until recently, by the technical procedures available. Among the latter, the ones likely to be of use include the following:

First is the classical type of microscopical histochemistry in which advantage is taken of the biochemical properties of the particular entity being investigated to demonstrate its localization in situ in histological preparations. Such methods have great usefulness and provide maximal anatomical precision but yield qualitative information only and are prone to giving fallacious localizations, as I think critical investigators working in this field are all well aware.

Second, and perhaps more promising, are methods that at least in theory are similar in nature, namely, those referred to by Dr. Nurnberger, in which use is made of the optical properties of certain tissue components for their in situ identification and partial quantitation. Of particular importance among these have been ultraviolet microscopy and histospectroscopy and the precise and elegant technique of x-ray absorption historadiography. Related methods might include micro-incineration, isotope autoradiography and interference microscopy.

Third are a whole group of methods which collectively are known as quantitative histochemistry. In these, the object is to prepare exceedingly small samples of tissue for quanitative chemical analysis, so that histological identification and study of the samples can be made either directly or by using alternate serial sections, thus providing for the establishment of correlations between biochemical and histological aspects of tissue structure. These methods have the disadvantage of providing relatively poor anatomical precision but the great advantages of yielding quantitative information and having exactly the same degree of operational validity as do standard macro-biochemical analyses of all types.

Fourth are the important methods of preparative cytochemistry. In these, tissue homogenates are subjected to differential high speed centrifugation, enabling preparation of pure samples of nuclei, mitochondria, microsomes and soluble nonparticulate components, each of which may then be analyzed by standard macro-biochemical procedures for structural and metabolic factors.

Each of the foregoing methods has been applied in some measure to the problem of the chemical nature of the neuroglia; but what has been learned thus far is fragmentary. I shall discuss first, and very briefly, the question of glial structural chemistry and then consider in somewhat more detail information relevant to the metabolic behavior of the neuroglia cells.

Before coming to this conference, I had planned to say that

nothing is known concerning the lipids and proteins that enter into the composition of the several species of neuroglia cells. This, however, must be modified somewhat in view of things we have been learning here. The work just presented by Dr. Korey represents one promising line of attack in this field which, as we have seen, has already provided some pertinent information. The studies reported by Professor Bairati represent the start of other important and potentially very rewarding investigations, particularly those in which use is being made of polarization optics and x-ray diffraction for analyzing the fine structure of gliofibrils and their constituent proteins. Nevertheless, in spite of these fine beginnings, it must be admitted that knowledge concerning the specific nature and structure of neuroglial lipids and proteins represents essentially *terra incognita*.

When we turn to a consideration of the metabolic properties of the neuroglia, some information is available although most of it is fragmentary and indirect and, in many instances, conflicting. First, let us consider the general problem of energy metabolism in the neuroglia. By this, I mean the means by which neuroglia cells convert the energy of the substrates, which they burn, into a utilizable form. There is no reason to doubt that this occurs chiefly through the mechanisms of glycolysis and oxidative phosphorylation, as in brain tissue as a whole, and that the rate of these processes can be more or less satisfactorily equated with the rate of oxygen consumption. Now, it seems to me that there is considerable, at least circumstantial, evidence to indicate that the rate of oxidative metabolism is significantly less in neuroglia cells than in the neurons.

In the first place, the well-known high oxygen consumption of gray matter as compared to white (Elliott, '55b) in spite of the fact that the total number of cells per unit volume is about the same in each, is a clear indication of the comparatively high metabolic rate of neurons. Even higher than that of gray matter is the respiratory rate of retina. Since this tissue has an even smaller volume fraction due to glial elements, it appears that the more neuroglia cells present in a sample of nervous tissue, the more a sort of diluting out of the high respiratory rate of the neurons tends to occur.

The second consideration has to do with the relative blood supply provided for neuroglia cells as compared with neurons. In general, the blood supply in terms of the length of capillary loops per unit volume of tissue is about one quarter as great in white matter as in gray (Cobb, '52), again in spite of the roughly similar total number of cell bodies. This also is consistent with a much smaller requirement for oxygen delivery per neuroglia cell than per neuron.

Third are the facts well-known to all neuropathologists concerning the differential sensitivities of neurons and neuroglia cells to hypoxia (Penfield, '32a, b; Glees, '55). Degrees of oxygen deprivation that result in irreversible damage to neurons often leave the neuroglia cells, especially the astrocytes, essentially intact and may even stimulate them to proliferate.

Fourth are the few direct measurements that have been made on the respiration of glial elements. Dr. Korey mentioned that in his preparations the Q_{O_2} may run as high as 5; but even such a rate would be less than half that to be expected in cerebral gray matter and probably very much less than would be observed in a pure culture of neurons. A few measurements of oxygen consumption have been made on areas of gliosis in human material. Dr. Elliott has reported some observations of this kind (Elliott and Penfield, '48) as also did Victor and Wolf ('37) in an earlier study on brain tumor metabolism. In both instances, the oxygen consumption figures were far below those of both normal gray and white matter.

Yesterday, there was considerable discussion about the relative numbers of mitochondria in neurons and neuroglia cells. I believe the consensus was that although these organelles are certainly present in significant quantities in all of the neuroglia cell species they are probably fewer in number per unit volume than in neurons. Since in brain, as in other tissues, biological oxidations are associated with the mitochondria (Brody and Bain, '52), these observations are also consistent with the general thesis of a comparatively low metabolic rate in neuroglia cells. Also consistent, is the general failure of microscopical histochemistry to demonstrate respiratory enzyme activity in neuroglia cells. This goes back nearly 40 years, to the time when Marinesco ('19) first studied the nervous system systematically for indophenol oxidase activity, which histochemically demonstrates the in situ localization of the cyto-chrome-cytochrome oxidase system, and was unable to demonstrate any such activity in neuroglia cells. These observations have been confirmed by many workers, both for the indophenol oxidase and for other respiratory enzymes, for example, such as succinic dehydrogenase (Mustakallio, '54). The content of such enzymes in neuroglia cells, even when they are demonstrable at all, is always significantly less than in nerve cell bodies.

Finally, for what they are worth, comparative studies on glial tumors bear out the same general impression. At least, this is true for gliomas of the spongio-astrocytic series as shown first by Victor and Wolf ('37) and again recently in the studies of Heller and Elliott ('55). Each of these authors has shown that both the astrocytoma and the glioblastoma multiforme display a very low rate of oxygen utilization. Moreover, in our laboratory Dr. Norman Allen has found recently that cytochrome oxidase activity is also comparatively very low in gliomas of these types (Pope, Hess and Allen, '57).

Next, it is necessary to state that there are certain facts which are simply not in accord with the foregoing. Abood and his co-workers in Chicago (Abood, Gerard, Banks and Tschirgi, '52) studied the respiration of cultures of newborn chick spinal cord that were considered to be exclusively composed of neuroglia cells and observed comparatively high Qo_2 values. Moreover, in some recently reported, but as yet unpublished, observations upon respiration in tissue cultures prepared by Dr. Ruth Geiger, Abood has found the cytochrome oxidase activity in cultures of neurons and neuroglia cells to be about the same. Also, some time ago, Howe and Mellors ('45) produced neuron degeneration and replacement gliosis in one thalamus in the cat by ablation of appropriate cortical sectors and then compared its cytochrome oxidase activity with that of the contralateral normal thalamic nuclei. On the basis of their results and certain calculations therefrom, these authors concluded that in normal thalamus 60 or 70 per cent of the cytochrome oxidase activity is contributed by the neuroglia. I believe there are certain difficulties inherent in the interpretation of each one of these experiments. Certainly, they are at variance with the rest of what I have listed as evidence for a relatively low oxidative metabolism in the neuroglia. Nevertheless, the weight of evidence, at present, seems to me in favor of the respiratory metabolism in neuroglia cells being significantly less than that in neurons.

If this conclusion is true of the neuroglia as a whole, it would appear to be doubly so for astrocytes. As mentioned before, these cells, instead of being destroyed by degrees of anoxia that are lethal for neurons and oligodendrocytes, are apt, rather, to be stimulated to hypertrophy and hyperplasia. Moreover, the studies already quoted on glial scars and gliomas are consistent with an especially low respiratory metabolism and oxidative enzyme content in astrocytes.

When, however, we turn to the oligodendrocytes, I suspect the story may prove to be quite different. In both of the studies mentioned upon metabolism of gliomas, oligodendrogliomas were found to have a very much higher rate of oxygen consumption than did the other tumors. Also, in mixed tumors containing a considerable portion of oligodendrocytes, Dr. Allen found the cytochrome oxidase content to be significantly higher than in purely astrocytic tumors. These findings on oligodendrogliomas may require some qualification since these tumors, though biologically benign, are usually extremely cellular and, therefore, the respiration per cell may not be so very great after all. It is at least possible that some of the glial tissue cultures, shown to have a relatively high respiratory rate, may have been composed largely of oligodendrocytes. In view of these facts and of certain other biological characteristics of oligodendrocytes (e.g., greater sensitivity to hypoxia than that of astrocytes), it seems altogether probable that oligodendrocytes contribute most of the respiratory activity of white matter which, though much lower than that of gray, is by no means negligible. This would lead to the further assumption that certain oxidative and glycolytic enzymes that are proving to be quite active in white matter reside in such cells. One enzyme, in particular, is noteworthy in this regard. This is glucose-6-phosphate dehydrogenase which, according to the results of Lowry ('55), is, if anything, higher in white matter than in gray. This finding suggests the possibility that, in the neuroglia cells of white matter (largely oligodendrocytes), the hexose monophosphate shunt is in operation, that is, the direct oxidation of glucose to phosphogluconate, then to a pentose, and so on, rather than via dismutation and the glycolytic and tricarboxylic acid cycles.

In summary, therefore, I suggest as a working hypothesis that astrocytes can be considered to have a fairly low rate of oxidative metabolism and that oligodendrocytes probably have a significantly higher one, perhaps even approaching that of neurons. Finally, whatever may ultimately prove to be their metabolic rates, the neuroglia cells certainly occupy a large amount of the total volume fraction of metabolizing brain tissue, so that even though the metabolic rate per neuroglia cell is fairly low, these elements must contribute a very important part of the total metabolism of the organ.

Next, I shall consider briefly the question of protein turnover in the neuroglia. One way of approaching this is to study the quantitative histochemistry of proteolytic enzyme activity in brain. This is not the time or place to discuss the subject of brain protein metabolism or the role therein of tissue proteolytic enzymes but, if we adopt the argument that enzymes that hydrolyze simple peptides do have some part in the retailoring process that goes on constantly during tissue protein turnover, then it is reasonable to suppose that the relative activities of proteolytic enzymes are a reflection of rates of protein synthesis as well as degradation.

In our laboratory, we have had considerable experience with the quantitative histochemistry of one such enzyme in various parts of the mammalian nervous system. This is an intracellular dipeptidase which hydrolyzes l-alanylglycine rapidly at neutral pH and in the absence of added metallic or other activators. It is widely distributed in animal tissues, appears to be associated with RNA nucleoprotein and has been used by many investigators as an index of protein metabolism and of cell population (Holter and Linderstrøm-Lang, '51). We have found it to be very active in several portions of both rat and human nervous systems but to have a nonuniform distribution consistent with localization in cell body material (Pope and Anfinsen, '48; Pope, '52; Pope and Hess, '54). In particular, in the somatosensory cortex of the al-

bino rat, l-alanylglycinase activity is high, relative to immediately adjacent zones, in layers II, IV, Vb and VIa (Pope, '52). Since
these are levels at which nerve cell bodies are either relatively
numerous (II, IV, VIa) or very large (Vb), this intracortical profile clearly suggests localization of proteolytic enzyme activity in
the nerve cell bodies. However, dipeptidase activity is considerable in layer I and is well-sustained in the subcortical white
matter. Indeed, if expressed on the basis of total nonlipid solids,
its activity is the same in white matter as that of its average in
the layers of the gray cortex. Differential cell counts have shown
that the toal number of cells per unit volume in subcortical white
matter (essentially all glial) is also the same as the average total
number (including neurons) in the several architectonic layers of
the gray matter. Moreover, within the cortex, the intralaminar
distribution of dipeptidase activity follows fairly well the total
number of cells per unit volume irrespective of species. All these
facts, therefore, suggest that proteolytic activity resides in the
cell bodies of both neurons and neuroglia cells. Similar studies
on the frontal cortex of man and, for what they are worth, on
human tumors of the glioma group (Pope, Hess and Allen, '57)
are consistent with the same general conclusion. However, a
somewhat more detailed analysis of these findings suggests that
it is not the number of cells, but rather the amount of actively
metabolizing cytoplasmic mass that is reflected by the proteolytic enzyme activity; and this would bring these observations into
line with others mentioned above on the distribution of peptidase
in many other animal tissues.

There is, therefore, some evidence to indicate that the proteolytic potential of neuroglia cells is fairly high and probably of
the same order as that of neurons. What this means in terms of
protein turnover is difficult to say; but it may be of some interest
in view of the potentialities that neuroglia cells have for proliferative activity and possibly even for the synthesis of materials important for the maintenance of neurons and of myelin.

With regard to specific biochemical functions or activities in
the neuroglia cells, there is very little to be said. A number of
enzymes and a few selected chemical entities have been found to
be preferentially located in such cells, either by histochemical

techniques or by inference from higher concentrations of these substances in white matter than in gray. Several have been referred to already during the course of this conference. The example of pseudocholinesterase was brought up by Dr. Scheibel. The first to suggest that this enzyme is located in the neuroglia were two groups of English workers (Burgen and Chipman, '52; Ord and Thompson, '52) who noted that its activity is high in white matter especially in the human brain. Its localization in the neuroglia has been clearly established by further work in Thompson's laboratory (Cavanaugh, Thompson and Webster, '54) and by the excellent histochemical studies of Koelle ('55). What the enzyme is doing there is unknown. At first it was thought that pseudocholinesterase must have some role in the formation and the maintenance of myelin, because triorthocresyl phosphate, a poison which may cause demyelination, is also a specific inhibitor of pseudocholinesterase. However, it has now turned out that a number of other inhibitors of this enzyme do not result in myelin breakdown, so that the question of its role in glial metabolism remains unsolved.

The intriguing possibility that carbonic anhydrase is localized in astrocytes and is concerned with electrolyte exchanges between serum and cerebral fluids has been thoroughly discussed by Dr. Tschirgi. Another enzyme which appears to have selectively high activity in white matter (Lowry, '55) and perhaps, therefore, to be localized in glial elements is 5-nucleotidase. The significance of this with respect to glial metabolism is unknown as is the similar distribution of β-glucuronidase (McNabb, '51) unless the latter plays some role in relation to the mucopolysaccharide ground substance of the brain postulated by Hess ('53). The important observations of Dr. Klüver concerning the localization of porphyrins in neuroglia cells have also been adequately covered in this symposium. Another recent report of interest is that of Friede ('53b) who calculated what he termed a glial index, that is, the number of neuroglia cells per neuron in different parts of the nervous system, and found that the concentrations of iron, vitamin C and riboflavin paralleled this glial index, thus suggesting a high concentration of these substances in neuroglia cells. Other than the fact that each of these bears some relation to biological oxidations, it is difficult to determine the significance of these findings.

In relation to the question of neuroglial chemistry, clues furnished by neuropathological observations must not be neglected. One such is the rather remarkable sensitivity which oligodendrocytes have to relatively minor changes in cerebral homeostasis with production of the phenomenon of acute swelling. This, indeed, has been referred to by Penfield ('32a, b) as "the most delicate index of disturbed cerebral function that we have." When at all severe, it is apt to be accompanied by the apparently analogous "ameboid change" or clasmatodendrosis of astrocytes which may be remarkably selective. Both processes are not uncommonly observed in pathological material in which the neurons are essentially intact. The production of these changes, when representing genuine pathological change and not artifact, demands biological study and explanation. A second relatively specific phenomenon brought up yesterday by Dr. Cammermeyer is the remarkable hypertrophy and hyperplasia of protoplasmic astrocytes that is often seen in hepatic encephalopathy. This disorder appears to be related to ammonia intoxication, so that the astrocytic change may be an indication that reactions in which ammonia is involved, such, for example, as glutamate turnover, are of critical importance to astrocytes. Another curious finding which certainly deserves exploration is the lack of productive glial reaction that is observed in subacute combined degeneration of the spinal cord, but which immediately begins following institution of specific therapy. It is, in other words, as though astrocytes themselves require vitamin B_{12} in order to exhibit their proliferative activity.

The foregoing clearly shows the fragmentary nature of present knowledge concerning the structural and metabolic chemistry of the neuroglia. May I conclude by offering a few suggestions as to ways and means of advancing knowledge upon this subject. I believe a twofold problem is involved. One is the problem of obtaining each of the neuroglia cells species in relatively pure samples without, at the same time, bringing about biological changes in the cells that potentially invalidate chemical observations made upon them. At the present time, the method of tissue culture, which has been so beautifully demonstrated for us here today, would certainly seem to be the one of choice. However, as a biochemist, I would like to second the note of caution sounded by Dr. Rose this morning. I think all of us would be easier in our minds about the use of tissue cultures if basic biological information were provided to show that cultured cells are indeed similar in their physiological and biochemical properties to their in vivo homologues. If this can be done (and studies of the sort herewith proposed should contribute information relevant to this problem), then the culturing of adult forms of neuroglia cells and the analysis of such cultures by ultramicrochemical techniques should be highly successful in delineating the biochemistry of neuroglia cells.

The second means of sampling might be to use methods whereby one can obtain neuroglia cells from the intact nervous system with an absolute minimum of disturbance. For this, two methods are especially appropriate. One is the use of direct cytochemical techniques such as that of x-ray absorption histospectroscopy. The second is to make use of the refined methods for harvesting specific cell types that are being provided by Lowry ('55) and thus to microdissect directly the cells to be studied and perform biochemical operations on samples of this type. In addition, properly controlled and evaluated investigations upon pathological material can also be useful. This might include studies on reacting neuroglia cells, on gliomas, and also on neuroglia cells in different stages of ontogeny and phylogeny. All of these approaches can be relevant provided the results are examined with a rigorous critique and, with luck, each should provide new facets of information that will be supplementary, complementary and mutually supportive. Finally, it seems to me that neuroanatomists can perform a considerable service by being on the alert for places in the brain where one can dissect out fairly pure microsamples of each of the several neuroglia cell species, and that those of us who are concerned in any way with neuropathology can also contribute by keeping our eyes open for the many clues that surely are to be found in neuropathological material which may help to solve some of these difficult problems.

ROUND TABLE DISCUSSION

DR. WINDLE: We should first direct questions to Dr. Nurnberger.

DR. FLEXNER: Is there mitotic activity in the ependyma in earlier stages?

DR. NURNBERGER: I saw no mitotic activity in any of the nuclei I encountered.

DR. FLEXNER: Have you no doubts in specific instances about the identity of these nuclei?

DR. NURNBERGER: I do have doubts about the identity of some of the nuclei. The majority of them are identifiable beyond any question but in the early chick embryo brain there are serious difficulties. I have no major reservations about the total counts.

DR. DEMPSEY: Some years ago in our laboratory, Dr. Falzone attempted to separate endothelial nuclei from hepatic cell nuclei. He had some success in centrifuging them in media of controlled density. Have you attempted any such fractionation as this? It would seem to me that it might be valuable in getting at this question of the DNA content of the different types of nuclei.

DR. NURNBERGER: In relation to the cell counts—no. We started out by centrifuging at very low speeds in order to sediment cellular debris, but the nuclei tended to mass so disturbingly that we could not disperse them afterward to our own satisfaction. Therefore we abandoned centrifuging as far as total counts went. We have not tried to separate one nuclear type from another but I think it might well be done in this way.

DR. ELLIOTT: Was the basis for recognizing these different nuclei that after grinding up and being fixed they looked like nuclei that were in the whole cell?

DR. NURNBERGER: Yes. These were all methylene blue stained and the pictures show the way they looked in the counting chamber.

DR. ELLIOTT: They look the same before grinding up? On what basis did you recognize what was an oligodendrocyte nucleus and what was a neuron nucleus?

DR. NURNBERGER: I accepted as neuronal those nuclei which

had a large central and single nucleolus. Nuclei from astrocytes and oligodendrocytes are easily differentiated, as the photomicrographs show. One of the difficulties I encountered was in distinguishing neuronal nuclei from very large nuclei seen in chick embryo brain homogenates, particularly in the early incubation period. These had a glassy, watery nucleoplasm, with delicate, poorly stained chromatin and perhaps one or two nucleoli centrally placed. Some of them were indistinguishable from neuronal nuclei. In the adult rat the only problem might have been with the nuclei of small nuerons but, as far as I know, almost all neurons that are studied in histological sections have a nucleus with a single central nucleolus.

DR. CLEMENTE: Was it your interpretation that the larger percentage of nonneuronal elements in the hypothalamus was due to an increase in both endothelial and neuroglia cells, or more preponderantly one over the other?

DR. NURNBERGER: I couldn't tell for certain from the counts because, at the time, I attempted only to differentiate neuronal from nonneuronal nuclei. On the basis of the indirect evidence previously mentioned, I propose that many of the noncharacteristic nuclei were nuclei either of neuroglia cells or perhaps of small neurons. It is difficult to distinguish some neuronal types in stained sections of certain hypothalamic areas. After disintegration by this technique the difficulties are, of course, increased.

DR. ROSE: The statement is often made that oligodendrocytes are easily the most numerous cells in the central nervous system. We have accepted this. Would you agree on the basis of your counts?

DR. NURNBERGER: I am afraid my counts cannot answer this question. We must do additional differential counts of the nonneuronal fraction to provide such information. This technique makes such counts possible but we still have this to do.

DR. TSCHIRGI: Do you know of any data concerning the development of the carbonic anhydrase in the central nervous system which might be correlated with your observations?

DR. NURNBERGER: I don't know about carbonic anhydrase but I have recalculated Nachmanson's data on cholinesterase levels in the chick embryo brain. If cholinesterase activity is referred to neuronal cell counts, activity per "average" neuron is noted to increase almost 100-fold from the eighth incubation day to hatching. Until someone establishes the cellular localization of true cholinesterase beyond question, this statement of activity increase must be tentative.

DR. FLEXNER: Somebody has. Koelle has good evidence now, histochemical evidence. The nerve cells on the side of specific and the neuroglia cells on the side of the nonspecific cholinesterase.

DR. NURNBERGER: Yes, I knew that, but I thought it was still debated. We calculated it per total neuron count per brain and it is on the basis of this reference to neurons that one has a sigmoidal elaboration of cholinesterase.

DR. BROWNSON: Like Dr. Rose, I was anxiously waiting for the quantitative separation of neuroglia cell types and on this basis I have done some satellite cell counts. Kryspin-Exner ('52) has done quite a bit on this subject, investigating cortical areas and reports were often very high for astrocytes—beyond 40 or 50 per cent of neuroglia cell population. In my own work, if I am counting satellites and not getting far from the edge of the nerve cell, the oligodendrocytes stay in the vicinity of 50 to 52 per cent and the astrocytes broke over 40 per cent. In many cases the microglia cell counts were down to 6 to 10 per cent. Whether or not I was getting out too far from the neuron is a question because the figures are very similar to the earlier reported work for whole cortex qualitative analysis.

DR. NURNBERGER: With the conventional types of fixation and dehydration, the amount of shrinkage that can occur during the process of preparing tissue for histologic study is rather impressive in the central nervous system. Twenty per cent contraction in one linear dimension has been reported fairly commonly for cortex, for example; if one translates linear contraction into volumetric contraction a 20 to 25 per cent contraction in one dimension means a 300 per cent reduction in volume. I believe it is virtually impossible to make any meaningful correction for a factor of this magnitude.

DR. POPE: I may be able to answer in part the question by Dr. Rose about the oligodendrocytes. A number of years ago, I had occasion to make some rough differential counts of neurons and neuroglia cells at different levels in the cerebral cortex and in the subjacent white matter of adult rats and humans. I can't remember the results accurately, but my recollection is that, per unit volume at almost all cortical levels, the number of astrocytes and the number of oligodendrocytes were about the same. In other words, in gray matter, astrocytes and oligodendrocytes each accounted for about 45 per cent of the neuroglia cells, the remaining 10 per cent being microglia cells. However, in the subjacent white matter the situation is very different, indeed. There, two-thirds, at least, of all the cells are oligodendrocytes. Therefore, if the proportions of cell types are calculated in terms of the relative volume fractions contributed by the total amount of white matter in the brain to the total amount of gray matter, it would certainly turn out that oligodendrocytes represent the most numerous cell type. This would vary somewhat as a function of the size of the brain because in general the larger the brain the more white matter relatively there will be. Therefore, in the primate brain the oligodendrocytes would almost certainly outnumber all other cell types.

DR. ALBERS: Dr. Pope explained the techniques which I have used in exploratory efforts to distinguish chemically something that might be related to the neuroglia cells, and which would better enable me to interpret the rest of the quantitative data that we are accumulating. No matter how carefully one dissects, there is always some contamination of each cell layer with neuroglia and endothelial cells. We have examined the enzyme content in tissue samples relatively rich in neuroglia cells. These samples were obtained by removing the cat's occipital cortex unilaterally. After allowing about 10 months for degeneration, we took both lateral geniculate bodies for our study, using the intact side for the control.

Taking a quick look at the histology (Fig. 70), there seems to have been quite an increase in the number of neuroglia cells. The number of recognizable neurons decreased on the operated side by about 40 per cent, while the number of neuroglia cells increased more than 4 times. In most cases, the neurons were rather

small and pyknotic and there may have been even smaller ones
that were counted as neuroglia cells.

We have applied a technique like Dr. Pope described for his
proteolytic enzyme, but using frozen dried sections, as in the
procedure that Lowry employs. We can cut out little samples

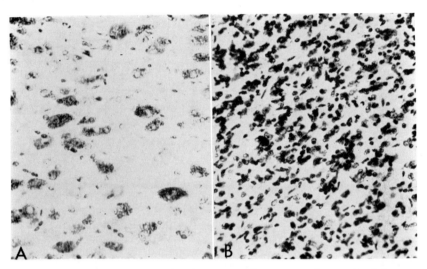

FIGURE 70. Photomicrograph of corresponding areas of zone A of the cat
lateral geniculate body. B. Appearance 10 months after cortical ablations.
A. Unoperated control section of the same region. Frozen dried 20 μ sections, stained with cresyl violet. Magnification, 250 ×.

under the dissecting microscope, including only what we know
to be completely degenerated areas, and samples from the corresponding area of the control material. Samples of the corresponding optic tracts were also analyzed. The aldolase data (Table IV) are given in moles per kilogram and per hour (MKH)
along with the standard error of the mean (SEM). For all practical purposes, there is no difference between the samples from the
control and experimental sides. The same holds true for *iso*-citric
dehydrogenase and, in addition, there is strikingly little of this
enzyme in optic tract.

Now, 6-phosphogluconic dehydrogenase, or rather the related
enzyme glucose-6-phosphate dehydrogenase, has been studied in

Biology of Neuroglia

white and gray matter by Lowry, as mentioned by Dr. Pope. This enzyme increases on the atrophic side by about 40 per cent and is one of the most significant differences that we have noted so far. The difference between glial and neuronal biochemistry in terms of these enzymes of general metabolism is not very great.

DR. ELLIOTT: I would like to elaborate a little on things that were mentioned by Dr. Nurnberger and Dr. Pope and try to

TABLE IV

ALDOLASE

Activity of Lateral Geniculate Gray Matter
and Optic Tract (Cat)

	MKH	SEM
Control geniculate	3.35	.09
Atrophic geniculate	3.23	.02
Control tract	0.93	.04
Experimental tract	0.95	.08
N = 6		

straighten out one or two points. I have worked for many years with the cerebral cortex and was driven to distraction by feeling that I must really know whether or not one was dealing largely with nerve cells. So Dr. Irving Heller and I ('54, '55) tried a rather indirect and crude approach which was fairly satisfying to us. We divided tissue samples into three parts. From one part we made slices and determined their metabolism, oxygen uptake, chiefly, but other things as well. On one part we determined total DNA. From the third part, using the citric acid method, double centrifuging, etc., we prepared a sample of nuclei for counting and determination of DNA. Thus, we would know the DNA per nucleus and the total DNA in the sample; by dividing one into the other we could get a rough cell count. The DNA per nucleus, which we found in the normal brain of dog, cat and man, was just about in the range that is found in almost any mammalian tissue.

We could get a cell count and relate metabolism to it. We studied cerebral cortex, where we had neurons and neuroglia cells; cerebellar cortex, where, Dr. George Olszewski of our Institute assured us, the majority of the cells are neurons, and white matter, where we were equally assured that there weren't any neurons. I will consider only the oxygen uptake. It is easier. We found that the cerebral cortex and the cerebellar cortex both respire at least twice as rapidly as white matter. But when we referred the oxygen uptake to the cell count we found that the cerebral cortex has the highest rate of respiration per cell. The corpus callosum respires a good deal more rapidly than cerebellar cortex, per cell. We concluded from this, perhaps naively, that neuroglia cells can respire more rapidly than some neurons, the neurons of the cerebellar cortex, but they respire much less rapidly than the average neuron of the cerebral cortex. Then we studied a number of gliomas. The DNA per nucleus was not the same as normal tissue. It was high—but that is another story. We calculated the cell density of each tumor from the total DNA and the DNA per nucleus found for the individual tumor. The astrocytomas, in fact all tumors except the oligodendroglioma, respired, on the weight basis and on the cell basis, very slowly. Their metabolic activity was very low. In two years of work, we only got one oligodendroglioma for cell counts. So we draw heavily on two oligodendrogliomas that Victor and Wolf ('37) had, because their results fitted in with ours nicely. As Dr. Pope said, the oligodendrogliomas respired a good deal more rapidly than any of the other gliomas. The rate for the oligodendroglioma per cell was about the same as, or perhaps a trifle higher than that for white matter of the corpus callosum; in white matter, a majority of the cells may be oligodendrocytes. It respired less rapidly per cell than the average for cerebral cortex. From our results, and estimating the ratio of neuroglia cells to nerve cells from the data given by Friede ('54), we have calculated[*] that, in the dog and cat, the cerebral cortex metabolism must be about 85 per cent due to neurons. It might even be a bit more than that because we were making the assumption that the neuroglia of the cerebral cortex had the same proportion of astrocytes and oligodendrocytes as in the white matter. Actually I believe there is a higher

---

[*] The estimates given in the above papers by Heller and Elliott were made before Friede's paper came to our attention. Summarized data and the method of calculation will appear in the proceedings of the Second International Neurochemical Symposium (1956).

proportion of astrocytes in the neuroglia of the cerebral cortex which would mean that the glial contribution to the metabolism of the cerebral cortex would be lower than estimated and an even greater proportion of the metabolism of the cerebral cortex would be due to neurons. We could not calculate quite so closely for the human because we did not get all the samples of the kind we wanted; but I feel sure that at least 70 per cent of the metabolism of human cerebral cortex is due to neurons or not more than 30 per cent is due to the neuroglia.

DR. POPE: Dr. Norman Allen in our laboratory last year obtained results that are so closely in agreement with those of Dr. Elliott that I think it is worth bringing out. He studied the activity of cytochrome oxidase, rather than the actual oxygen uptake of tumors. This enzyme is, of course, the one that plays such a key role in the transport of electrons to molecular oxygen during intracellular oxidations. What Dr. Allen did was to obtain a series of glial tumors and study the cytochrome oxidase activity by microtechniques, using very much the same type of experimental design that I indicated we used in cerebral cortex. In this way he was able alternately to measure the oxidase activity and make differential cell counts in small serial frozen sections. This also enabled him to control his results histologically for areas of necrosis and hemorrhage, which are such a problem in the case of glioblastomas, and also for inclusions of infiltrated brain. He found that, in astrocytomas, the cytochrome oxidase activity was about half that which one gets in normal human cerebral white matter. In a few instances in which the activity was higher, it turned out that there were nerve cells contaminating the sample and, by a rather round-about calculation, it was possible to show that the contribution which the nerve cells probably made to the activity just about accounted for the difference. Unfortunately, there were no pure oligodendrogliomas in this series of neoplasms. There were, however, two in which oligodendrocytes were an important element in the architecture of the tumor. One of these was a mixed astrocytoma-oligodendroglioma, the other was a glioblastoma that had a signficant number of oligodendrocytes in at least one major part of it. I should have said that the cytochrome oxidase activity in pure glioblastomas, when cor-

rected for areas of necrosis and hemorrhage, was somewhat higher than that in the astrocytomas, suggesting that, with differentiation, astrocytes may, in fact, lose some of their oxidative potential. On the other hand the two mixed tumors, both the astrocytoma and the glioblastoma that contained oligodendrocytes as
well, had significantly higher cytochrome oxidase activities, of
the same order or higher than that of human cerebral white matter. I think Dr. Allen's results in every way dovetail with what
Dr. Elliott reported and in general support the thesis that oligodendrocytes have a considerably higher respiration than do astrocytes, though not as high as neurons.

DR. KLÜVER: The interesting study of Dr. Albers reminds me
that Dr. Bucy and I recently published a rather detailed investigation of the temporal lobe in the rhesus monkey in which we
showed that bilateral temporal lobectomy leads to an almost
complete degeneration of the anterior commissure (Bucy and
Klüver, '55). In cresyl violet preparations, the region of the degenerated tract showed an intense gliosis.* This suggests at least
one way of transforming a sizable tract into neuroglia cells. Histologically, most of these cells appear to be oligodendrocytes. In
Nissl-stained sections, the picture of an intense gliosis remains
unaltered and the result seems to be the same, no matter whether
such monkeys are killed a few months, 2 years, 5 years or 10 years
after the operations. Although certain facts may force us to view
neuroglia cells dynamically or attribute trophic functions to them
(Friede, '53a), the constance of the picture of the Nissl-stained
sections through the years reminds one of the old idea that the
neuroglia serves as a nerve glue.

DR. LUMSDEN: In addition to what Dr. Klüver has said, I believe that the reactive changes one sees in astrocytes in suitable
conditions are reversible. I find nothing surprising in the idea that
these astrocytes remain alive for the rest of the life of the organ.

DR. ELLIOTT: Dr. Pope mentioned my having studied gliosis
once. I never really did but, while studying material removed
during Dr. Penfield's operations on epileptic patients, I quite
often got bits of cerebral cortex which were, to my completely

---

* This is shown in Plate 10, Section 899, in Bucy and Klüver ('55).

inexperienced feel, gliosed. They were tough and much too easy to slice. They would metabolize just as well as difficult-to-slice cerebral cortex, except once or twice when we got samples in which the process had gone too far and then there was practically no metabolism. Apparently there had been proliferation of neuroglia cells in many samples which had really not made a great deal of difference to the metabolism, had not diminished the number of respiring neurons very much but, in a few, metabolizing neurons must have disappeared and there was little respiratory activity left.

DR. KETY: Although studies on the enzymatic constitution of these various cells seem quite relevant, since it is unlikely that these enzymes will differ in concentration in the state in which they are examined from that in which they existed in the body, I am a little in doubt as to the relevance of Q_{O_2} measurements to the living functioning brain. One thinks of an analogy perhaps to the difference between an Olympic runner and an executive. If these are both studied while they are asleep or under anesthesia and it is discovered that their oxygen consumption is the same, should it be concluded that running takes no more oxygen than sitting? Can one with ease relate values for Q_{O_2} obtained in vitro with actual metabolism during functional activity? We have some observations made at the National Institutes of Health with Drs. Sokoloff, Freygang, Landau, and Rowland on the local blood flow in certain of the areas that Dr. Elliott mentioned. Unfortunately, we don't have measurements on the oxidative metabolism on these same areas in the living state but the blood flow ratios do give one some limits beyond which it is unlikely that the oxidative metabolism ratios will deviate. I realize that Dr. Elliott was speaking about the oxygen uptake per million cells and, of course, these are the blood flow values per gram of tissue but we found the cerebral cortex and cerebellar cortex to be quite comparable in terms of blood flow while the corpus callosum was not different from other areas of white matter. As Dr. Pope mentioned previously, the ratio between these two areas was something of the order of 5 or 6 to 1. Now, it is not likely that the oxygen uptakes will stand in very different ratios from the blood flow. Perhaps on the basis of your calculations, Dr. Elliott, you might see whether this kind of finding is compatible with the Q_{O_2} finding as you calculated them for the number of cells.

DR. ELLIOTT: On dry weight, our cerebral cortex and cerebellar cortex were about 4 times as active as white matter; twice as active on the wet weight basis. You may remember a while ago I ('55b) did some calculations and figured that the sort of things that we measured was for your sitting executive who was tending to go to sleep. We have not got satisfactory measurements for the actively functioning brain. You are the nearest to having that measurement.

Chapter 15

The Biology of the Neuroglia: A Summary

PAUL GLEES

I WONDER whether those, like myself, who oscillate between morphology and physiology, are justified in drawing so much attention to biochemistry and physiology of the neuroglia, which is essentially in the morphological field of research. Is the neuroglia a physiologically active part of the nervous system? I have listed here several points worth discussing.

Let us start with the morphological aspect. There are two main issues: Have we to discard the classical view that the neuroglia is only a supporting tissue—supporting in the mechanical meaning of the word; do neuroglia cells form functionally important membranes around capillaries, membranes which have to be crossed for the purpose of interstitial metabolic transport? What we have seen in tissue cultures of neuroglia cells, in fixed preparations, has not as yet disposed of the most likely function of the neuroglia—that of support. In particular, the pathological changes of neuroglia cells, as in scar formation, seem rather to point in a static function only. Dr. Klüver's remarks about the persistence of neuroglia cells in the anterior commissure following temporal lobe removal, support this static conception.

If the function of neuroglia cells is essentially supporting and holding nerve fibers and nerve cells in position, then the nervous system would be provided and perhaps burdened with an enormous number of neuroglia cells, ten times as high as neurons, many of them waiting to be called upon for repair work. But this elaborate provision for repair would supply the injured nervous system with rather useless scar tissue. If scar formation were the main function of this apparent surplus of neuroglia cells, it would be an extraordinary arrangement for the normal brain to give housing to so many cellular elements for an emergency that may never occur. Thus, from a biological point of view it seems un-likely that the repair function of the neuroglia can be its only purpose.

Although the function of microglia cells in the removal of debris has been clearly established, it may well be possible that the delicately branched resting microglia cell has also a function to fulfill apart from waiting for a cerebral trauma to occur. What favors a purely morphological static conception, is the histological picture of the numerous neuroglia cell processes and their being attached between vessels (as far as astrocytes are concerned). However, with the same reasoning we might also ask: why should not the processes of neurons, at least the dendrons, be also tentacles for supporting the cell body? We know that in the early time of neurohistology, Golgi assumed that dendrons were only supporting; then opinion was changed to thinking that their func-tion was receptive and, at the present time, we are still not cer-tain whether dendrons are only receptive expansions of the cell body.

The oligodendrocyte deserves special consideration for reasons other than because we all find it very difficult to define this cell. We refer to oligodendrocytes either as cells which ensheath the myelinated fiber in the white matter or, as satellite cells in the gray substance (Fig. 71). I think there must be some difference between so-called satellite cells of the gray matter and the neu-roglia cells within the white matter. I am encouraged to take this view by referring to the findings of Drs. Pope and Elliott, who stated that the oligodendrocytes have a higher metabolic rate than any other neuroglia cells. Dr. Pope mentioned, too, that oligodendrocytes have a certain proteolytic activity. Therefore, we ought to investigate, to start with, all the differences between the satellite cells in the cerebral gray matter and those in the white matter. How would we do this? If we use the proliferated neuroglia cells for such a study by following Dr. Klüver's sug-gestion of an examination of anterior commissure tissue, a cau-tious view must be taken. The anterior commissure after bilateral temporal lobe removal would be contaminated mainly with pro-liferating astrocytes. I doubt whether the anterior commissure would give us a clear answer for an investigation of oligodendro-

cytes alone; but, if there were any means of depriving the cerebral gray matter of its neurons, thus leaving only the satellite cells
and protoplasmic neuroglia cells, we could make useful functional
studies. We ought to find out how to achieve the selective death
of nerve cells by anoxia, x-ray, or some other means of killing the
neurons within the cerebral cortex is possible; then we could
study the metabolic activity of the neuroglia in comparatively
large portions of cerebral cortex deprived of its neurons. We cannot deny that astrocytes of the white matter seem to be essentially ensheathing and supporting cells. For this reason, studies
of glial tumors which are mainly composed of astrocytes probably cannot unravel the more important functions of satellite cells,
including the protoplasmic neuroglia cells of the cerebral gray
matter. I suggest that the oligodendrocytes and protoplasmic
astrocytes around the neurons must have different functions from

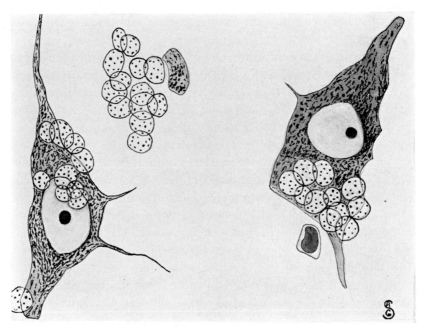

FIGURE 71. Great numbers of satellite cells—probably oligodendrocytes—
can be found in close contact with the cell bodies of medium and small
sized neurons of layer 5 of the human motor cortex. Nissl stain; magnification, 1000 ×.

astrocytes of the white matter. I had originally based this suggestion on the conception that nerve cells have become so specialized in generating nervous activity that they needed slaves, the satellites, to support them with nutrient material in order to keep them going. If this assumption is correct, I wonder whether this explains why oligodendrocytes have a higher metabolic rate than astrocytes. Is this rate higher than one would expect from a resting cell? Is this rate at least sufficiently high to be involved in the acting of an intermediary in neuronal metabolism?*

These satellite cells are particularly numerous around the small nerve cells of the cerebral cortex. It is not sufficiently appreciated by neuropathologists that their presence is quite a normal appearance, although Spielmeyer ('22) most emphatically refuted that neuronophagia is a justified definition. Spielmeyer described the satellite cells as occurring mainly in the third layer of the cerebral cortex and called them Traubenzellen. However, these cells are just as plentiful in the upper layers of the cerebral cortex, where they cluster around the small cells, and the large cells of Betz have only few satellites. What could this unequal distribution be caused by? Have small nerve cells a more continuous activity than big ones, needing more metabolic support of neuroglia cells? I can draw one negative conclusion, namely, that the satellites are not mechanically supporting. For if they had this function, the large cells of Betz would certainly need more of these supporters than the cortical small neurons, where the total mass of satellites exceeds by far the mass of enveloped neurons.

I would like to come back to the histological picture of the type of astrocytes we find in the cerebral gray matter. Their cell bodies send out fine delicate branches which envelop the neuron (Fig. 72). The branches are too delicate to assume that they can be capable of supporting the neuron. This at once produces another challenging and fundamental question: What is the significance of cellular branching in the nervous system? This extensive branching is alike for both nerve cell and neuroglia cell. In the

---

* Some functional studies of neuroglia cells following x-radiation, which have been carried out by Fantis and Gutmann ('53) show that the metabolin of astrocytes can be studied in situ.

case of neurons we assume that the branching is essential for receptive and conductive functions. But what about neuroglia cells? Why have the astrocytes and the resting microglia cells in the gray matter so many branches? We might assume that this is

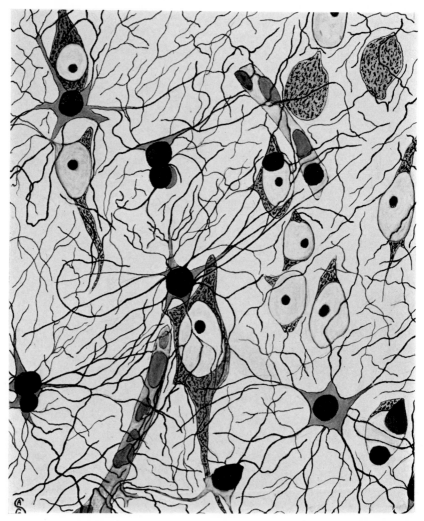

FIGURE 72. Arborization of processes of astrocytes in the gray matter of layer 5 of the temporal lobe of *Macaca mulatta*. The astrocyte in the middle of the field envelopes the cortical neuron and the adjacent capillary wall. Hortega silver-carbonate stain; magnification, 1000 ×.

a particular physical adaption to the gel-like structure of the brain. But if we take this view, we must assume that the branching of nerve cells should also be caused by similar physical conditions and that their branches may not be essential for nervous function. I have the impression that the elaborate branches of neuroglia cells may be for the purpose of intercellular metabolic exchange. For the branching of both nerve cell and neuroglia cell increases in magnitude during phylogeny and ontogeny; and it seems that the more viscous brains show no greater branching of neuroglia cells than brains of firmer consistency. To emphasize my point again, the intense arborization of neuroglia cells could be the morphological expression of a special metabolic activity. In the same way, nature shows an increase in branching during the development of plants. Seasonal variations cause corresponding variations in branching of plants which most likely means an increase or decrease in surface area and therefore an increase or decrease in metabolism. With this general biological assumption in mind, it seems unlikely that the dense arborization of neuroglia cells would be necessary for resting cells; but such branching could be meaningful if neuroglia cells contribute to neuronal metabolism. However, Dr. Bairati reminds us that the protein of glial fibrils is a keratinlike substance and we usually associate these substances with low metabolic rates. Would this also apply to the processes of astrocytes? If this were the case, supporting function would then be more likely.

The picture of Drs. Lumsden and Bairati have cleared up another point, namely, the relationship of neuroglia cells to capillaries (Fig. 73). Previously, I was uncertain whether capillaries are endowed with a complete glial sheath. I realize now that the astrocytes form distinct end-feet on capillary walls, so closely in contact with capillaries that metabolic products going in or out must pass through glial elements.

Coming back to the initial question—whether we exaggerate the physiological significance of the neuroglia—I will compare muscle or liver with brain tissue to make my point clear. The contractile part of muscle tissue or the cells of liver correspond, in our comparison, to the neuronal tissue only. None of us is concerned about the normally present supporting tissue in either liver or muscle but we all feel the urge to clear up glial function. What are the reasons for the different evaluation of supporting elements in brain and other organs? Have neurohistologists over-emphasized the neuroglia?

I don't think so, for the possibility of conveying nutritional material has been described; but there is another possibility: Have neuroglia cells a secretory function? Morphologically, there is as yet little to support this view. On the other hand, biochemical aspects of cortical synapses demand, somewhere, somehow, a se-

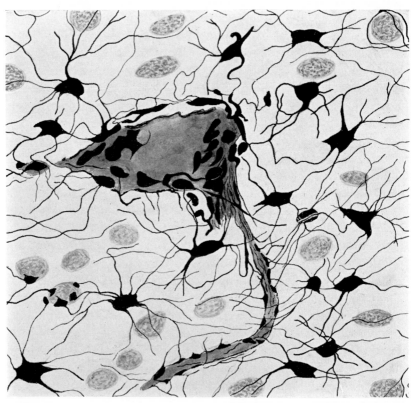

FIGURE 73. Ensheathing of cortical vessels. The middle of the field shows a transverse oblique section through a cortical vein, the walls of which are partially seen from their surfaces. Numerous intensely black glial end-feet can be seen. The entering cerebral capillary has smaller end-feet attached and numerous enveloping fibers. Occasionally the end-feet can be seen in close contact with cerebral neurons, as shown in the upper left. Magnification, 1000 ×.

creting mechanism. This secretion might come from terminating nerve fibers; but neuroglia cells, particularly the satellites, should not be excluded. Thus, I have to make another plea for functional studies of the satellites.

Why do we deny neuroglia cells any nervous function? What is the actual evidence against nervous function? Why do we assume, although both neuroglia cells and neurons come from the same matrix, that one is definitely nervous, while the other is resting, supporting or sedentary? We say, of course the neuroglia cells cannot be nervous in function because neuroglia cells have no axons. But we know there are nerve cells whose axons cannot be demonstrated. To exclude a neuroglia cell from being nervous in function cannot be justified by the absence of an axon. Then, of course, I am at once reminded how absurd this idea of nervous function is because neuroglia cells have no Nissl substance. But are we quite certain that Nissl substance is a definite characteristic of nerve cells? There is a large population of cells for which it is impossible to say, this is a nerve cell, or this is a neuroglia cell in Nissl stains. Moreover, Dr. Palay has drawn our attention to the fact that astrocytes have around the nucleus electron dense particles which may resemble Nissl substance.

I do not wish to suggest that the neuroglia participates in fast nervous events but we might speculate that the cortical neuroglia cells have the faculty of storing memory. I suggest such a function only for the satellite cells in the cerebral gray matter and, of course, not for astrocytes or oligodendrocytes in the white matter. We should deny nervous function to the neuroglia only when we are absolutely certain that this is not the case; we may all be biased by certain neurohistological dogmas.

There is another possibility of which I have been aware, which may be to some extent an indirect nervous function. Marshall ('53) has mentioned that the neuroglia may contribute to the spreading depression of the cerebral cortex, this slow rising DC potential which may be extraneuronal; and Dr. Denis Williams has suggested that a part of the slow rhythmic electrical activity of the brain could be caused by neuroglial activity. We know from the recent studies with micro-electrodes by Li and Jasper ('53) that there is little coincidence between individual neuron discharges and this slow cerebral rhythm. It does not appear at the moment that the slow electrical rhythm is just a summation of the fast action potentials; perhaps scientists like Kornmüller ('50) may be right in considering that the neuroglia might contribute either to the slow AC or DC potentials. If this were true, then the neuroglia would at least indirectly interact in nervous function or, if you like, in mental function. Then, too, we have to fit in the Scheibel's observation that there are nerve fibers terminating on oligodendrocytes, which can mean two things: Either they did not see the dendrons to which these terminations went, or the oligodendrocytes receive nervous stimuli. In the latter event the oligodendrocytes could either be incited to secrete or somehow incorporated into nervous functions, such as storing memory. Coming back to a possible electrical activity of neuroglia cells, I should mention that Phillips ('56), in our laboratory at Oxford has made intracellular recordings in the motor cortex. While most of the records showed oscillating activity, some showed constant resting potentials. This may represent the electrical charge of neuroglia cells or of inactive resting nerve cells. Coombs, Eccles and Fatt ('55) also referred to long lasting resting potentials in the spinal cord. If these observations could be followed, it might be possible to reach a decision on the question of whether neuroglia cells have any fluctuating activities at all. This fluctuating activity could result in a discharge of slow electrical potentials.

I find Dr. Murray's work on serotonin of great interest; but there we come to a crucial problem of tissue cultures. What is the meaning of this pulsating activity of oligodendrocytes and can we in any way imagine that such activity occurs within the intact brain? If processes alter their relative positions, this fact should have considerable bearing on our neurophysiological conceptions, because neuroglia cells are sufficiently close to intervene between synaptic fibers and neuronal surfaces. If neuroglia cells alter their intercellular positions, then Ramon y Cajal's ('25) original suggestion that they indirectly could affect synaptic activity would not be such an absurd one. We must leave the essential question—what is the actual functional role of the neuroglia in the central nervous system—still unanswered.

SECTION V

The Neuroglia in Clinical Neuropathology

Chapter 16

Implications of the Biology of the Neuroglia And Microglia Cells for Clinical Neuropathology

RAYMOND D. ADAMS

I N THESE past two days we have seen and heard the first results of modern histological craftsmanship. We note with interest that the apparatus and methodology by which man hopes
to plumb the depths of the cell as an elemental organism are now
at hand or soon will be developed. Microchemistry promises to
reveal the most intricate metabolic activities of the neuroglia and
biophysics to analyze the diminutive structures, some of little
more than molecular size, which reside in the nucleus, cytoplasm
and processes of these cells. The data yielded by these methods
may become the basis of new conceptions of nervous structure
and function.

The studies which have been reviewed thus far in this symposium have approached the neuroglia cells from the viewpoint
of the biologist and have as their abiding purpose the determination of all of the objective manifestations of these cells, either as
isolated units or as members of the normally constituted nervous
tissue. My task today, if I understand my assignment correctly,
is to set before you some of the properties of these cells as they
may be determined from the study of disease and, in particular,
vascular and inflammatory disease.

At the very outset I suppose one might question the legitimacy
of using a pathological process to disclose the normal properties
of cells, but there are several points which may be raised in defense of this approach. In the case of the supporting and interstitial elements, at least, a morbid dissolution of the tissue appears

245

to be one of the most effective methods of revealing their natural function; and one may conclude that whatever else they do in states of health, they play a vital role in tissue reparation. Then too, it is a matter of record that much of what we know of these cells was learned through the study of pathological forms. In fact, the original ideas as to their function in the nervous system came from human pathology and only later were they tested in the experimental laboratory.

THE ROLE OF THE NEUROGLIA IN NEURO-PATHOLOGICAL PROCESSES

In neuropathology it has become virtually axiomatic that the astrocytes and microglia cells are the indicators of disease. They are used in much the same manner as a chemist uses litmus paper to indicate to the eye the acidity or alkalinity of a solution. And, as a corollary of this axiom, it may be said that any neuropathological process manifested only by changes in the nerve cell, its axon or myelin sheath, leaving the neuroglia unaltered, must always be regarded with the greatest suspicion. Often closer study will prove such changes to be artifactual. There are exceptions to this statement, as with all rules. In acute disease leading to a fatal issue within minutes to hours, these reactive glial changes may not have time to develop; or in extremely chronic disease, where only a relatively acellular fibrous gliosis remains, they may escape notice.

Since the beginning of neuropathology as a special field of endeavor, two basic glial reactions have come to be recognized. These are astrogliosis and microgliosis. It may be said that they form two of the cornerstones of the whole edifice of neuropathology, the other two being the vascular reactions, which are not altogether separable from the glial reactions, and the specific nerve cell changes. These two fundamental glial reactions may occur singly or together and they comprise a series of cell changes which have an orderly relationship to one another. Unfortunately the terminology by which they have come to be designated is rather cumbersome. In the series of astrocytic reactions there are the hypertrophied and the swollen or plump astrocyte (Gemastetezellen of Nissl) and often termed "cellular gliosis." Under special circumstances the giant astrocyte (Monsterzellen) and the ameboid astrocyte appear. And, as the most chronic astrocytic reaction, the fibrous (piloid) astrocyte, proliferates and gives rise to "fibrous gliosis." Similarly, in the series of microglial reactions there are the hypertrophied, ameboid, lamellar or pleomorphic microgliacytes, the rod cell (Stabchenzellen of Nissl), the fat granule cell of Gluge (Kornchenzellen and Gitterzellen), also called the globoid microglial phagocytes or macrophages. Other changes involving the neuroglia cells have been described and are commonly mentioned in neuropathological writings, e.g., ameboid astrocyte, more correctly termed ameboid degeneration of astrocytes with clasmatodendrosis, the formation of filling bodies (Fullkorperchen) and dendrophagocytosis, isomorphic and anisomorphic fibrous gliosis, microglial satellitosis and neuronophagia.

These cell changes and reactive processes are fully described in the writings of del Río Hortega ('32) and Penfield ('32a, b) and the details need hardly to be reiterated. However, as every student soon discovers through personal experience, some of these cell changes are easily verified as faithful signs of disease and others are indefinite and highly unreliable. Some purpose may be accomplished therefore if I summarize the major pathological reactions of the astrocytes and microgliacytes from the viewpoint of one who attempts to work with them in the laboratory. I am sure that my opinions are not fully shared by many professional neuropathologists but, nevertheless, they may provoke discussion which will clarify certain points.

ASTROCYTOSIS AND ASTROGLIOSIS. These terms are used more or less synonymously in many writings. However, the more precise meaning of the word astrocytosis is a proliferation of neuroglia cells, i.e., an increase in the number and size of astrocytes; astrogliosis in contrast refers to an excessive production of gliofibrils of astrocytes. The astrocytes, like all other elements in the nervous system, appear to have certain metabolic needs which must be satisfied. If, for example, there is a critical degree of anoxia or ischemia, they degenerate as do the nerve cells, the oligodendrocytes, microgliacytes and many of the cells in the small blood vessels. Their cell nuclei, in the conventional aniline stains, become shrunken and pyknotic, with irregular or serrated borders; and shortly the reaction to basic stains is altered or lost. The processes of the cell become fragmented—a process known as clasmatodendrosis—and finally the cell components are converted into a granular, amorphous debris, no longer identifiable as part of a cell. As stressed by Penfield and Cone ('26a) the ameboid astrocyte described originally by Eisath and Alzheimer, is a degenerating or dead cell and the processes of this cell whether normal or previously hypertrophied will be fragmented (clasmatodendrosis) or phagocytized (dendrophagocytosis). Both protoplasmic and fibrous astrocytes undergo this series of changes.

Hypertrophy and probably slight hyperplasia of astrocytes attend the degeneration of nerve cells and myelinated fibers, as in Wallerian degeneration. The enlarged astrocytes develop thick processes with increased numbers of branches, as seen in the gold chloride sublimate stain of Ramon y Cajal, and increased numbers of gliofibrils, as seen in a phosphotungstic acid hematoxylin (PTAH) or Holzer stain. In the earlier stages of this reaction, the nuclei are enlarged and hyperchromatic and the cytoplasm becomes visible, which permits their detection by the usual cell stains; but in the later stages, or in very chronic degenerative processes involving nerve cells the nuclei are small and the PTAH and Holzer techniques must be called upon if an accurate picture of the abundant astrocytes (fibrous gliosis or astrogliosis) is to be obtained. This process of "replacement gliosis" is analogous to the "replacement fibrosis" of diseases in other organs. With tract degenerations the astrocyte fibers are oriented parallel to the degenerating nerve fibers (isomorphic gliosis) and in degenerations of nerve cells in the gray matter or in destructive lesions of white matter a more haphazard orientation occurs (anisomorphic gliosis).

The conditions for astrocytic proliferation or hyperplasia appear to be ideal in diseases which destroy the parenchyma, i.e., nerve cells and myelinated fibers, or the whole tissue. In severe injury to the nervous system, as in infarction, the astrocytes which proliferate are usually those that have escaped destruction in the margins of the lesion. At first they enlarge in all dimensions and their nuclei swell, a change which may be noted within a few days of the injury. Nuclear hyperplasia, always without visible mitoses, is evident by the fourth and fifth days and becomes increasingly prominent in the following weeks (astrocytosis). The dividing cells have an abundant, eosinophilic vitreous cytoplasm. These are the swollen or plump astrocytes of Nissl. Often the division results in the formation of cell clusters (Gliarasen). As a rule the glial proliferation at first exceeds the needs of the tissue because many of these cells later are seen to have disappeared. Fiber formation becomes increasingly prominent with the passage of time and the cell bodies become smaller and less numerous as the fibers become more abundant (astrogliosis). These are the typical reactions of fibrous astrocytes and protoplasmic astrocytes, the latter always being converted to fibrous forms. Some few of the astrocytes attain enormous size with extremely large nuclei in proportion to the volume of cytoplasm, forming the so-called giant astrocytes which may be identified erroneously as neoplastic cells. Any of these proliferating astrocytes may likewise degenerate, particularly if the disease which stimulated the hyperplasia was progressive, and this process is usually manifested by clasmatodendrosis and karyorrhexis. As the processes of repair are consummated the reactive astrocytes appear to return to a more quiescent form. The cell bodies are more sparse, the nuclei are smaller with less chromatin, nucleoli diminish in size and the cytoplasm is no longer prominent. However, many of the cells continue for a long time to retain abnormal characteristics, their large cytoplasmic expansions and excessive fibrillar structure distinguishing them from normal astrocytes.

Reparative gliosis is induced by any lesion whether vascular, inflammatory, traumatic or of other type, which changes structural relationships within nerve tissues. Under these circumstances the astrocytes exhibit most clearly their well-recognized supportive function. Nevertheless certain disease processes may exert their effects on the astrocytes themselves and evoke proliferative activity, as in certain metabolic states, such as hepatic coma, where the nature of the stimulus has not been determined. The enlarging and proliferating protoplasmic astrocytes in liver disease correspond to the Alzheimer Type I and Type II cells and their degenerating forms have been described by Opalsky ('30).

Another point of importance concerning the repair of lesions in nervous tissue is that astrogliosis usually is accompanied by some degree of fibroblastic reaction, especially in the pia and walls of blood vessels, and this appears to vary from one disease to another. There are in fact two types of connective or supportive cells in the central nervous system, the fibroblasts and astrocytes, and they react somewhat dissimilarly. The main stimulus to fibroblastic proliferation (fibrosis) appears to be injury of fibroblasts and possibly the deposit of fibrin, which accounts for the prominence of this reaction around abscesses, tuberculomas, hemorrhages and in the cavitating center of infarcts. The main stimulus to astrocytic proliferation is injury of astrocytes, and if they are destroyed, as in the center of an infarct, there is little or no possibility of astrogliosis.

HISTIOCYTOSIS AND MICROGLIOSIS. The natural stimuli to histiocytic and microglial proliferation appear to be abnormal blood supply, diminished oxygen supply and altered tissue tension. The form of the reacting cells is determined partly by the location and partly by the nature of the destructive process. Lesions in which products of degenerating myelin or hemorrhage are produced invariably result in the formation of macrophages. As these cells multiply they undergo mitotic division and the larger cell forms always exhibit vigorous phagocytic activity. A few of the macrophages probably are derived from surviving microglia cells in the margins of the lesion but the majority are formed by the adventitial and pial histiocytes. Macrophages appear in human material within 48 hours of the nervous injury and increase greatly in number during the following weeks. They are more abundant in lesions which involve the white than gray matter and incomplete destruction of the latter usually results in the formation of ameboid or rod cells rather than the globoid forms of histiocyte and microgliacyte. In all of the more chronic and incomplete lesions of the cerebral and cerebellar cortex the bipolar, rod-shaped histiocyte or microgliacyte, first observed by Alzheimer in general paresis, are abundant. Acute nerve cell destruction calls forth the ameboid or pleomorphic microgliacytes which remove the remnants of the degenerate nerve cells, a process which is called neuronophagia. Thus, the three reacting forms of histiocytic or microgliacytic elements, *macrophage, rod cell* and *ameboid histiocyte,* each appears to develop under rather specific conditions. There is nothing about their appearance that enables the pathologist to decide whether any one of these cells had its origin in the resting microgliacytes, or the adventitial and pial histiocytes. However, most of them appear to arise in the blood vessels and meninges and it is doubtful whether these cells can be identified except as they become activated and sever their attachments to the adventitia.

The fate of macrophages is unsettled. In older lesions they throng the perivascular spaces and become smaller and more flattened as they apply themselves to the adventitia of the vessels. Some eventually come to lie in close relationship to the endothelial cells. Whether they discharge their content of phagocytized material into the vessel lumen and resume their life as inactive histiocytes or actually migrate into the vessel and thence to the lung and spleen, as suggested by some pathologists, cannot be stated at this time. One never sees these cells transgressing the endothelial lining.

OLIGODENDROCYTOSIS. The oligodendrocyte does not appear to participate in any of the standard histopathologic processes of the nervous system. It appears to be extremely sensitive to injury and degenerates almost as readily as the nerve cell; and in the white matter it seldom can be found if the myelinated fibers have degenerated or have disappeared. Swelling of the oligodendrocytes is the rule in post-mortem materials. Perivenous, perineuronal and interfascicular multiplication of oligodendrocytes undoubtedly occurs but nothing is known of the stimuli which cause them to increase in number or of the significance of this reaction. Perineuronal satellitosis by oligodendrocytes, a normal phenomenon in many areas of the brain, is an equally mysterious change and one of relatively little value in neuropathology at the present time. The appearance of cytoplasmic material which takes a mucin stain, the mucocytic change of Grynfeltt ('23), is still of doubtful meaning and its relation to the grapelike bodies of Buscaino even more obscure (Liu and Windle, '50). As pointed out by del Río Hortega ('28), the cytoplasm of presumably normal oligodendrocytes occasionally stains in this fashion.

CRITIQUE OF THE STANDARD NEUROGLIAL
REACTIONS

The neuroglial changes which are listed above have become so traditional in neuropathology that there is a tendency to accept them unquestioningly as established reaction types. However, practical experience in the laboratory teaches that all of them are not of equal value and it may be predicted that certain of these neuroglia cell changes, like the equivalent nerve cell changes, so much in vogue in Germany early in this century, will prove to have limited application.

The separation of the different glial and mesodermal cells on the basis of their morphology and staining properties, either by the usual cell stains or metallic impregnation methods, is often uncertain. I doubt if there is any presently available method which will permit their identification in all instances. It comes as no surprise then that those of us who employ tissue culture and the other newer histological methods should have trouble in identifying cell types. The neuropathologist, while usually having no trouble in identifying the nerve cell, astrocyte, oligodendrocyte, microgliacyte, histiocyte and fibroblast by the more conventional stains, finds it easier to differentiate between them if they are engaged in a pathological process. It may, for example, be observed that diseases which induce change in astrocytes often leave the oligodendrocytes and nerve cells unaltered. Perhaps the histologist should take advantage of this knowledge and turn his attention to the reacting neuroglia cell instead of confining himself completely to the resting forms.

The whole series of microglia cell reactions, so brilliantly set forth by del Río Hortega ('16, '19) and now co-ordinated with the reactions of the reticulo-endothelial system, has found acceptance in every neuropathology laboratory.* Almost forgotten are the old arguments concerning the neuroglial (astrocytic) origin of

---

* The concept of the reticulo-endothelial system is not above criticism for the reacting histiocytic forms arising in blood vessels do not appear to be derived from the endothelial cell but from the adventitial cell. In other words it is to the reticulo-adventitial rather than reticulo-endothelial system of cells that we are referring when we use this term.

the macrophages, the lamellar cells and the rod cells. However, as important as this work is, it fails to stress the role of the adventitial and pial histiocyte in those processes which call forth these different cell types. Close inspection of the brain lesions in many acute diseases will show that most of the pleomorphic histiocytes, lamellar cells, rod cells and macrophages emanate from the outer coats of the blood vessels and the pia and not from the microgliacytes. Moreover, the proof of their microglial origin by the use of a metallic impregnation such as silver carbonate method of del Río Hortega does not settle the point, for all histiocytic elements of the reticular and adventitial systems of every organ take up the silver salts. One has the impression that there are relatively few microgliacytes in healthy, mature brain tissue. Whenever they are found in any large number some pathological process was underway at the time of death and they can be seen streaming from blood vessel walls and pia. This view was first put forth by Cerletti ('03) and has been affirmed most recently by Hassin ('40).

The astrocytic reaction types, so clearly outlined by Penfield ('32a, b) and others, have stood the test of time and are now accepted by nearly all neuropathologists. The natural cycle of the protoplasmic and fibrous astrocyte from a resting state to the reactive, hypertrophied, plump cell and then to a small nucleated fibrous form is well-demonstrated in acute processes of all types; and in chronic diseases the latter may be seen to dominate the picture. Nevertheless, certain aspects of geneology of the reactive astrocytes are in need of further study. The giant or monster cells with their large, irregularly shaped and sometimes multiple nuclei and enormous cytoplasmic expansions are poorly understood. All gradations are found between these cells and Nissl's plump astrocytes which suggests that the necessary pathological conditions for their development are the same as those for the plump astrocyte. They are usually found in chronic disease processes, as Penfield ('32a, b) pointed out, and are of undoubted importance. It has been said that they may represent degenerative or regressive forms but such a supposition is supported only by the fact of their bizarre nucleation and the occasional fragmentation of their processes in post-mortem material. In contrast,

ameboid astrocyte, clasmatodendrosis and dendrophagocytosis
are merely descriptions of degenerating cells and are easily confused with post-mortem changes. They offer little assistance to
the neuropathologist in interpreting the signs of disease.

Oligodendrocytosis, either as a perineuronal satellitosis or as a
vascular perigliosis, are other changes in the neuroglia cells which
cannot at present be interpreted. Undoubtedly these changes do
occur and they must have some obvious significance but it is not
as yet known. Swelling of oligodendrocytes is another common
finding in post-mortem material, especially in the brains of infants and children and in biopsy material. The fine distinctions
drawn by Penfield and Cone ('26a, b) between so-called acute
swelling and an autolytic change, on the basis of degree of swelling of cytoplasm, pyknosis of nuclei, hydropic change with vacuolization and the formation of protoplasmic girders, all said to be
greater in acute swelling, are of doubtful validity.

In general it may be said that any neuropathological process
which consists of only such indefinite changes as acute alteration
or dropping out of nerve cells, clasmatodendrosis and dendrophagocytosis of astrocytes, satellitosis, swelling of oligodendrocytes, and modifications of the staining properties of myelin and
axis cylinders without corresponding astrocyte, histiocyte and
microglia cell changes are usually too ambiguous to gain credi-
bility.

THE QUESTION OF PRIMARY VERSUS SECONDARY
NEUROGLIAL REACTIONS

Implicit in the above statements is the general notion that
neuroglia cells are either destroyed by disease or react to repair
the effects of disease. The "prehension, elaboration and transportation of substances," those functions assigned the pathological
microgliacytes by del Río Hortega, and the support of parenchymal elements, the function generally postulated for normal and
pathological astrocytes, are most clearly in evidence after pathological changes have taken place in the neurons. In this sense
they are secondary to the parenchymal lesion. The question of
whether or not there are in addition pathogenic processes which
interfere directly with the metabolism of the neuroglia cells and

induce some cytological response which is entirely unrelated to those of other components of the nervous system has been given considerable attention. Del Río Hortega ('28) and more recently Greenfield ('33) have suggested that in some of the degenerative diseases of the myelinated nerve fibers of the brain, the so-called metachromatic leucoencephalopathies, the degeneration of the oligodendrocyte is the initial change. Adams and Kubik ('52) discussed the degeneration of this cell in relation to the plaque of multiple sclerosis. This is a difficult point to settle by ordinary histological methods. In most lesions of demyelinative type it is true that no oligodendrocytes can be seen or the few that do remain could be related to surviving myelinated fibers. However, the same could be said of most infarcts and there seems to be no way at the present time of deciding whether the degeneration of the oligodendrocyte or the myelinated fiber was primary. In the encephalopathy that accompanies fatal liver disease the protoplasmic astrocytes enlarge and increase in number usually in the absence of other glial or parenchymal change (Scherer, '33; Cammermeyer, '47; Adams and Foley, '53). Moreover, in Wilson's disease, where there is a similar reaction of the protoplasmic astrocytes, the excess copper content of the brain is apparently concentrated in these cells, according to Uzman (personal communication). This too would suggest that disordered liver function can induce a change in the brain which is reflected more clearly by the astrocytes than any other cell or nerve structure. Again it has not been possible to exclude obscure parenchymal changes though the standard staining or impregnation techniques fail to demonstrate them. These pathological reactions deserve our closest attention; for, if clarified, they may inform us of new functions for neuroglia cells.

NEUROGLIA AND MICROGLIA CELL REACTIONS IN VASCULAR DISEASES

After these preliminary remarks I turn now to the main topic of my discussion, that of the neuroglia and microglia cell reactions in cerebrovascular diseases and in encephalitis.

Vascular diseases of the brain, which comprise all those diseases which depend on some primary alteration of blood vessels or of circulation, result in two important pathological changes in nervous tissue, infarction and hemorrhage. The microscopical pathology of these two conditions is so different that they must be described separately.

INFARCT NECROSIS. This is the most frequently encountered process in neuropathology and the microscopical permutations are so common and so readily observed that the neuropathologist tends always to use them as a standard of reference against which all degenerative and reparative changes in nervous tissue are judged. One would have supposed that by now a **neuropathological timetable** would have been constructed for this most comprehensible of all lesions for there is no doubt that such standards are badly needed in neuropathology. They would assist in diagnosis, both in ascertaining the character of a lesion and in estimating its age. Nothing would appear to be more simple than to establish the whole range of cytological alterations incident to ischemia by the study of a selected group of carefully dated infarcts in human brains. However, the obstacles to this enterprise are formidable. There is often uncertainty as to the exact age of a lesion, i.e., the interval between its onset, as decided by the recorded clinical history, and death. The histological change also appears to vary with the completeness and permanence of the ischemia. The most pronounced and impressive cytological change is observed in infarcts where the circulation must have been fairly well preserved or restored (liquefactive or colliquative necrosis); the least cytological change occurs in lesions which have been completely and more or less permanently deprived of circulation (solid or coagulative necrosis). The difference here is the conventional one between dry and wet gangrene. It would seem, then, that the biochemical changes which call forth vigorous glial reactions and the transport of cells into the lesion depend on the maintenance of circulation; and the histological reactions in total ischemia, a rather infrequent event to be sure, are delayed or prevented altogether. Another confusing factor is hemorrhage which occurs only in infarcts with a relatively good circulation and which may occur as an agonal process (Cammermeyer, '47). All of these factors, which cannot be accurately evaluated, make comparison of dated infarcts exceedingly difficult. Moreover, animal experiments, carried out with the intent of obtaining more reliable data on these points, have limited application. The experimental disease is usually different from that which occurs in humans and the cytological processes always proceed more briskly.

It is our impression that little in the way of demonstrable change takes place in the first 24 hours after the onset of ischemic necrosis. Within the anemic zone oligodendrocytes, astrocytes and microgliacytes, nerve cells, myelinated fibers and some of the small vessels are destroyed, but they retain their normal staining properties. The endothelial and adventitial cells of surviving blood vessels are the first cells to react, becoming larger and more prominent and towards the end of this period a few neutrophilic leukocytes migrate into the necrotic tissue. Then, between 24 and 48 hours, the cells of blood vessels, both endothelial and adventitial, become enlarged and begin to increase in number. The first macrophages appear in about 48 hours and are seen to originate in the adventitial histiocytes of surviving vessels within the lesion and in the pia. They can actually be seen in the process of migrating away from the vessels and from the pia mater where histiocytes are now vigorously multiplying. These macrophages increase greatly in number in lesions of more than 2 days and in small infarcts they literally replace the entire necrotic zone within 3 to 4 weeks. Neutrophilic leukocytes, which are particularly numerous in hemorrhagic infarcts of a few days standing, begin to degenerate within 2 to 3 days and have usually disappeared in 7 to 10 days. Surviving microglia cells in the margins of the lesions begin to react at about the same time, forming first the pleomorphic cell types and then macrophages. This reaction is always inconspicuous in comparison to that of adventitial and pial histiocytes and accounts for only a minority of the macrophages in the infarct. Both ameboid and rod-shaped histiocytes tend to form in the incompletely destroyed cerebral and cerebellar cortex and are more numerous than the macrophages. The macrophages are at first small and mononuclear but with the passage of time they become larger and often multinucleated. In infarcts of several weeks duration they also crowd the interstices of the meninges and the perivascular spaces. After several months they become fewer in number and tend to aggregate in the perivascular spaces. They are much diminished in number in year-old lesions but a few still remain after the passage of several years. The cytoplasmic inclusion material which has been phagocytized is at first finely granular and Scharlach positive but within a few days larger droplets of cholesterol ester appear. In older macrophages the fatty material becomes metacromatic as though composed of more complex lipids. There is also phagocytosis of red blood corpuscles in hemorrhagic infarcts and after 6 to 7 days blood pigments (hemosiderin) are seen within the cells (Strassmann, '45).

The earliest astrocytic reactions are to be seen in the subpial zone and in the boundary between normal and healthy tissues at about the third to fourth day. The nuclei are at first enlarged, though the cytoplasm is still invisible in hematoxylin and eosin and Nissl stains, and gliofibrils are altered relatively little. Within 4 to 5 days, multiplication of astrocytes becomes evident though mitotic figures are never visible. The cytoplasm becomes more abundant as the days and weeks pass and acquires a vitreous quality. The processes become very thick and stain unusually well in silver or gold impregnation stains. In lesions of more than 1 to 2 weeks standing, plump, hyperplastic astrocytes, occurring in clusters, are present in increasing numbers and always some multinucleated and giant astrocytes are seen. After several months the astrocytes become less numerous, smaller and more fibrous though usually plump forms and a few giant astrocytes are still visible. Along the border of the older infarcts phosphotungstic acid hematoxylin and Holzer stains reveal a dense network of gliofibrils. In the center of the infarct, filling the residual cavity, there is always a delicate web of blood vessels, fibroblasts and reticular connective tissue but no astrocytes.

The above remarks apply to infarcts in which cavitation has occurred. If the lesion is small and lesser degrees of ischemia have prevailed, the damage to interstitial cells is less, as pointed out by Globus ('28). Astrocytes all through the lesion may then survive and proliferate and the same is true of the cells of the small blood vessels, which form cellular cords (so-called vascular proliferation), all together giving rise to a complex astroglial and mesodermal scar. It is lesions of this type that demonstrate most clearly the differing susceptibilities of cells to ischemia. Oligo-dendrocytes are observed to be about as sensitive to ischemia as the nerve cells and myelin, whereas the astrocyte is more hardy; and the cells related to blood vessels, i.e., histiocytes, fibroblasts and endothelial cells, are the most resistant of any of the tissue elements.

HEMORRHAGE. Accurate documentation of the cytological re-action of the tissues to hemorrhage cannot be found in any of the standard textbooks of neuropathology. The most that can be said at this time is that hemorrhage into the brain tissue, if not at once fatal, is followed by processes of repair which begin at the periph-ery and slowly extend to the center. The blood clot and its fluid contents, i.e., serum, are absorbed. Along the margins of the hemorrhage, red blood corpuscles are ingested by macrophages; this begins at approximately 48 hours. However, the red corpus-cles within the clot often retain their identity for weeks and slow-ly disintegrate with the liberation of hemoglobin. The latter may form hematoidin crystals but much of it is transformed by macrophages into hemosiderin. Proliferation of vascular adventi-tial histiocytes and fibroblasts is prominent. Fibroblasts, while not at first numerous, later proliferate and within a few weeks encapsulate the clot and invade it. If the hemorrhage is small it may be replaced by a scar composed of a granulation tissue con-sisting largely of histiocytes, fibroblasts, reticular connective tis-sue and collagen. If the hemorrhage is large, a clean-walled cavity eventually forms and is seen to be filled with clear fluid and lined by fibroblastic connective tissue, colored golden-yellow by many hemosiderin filled elongated histiocytes and macrophages. The amount of connective tissue is small unless there was much fibrin to organize. The surrounding astrocytes proliferate to some extent but not abundantly—a process which begins within 4 to 5 days. The end result is a lesion which differs from an old hemorrhagic infarct by its fibrous encapsulation and the lack of an inner network of connective tissue and vessels.

The above discussion, of course, does not encompass all the pathology of cerebrovascular disease for there are many other types of lesion coming to our attention almost daily. However, time is insufficient to describe each one in detail and to do so would probably advance our understanding of the glial reactions little more than would a more systematic study of the common processes of infarction and hemorrhage.

ENCEPHALITIS

In all forms of encephalitis diffuse and focal infiltrations of histiocytes and microgliacytes are a prominent finding. These cells have at times been referred to as polyblasts (Wickmann) and endothelial leukocytes (Mallory) and aggregates of them have been given special names such as the Babes nodule in rabies and the Durck granuloma in falciparum malaria, which in the latter instance is merely a necrosis of white matter of miliary size. These plemorphic cells appear early in the course of viral infections but always in relationship to some fairly obvious reaction on the part of the mesodermal elements, both adventitial histiocytes and microgliacytes, from which they take origin. It is characteristic of the viral encephalitis that these cells, which act as neuronophages, retain their plemorphic or ameboid form. According to the study of Howe and Bodian ('42), they represent a histiocytic reaction to nerve cell destruction and do not occur except in the instance of nerve cell death. Macrophages, however, do appear if there has been intense inflammatory necrosis leading to cavitation of the tissue or extensive destruction of white matter and hemorrhage. Astrocytes undergo a hyperplasia with the formation of hypertrophied and plump forms and the end result is a fibrous gliosis. If over considerable areas of the brain the neuroglia cells like the nerve cells have been destroyed by intense inflammation, softening develops; and with less severe damage a glial-mesodermal scar is the usual result. In the slightest injury, limited to nerve cells, a pure glial sclerosis is the outcome. In subacute lesions, i.e., in subacute sclerosing encephalitis, extreme gliosis and sometimes giant astrocytes are seen in the gray and white matter (Van Bogaert, '45).

In some virus infections the astrocytes and oligodendrocytes share demonstrably in the degeneration induced by the virus infection. Not only may there be a total destruction of the tissue, which may extend into the white matter, but eosinophilic inclusion bodies may appear in the neuroglia cell nuclei (Dawson,

'34). This has been noted in herpes simplex, inclusion body encephalitis and B virus myelitis. These diseases contrast in this respect to poliomyelitis where the glial changes appear usually to be secondary to nerve cell destruction or the inflammatory necrosis of tissue.

The perivascular cuffing and the infiltrations of the pia-arachnoid by inflammatory cells are often most abundant around third and fourth ventricles and at the base of the brain in the subacute stage of the disease; and they seem to bear no close anatomical relationship to the nerve cell destruction. Astrocytes, histiocytes and microglia cells proliferate beneath the ependyma and the pia. In some instances the meningeal inflammation appears to be the result of a surcharge of perivascular spaces by inflammatory cells, i.e., an extension of the inflammatory cells from the Virchow-Robin spaces to the leptomeninges, and in others, e.g., B virus and pseudo-rabies infections, the virus appears to act directly on mesodermal elements of the meninges with the formation of inclusion bodies and focal necrosis of meningeal and vascular cells.

In encephalitis of suppurative and granulomatous types other combinations of astroglial, microglial, histiocytic and fibroblastic proliferation may be observed and they impart certain identifying characteristics to the pathological process. The glial reactions however differ in no important ways from those which have already been described and they seem always to depend on such factors as ischemia, inflammatory necrosis of tissue, toxic effects and altered pressure relationships. Again the fibroblast participates in the inflammatory process if the fibroblasts and the vessels are injured or if there is a large deposition of fibrin to be organized. In fungous, tuberculous and luetic infections, the histiocytes and possibly microglia cells play a unique role and proliferate as closely packed sheets of epithelioid cells, so named because of their resemblance to regenerating epithelium. Incomplete division of some of these cells is believed to result in the formation of foreign-body giant cells of Langhans. These proliferative mesodermal reactions are characteristic of the granulomatous reactions of tuberculosis, syphilis and fungous infections of the meninges and brain. These and other interesting details serve to differentiate these pathological processes from those which attend acute suppurative and viral infections but time does not permit further exposition of the details of these reactions.

CONCLUSIONS

It may be said that the neuroglia and microglia cell reactions exercise an important role in many pathological processes and that their most important functions are revealed under the special conditions of disease. To the neuropathologist belongs the obligation of rendering these functions intelligible and in doing so he will surely obtain some intimation of the normal activities of these cells in states of health. The biologist who, on the other hand, essays to learn the secrets of normal cells should not neglect the clues offered by morbid processes in the brain.

All the pathological neuroglia cell types are not to this day fully elucidated. Some, which have been outlined under the heading of astrocytosis and microgliocytosis, have attained the stature of established reaction types. Others, particularly the regressive forms of reacting astrocytes and the several oligodendrocytic changes, are as obscure as when first described and as yet provide little insight into disease processes. The neuropathologist must continue to investigate these cytological changes if their meaning is ever to become clear.

The construction of a series of biological timetables for the several common histopathological processes in the nervous system, in which the neuroglia cells would figure importantly, has not been accomplished as yet. Even in such a common condition as infarct necrosis, the order of cytological events can only be roughly outlined at this time. The advantages which would result from detailed information of this type are obvious.

Finally, it should not be forgotten that there is a certain artificiality in our common task of studying the neuroglia cells apart from their natural habitat and as isolated entities in a pathological process. In doing this, we risk creating as many problems as we hope to solve. When cells are studied only as individual structural elements, many of the very properties which render them capable of organizing and functioning as a living tissue will elude us. And, it need hardly be pointed out to a group such as this that in our daily work as neuropathologists we are concerned not merely with cell changes but with structure and function of tissues and organs. In other words, it is obvious that tissues are endowed with potentialities far greater than those of the constituent cells; and many of these potentialities will be realized only when we study in a tissue all of the multiple effects of a pathogenic agent.

CONDENSED DISCUSSIONS OF THE NEUROPATHOLOGICAL SYMPOSIUM

DR. WOLF: Those of us who have had the privilege of sitting on the side lines of this conference had a most stimulating experience. No hard and fast conclusions have emerged, nor could they as yet, as to the functions of the neuroglia beyond the well-known reactions of the cells to disease and neoplasia which might serve the neuropathologists in seeking for aberrations of such functions in abnormal processes in neural tissue. Yet many fascinating hints have been given which may prove fruitful or perhaps turn out to be fanciful and for these we are very grateful. Can malfunction of the neural tissue yield data which may aid us in recognizing some of the as yet unknown functions of the neuroglia cells? In particular can we detect malfunction of the neuroglia cells themselves and its effect upon the neurons and perhaps myelin which could serve us in illuminating their normal functions? This is our path today and I hope we may make as brave a beginning at it as the conferees have done.

DR. LINDENBERG *(discussing Neuroglia in Traumatic Encephalopathies):* This presentation is restricted to cases in which the brain was exposed to blunt forces. The most common lesions related to the impact force are, besides hemorrhages, contusion necroses in localized areas of the cerebral cortex. They originate at the moment of the impact due to compression waves of necrotizing degree acting on the molecular structures of the cells. The neuroglia cells within such areas of tissue necrosis usually do not develop necrobiotic changes as in vascular softenings but retain their structure, gradually losing their staining property. The microglia cells rarely recover and participate in the phagocytosis of the dead tissue. This sudden coagulative necrosis is the only alteration of the neuroglia in which the mechanical forces are the sole causative factor.

If such an area of contusion necrosis is survived for several days, the astrocytes and microglia cells in its vicinity develop progressive changes within 2 to 4 days after an accident, whereas the oligodendrocytes closest to the lesion may die. Such glial reaction also occurs around traumatic hemorrhages. The width of this zone of marginal glial response depends to some extent on the size of the contusion necrosis or hemorrhage. These proliferative changes have been ascribed to the injury (Rand and Courville, '32a, b; Rand, '52), however they occur also around nontraumatic necroses or hemorrhages. What factor stimulates the neuroglia cells to react with progressive changes? Both areas of necrosis and hemorrhages are generally space-consuming during their early phase and exert pressure on capillaries in their vicinity, thus producing hypoxia and anoxia in the marginal tissue. Therefore, there is reason to believe that the glial proliferation is primarily due to oxygen deficiency. If the primary lesions are larger and therefore exert more pressure on their vicinity, the marginal tissue may secondarily become necrotic. Beyond this zone of marginal pressure necrosis there is the zone of glial proliferation. The most pronounced reaction of astrocytes is closest to the necrotic tissue, i.e., in an area where the hypoxia is of an almost necrotizing degree. The reaction of the microglia cells also seems to be dependent on the degree of hypoxia but the behavior of these cells indicates that their reaction is also determined by chemical substances diffusing from the necrotic tissue into the marginal zone. They multiply in the marginal zone, migrate into the dead tissue and there they form phagocytes. If a contusion necrosis does not increase in volume during its early phase and therefore exerts no significant pressure on the adjacent tissue, the neuroglial proliferation may concern mainly the microglia cells which may show no or very little protoplasmatic reaction but may exhibit multinucleation.

In areas remote from the contusion hemorrhages and necroses, one may find localized or diffusely spread progressive reaction of astrocytes or of microglia cells or of both cell types which must be attributed to various types of hypoxia secondary to the head injury—for instance, due to prolonged shock or compression of arteries. The intensity of the progressive changes of the neuroglia cells varies to a great extent, possibly depending on the rate and degree of hypoxia. Extensive glial reactions occur in the vicinity of small areas of necrosis caused by arterial compression. The cells, mainly microglia, show a wall formation similar to that of dedifferentiated neuroglia cells around necrotic areas in gliomas. On the other hand, in an area of selective necrosis of nerve cells and some oligodendrocytes due to hypoxia, the astrocytes and the microglia cells may remain surprisingly passive. Eventually, a glial fibrosis may develop without any change in the shape of the astrocytes.

In cases which died at the moment of injury, one usually finds throughout the brain acute swelling of various degrees of the oligodendrocytes, and swelling, vacuolization and breakdown of dendrons (clasmatodendrosis) of the astrocytes associated with vacuolization, homogenization or acute shrinkage of the nerve cells. These changes, if widespread and involving all parts of the brain, are not related to the impact forces which travel through the brain at the moment of the impact but are due to the fact that the instantaneous death of the individual caused a sudden stagnant anoxia for the tissues. During the early phase of anoxia, the cells are still alive but the breakdown products of their metabolism are not removed because of the circulatory standstill and act on the structures of the cells (Lindenberg and Noell, '52; Lindenberg, '56). In regard to the biology of the astrocytes, it is of interest that, under such generalized stagnant anoxia of death and under the same temperature condition, not all astrocytes exhibit the same degree of alteration at the same time. Swelling and clasmatodendrosis start in the deeper white matter, progress to cortex and striate bodies and then spread to the astrocytes of the subcortical white matter while those cells of the pallidum and most parts of the brain stem may still show no essential changes. This chronological and regional sequence of the disintegration of the astrocytes is apparently indicative of some difference in the metabolic activities of the astrocytes from area to area. The oligodendrocytes show no such regional differences, except that their swelling is usually more pronounced in the white than in the gray matter. The microglia cells reveal no such major changes while astrocytes and oligodendrocytes disintegrate. If somatic death is not instantaneous but is preceded by a phase of critical hypoxia lasting for about one hour, none of these changes develop and all cell types, including the nerve cells, maintain their normal structure. This is apparently due to the fact that during the phase of critical hypoxia some of the substances necessary for normal metabolism are utilized and that those breakdown products of metabolism, which cause the cellular alterations in sudden anoxia, are removed from the tissues by the circulation. In spite of the normal appearance of these cells, their chemical composition should differ from that of normal cells taken from the living and fully functioning brain if immediately deep frozen. It would be of interest to know whether these two types of normal cells would show any difference in their structure under the electron microscope and whether the exposure of the cells to severe hypoxia for various periods of time prior to their explantation into culture medium would affect their growth.

DR. ROIZIN (*discussing Neuroglia in Metabolic Disorders*): Dr. Windle and Dr. Pomerat have expressed the hope that this Symposium may restore the proper prestige to the neuroglia which was somewhat overshadowed by the masterminded neuron. I am quite sure that the majority of us share the same feeling. With an increasing realization of the role played by the neuroectodermal and mesodermal elements in the maintenance of the neural tissue functions and its metabolic activity, we hope to be in a better position to understand certain mechanisms involved in metabolic disorders and some of the pathogenetic processes which determine different disease conditions. Since the space allotted is insufficient for a complete review of this vast field, I have selected only a few examples and shall briefly point out some of the highlights.

In the Tay-Sachs variety of familial amaurotic idiocy, the microglia cells, astrocytes and, to a lesser degree, the oligodendrocytes undergo various degrees of proliferative and degenerative alterations, especially in the brain cortex (Hassin, '24; Klenk, '40;

Thannhauser, '50). With Hortega's silver carbonate impregnation, it is possible to demonstrate, in the gray matter of the cerebral cortex, various stages of metamorphosis of microglia cells into the so-called "rod cells." Ramon y Cajal's gold sublimate impregnation frequently reveals the "mulberry" type of astrocyte changes (Globus, '42b). These metal impregnation techniques, combined with fat stains, disclose that the above mentioned neuroglia cells are also undergoing various degrees of lipid degeneration.

In previous studies (Roizin and Ferraro, '42), we have demonstrated that the intraneuronal inclusions in a case of myoclonus epilepsy consisted predominantly of a complex glycoprotein compound. In subsequent studies (Roizin, '55), I have noticed that oligodendrocytes and some microglia cells also appear to be affected. Combined metal impregnation techniques with various histochemical methods revealed the presence of various degenerative products in the involved oligodendrocytes and microglia cells. Table V summarizes some of the most prominent histochemical findings.*

In degenerative processes of abiotrophic character or those observed in the course of presenile and senile processes of the central nervous system, the neuroglia cells and the microglia cells are involved in various degrees (Ferraro, '31; del Río Hortega, '43; Roizin, '52). Even in the earliest states of neuronal degeneration, it is possible to demonstrate with combined metal impregnation techniques and fat stains that some microglia cells contain sudanophilic material. Particularly during various phases of evolution of the senile plaques, microglia cells and astrocytes disclose first proliferative reaction, followed later on by a regressive and degenerative alteration. The oligodendrocytes are also frequently found undergoing multiple degenerative changes in the areas where plaque formations are taking place. Of particular interest is the metamorphosis of oligodendrocytes and microglia cells into amyloid bodies. Finally, when the degenerative processes are followed by atrophy, then fibrillary gliosis appears to dominate the pathological picture (Roizin and Kallmann, '56).

During different phases of neuronophagia, associated with dis-

---

* For more complete technical details, see Roizin and Ferraro ('42).

ease processes of a degenerative nature, oligodendrocytes and especially microglia cells appear engaged in phagocytosis or metabolization of the involved neurons (Roizin, '54). In the course of human and experimental demyelinating disease (Roizin, Helfand and Moore, '46; Ferraro and Roizin, '51), it is possible to demonstrate several types of neuroglia cell reactions. During the acute and subacute stages of demyelination, microglia cells appear principally involved in the process of phagocytosis and metabolization of the fat products of myelin disintegration (Table VI). In the same period of time, one can see, in combined metal impregnation and fat staining techniques, the metamorphosis of the microglia cells into macrophages, also called gitter

TABLE V

QUALITATIVE HISTOCHEMICAL REACTIONS OF THE INTRAGLIAL
DEGENERATIVE SUBSTANCES

Method	Color	Intensity of Reaction
Lugol and H$_2$SO	dark brown	++/+/±/−
Siegert	dark brown	++/+/±/−
Gieson (picro-fuchsin)	yellow or red	+/0/−
Benhold (congo-red)	dark red	+/±/−
Birch-Hirshfeld (Bismark-brown)	red	+/±/−
Methyl-violet and gentian violet, crystal violet, toluidine blue	metachromatic	++/+/±/−
Hematoxylin and eosin	blue	+/0/−
Nissl	deep green or bluish	+/±/0
Best-Bauer	red	++/+/±/−
Pyronin Y and methyl green	red or green	++/+/±
Alzheimer-Mann	bluish or purple	++/+/±
Weigert (fibrin)	purple	++/+/±
Russel (hyalin)	red	++/+/±
Scarlet R	red	−
Sudan black B	dark green	−
Lorrain-Smith	rose	+/−
Smith-Dietrich	blue-black	+/−
Tirmann-Schmelzer, Perl (Lison, Mallory, Gömöri)	blue	+/±/−
Stölnzner (Bertrand)	black	+/−
Kossa	black	−

+ = positive reaction; ++ = intense reaction; ± doubtful reaction; 0 = non-specific reaction. The intensity of the reaction varies not only in different regions of the brain but also in various elements of the same region; hence various markings indicate different types of reaction.

TABLE VI

Qualitative Histochemical and Histological Characteristics
of the Lipids of Myelin Disintegration

	Stage of Demyelination					
Methods	*Acute*		*Intermediate*		*Chronic*	
	Macro-phages	Extra-cellular	Macro-phages	Extra-cellular	Macro-phages	Extra-cellular
Sudan III R, Black	+++	++++	++/±	++/±	+/±/–	±/–
Nile blue	+++	++++	++/±	++/±	+/±/–	±/–
Osmic acid	+++	+++	+/±	+/±/–	–	–
Smith-Dietrich (modified)	+/±	+/±	+/±/–	+/±/–	+/±/–	+/±/–
Double refraction	++/±	++/±	+/±	+/±	±/–	±/–
Solu- Acetone	++/±	+++/±	+/±/–	+/±	±/–	±/–
bility Alcohol	+++/±	++++/±	++/±	++/±	±/–	±/–
in Ether	+++/±	++++/±	++/±	++/±	±/–	±/–
cold Chloroform	+++/±	++++/±	++/±	++/±	+/±/–	+/±/–

+ to +++ = various degrees of positive reaction.
± = doubtful or traces; – = negative or absent.

cells or the so-called compound granular corpuscles. The astrocytes, particularly the fibrous type, reveal more pronounced proliferative reaction in the subchronic and chronic phases. This was
generally much more readily demonstrable and much more intense in human material as compared with that observed in
rhesus monkeys (Ferraro and Roizin, '51; '54).

In experimental encephalomyelitis in monkeys, I have demonstrated (Roizin, '49) that, in the early stages of the disease process, the perivascular neuroglia cells show increased activity of
indophenol oxidase and peroxidase which, in many instances,
were very prominent in the surrounding tissues also. In similar
instances, acid phosphatase displayed increased activity though
it appeared much more prominent in the areas surrounding the
inflammatory allergic reactions.

Conclusion: A brief review of a few degenerative processes of
the gray and white matter of the central nervous system in human and experimental conditions illustrates that in association
with structural and histochemical neuronal or myelin alterations, the various neuroglia cells appear also involved in different
manners and degrees. Furthermore, from an evaluation of the

results obtained with a variety of histochemical and metal impregnation techniques, the conclusion is reached that the neuroglia cells are concerned with oxidation and phosphorylization processes as well as with the pathological disintegration of lipids, proteins and carbohydrates which is attained, particularly by the microglia cells, by lipolytic, glycolytic and proteolytic functions.

DR. COHEN (*discussing Chemical Basis of Pathological Demyelination*): Dr. Roizin and others of the conferees have discussed the possible relationship of neuroglia to myelination. I would like to confine most of my remarks to evaluation of some of the earlier statements as to the chemical basis of pathological demyelination and secondly to directions suggested by this conference to better study the role of neuroglia cells in pathological processes.

Weil ('48) compared the cerebral content of certain phosphorylated compounds in four cases of multiple sclerosis to three normals and concluded that lipid phosphorus decrease and nucleic acid phosphorus increase were generalized in the brain. He then suggested that neuroglia cells were retaining phosphorus, thus preventing this element from becoming available for lipid metabolism. This concept seemed interesting, though difficult to accept from a chemical metabolic concept. We then investigated a series of nearly 1,000 tissue blocks from approximately 100 normal and pathologic brains (Cohen, '55). Histological controls were utilized so that the chemical determinations were carried out on tissue with a known cellular content. This study demonstrated that the nucleic acid phosphorus increase noted by Weil was proportionate to the number of cells in each section and, therefore, the phosphorus content per cell was not increased. Thus phosphorus could not be said to be specifically retained in the cells. In addition, lipid phosphorus was decreased only when there was demyelination, whether this followed vascular processes, neoplasms or primary demyelinating conditions. The obvious conclusion to be drawn from this study is that adequate histological controls are essential before chemical and metabolic interpretations can be made from this type of quantitative experiment, which has been clearly emphasized by Drs. Nurnberger, Pope, Korey and Elliott in this conference. Dr. Elliott's statement that DNA phosphorus is an excellent indicator of cellularity is consistent with the results of our study.

Finally, I would like to consider the concept adopted by some pathologists that morphological changes in tissue are necessary concomitants of disease. While this is theoretically possible, the techniques presently at the neuropathologist's command are inadequate for the demonstration of all pathological changes which might occur. Pathological techniques have been refined by utilizing special stains to demonstrate changes unrecognizable when the tissue is handled routinely. The present conference adequately demonstrates that more tools are now available to search for structural changes which may accompany functional alterations. Drs. Lumsden and Costero have demonstrated that tissue culture has application in studying pathological material, although the translation of the tissue culture change to change in situ appears more difficult. The reports that we have heard concerning the electron microscope makes it likely that this is an especially fruitful means of pursuing pathological changes. While there may be disagreement as to the exact designation of certain cells demonstrated in electron microscopy, the micrographs we have seen the past few days demonstrate a consistent enough pattern. It would seem that the application of electron microscopy to evaluation of pathological changes is now feasible, particularly since the different varieties of histological change can be produced experimentally. For example, demyelination may follow experimental cyanide intoxication and certain infections and injuries. Vascular disorders are also simple to produce. These alterations as well as those in surgically removed human cerebral tissue can now be studied by electron microscopy.

Dr. Malamud (*discussing Neuroglia in Heredodegenerative Processes*): In heredodegenerative disorders, the neuroglia and microglia cells play their customary role of repair and phagocytosis but the intensity with which each element reacts may differ considerably. Three different kinds of glial reaction predominate in three types of degenerative disorder, as follows:

Reparative Astrogliosis. The majority of degenerative diseases of the central nervous system are characterized by a slow decay of nerve cells and fibers, whether because of an inherited low vitality or because of unknown endogenous or exogenous influences. To this category belong the senile and presenile dementias, the motor neuron diseases, Huntington's chorea, hereditary cerebellar ataxia, Friedreich's ataxia, certain forms of paralysis agitans and other less common disorders. In all these conditions a reacting astrogliosis is found to occur that is directly proportionate to the degeneration of neurons. The only variable is the individual capacity to react.

To illustrate, in Pick's disease the frequent laminar degeneration of neurons in the third layer of the cortex is accompanied by proliferation of fibrous astrocytes in exactly the same area. The more diffuse degeneration of the neurons and the senile plaque formation in Alzheimer's disease produce a mirror image in the spatial distribution of the astrocyte reaction.

This neuroglial reaction appears to be in the nature of replacement or reparative gliosis. There is little indication that the neuroglia cells in such instances react independently of the parenchymal degeneration. The microglia cells usually play an insignificant role and the oligodendrocytes show no demonstrable reaction.

Dysgenetic Astrogliosis. In certain forms of heredodegenerative diseases, an apparently independent activity is assumed by the astrocytes that proliferate quite out of proportion to any observable neuronal degeneration. Their hyperplasia suggest a close relationship to neoplasms, into which, in fact, they may become transformed. The specific conditions in which this occurs are tuberous sclerosis, von Recklinghausen's neurofibromatosis and syringomyelia. Apparently the underlying dysgenesis of these disorders in some way creates conditions for stimulation of astrocytes (and fibroblasts) to hyperplasia and tumor growth.

To illustrate, in tuberous sclerosis the cortical nodules are characterized by a disorderly arrangement of immature and giant neurons, amongst which myriads of glial elements proliferate in a manner suggestive of a diffuse glioma. That the neuroglia cells are astrocytes is evident from the dense fibrous network that they produce. Similarly, in von Recklinghausen's disease, areas of hyperplastic gliosis are often observed in the central nervous system as, for example, a local overgrowth of fibrous astrocytes in the meninges of the cerebellum. The central gliosis in the spinal cord of syringomyelia has much the same background and propensity to tumor formation.

Metabolic Microgliosis. In those heredodegenerative disorders where a metabolic disturbance is the fundamental pathologic process the predominant glial reaction is that of microglia cells. Here belong the lipoidoses, the familial demyelinating disorders, Hallervorden-Spatz disease, etc. In each instance microglia cell reaction predominates in the process of phagocytosis and transportation of abnormal metabolites.

To illustrate, in Tay-Sachs' disease the abnormal lipoid is deposited as granules in the ballooned nerve cells. This material in the neuron which stains weakly with Sudan stains is accompanied by a microglia cell reaction that often transforms the lipoid to a sudanophilic fat. In Krabbe's disease the demyelinated white matter is accompanied by an intense microglia cell reaction that is often characterized by diffuse and perivascular globoid cells.

The types of glial reaction outlined here may thus be said to reflect the different pathogenesis of the three types of degenerative disorder, although the fundamental nature of the latter remains obscure.

DR. LUMSDEN (*discussing Neuroglia Cells in Neoplasms*): Tumors of the astrocytoma-glioblastoma series are particularly easy to grow in tissue culture. The method reveals the great plasticity of living cells in conditions which favor migration. Clearly, its value in future research on the biology of these tumors must therefore stand or fall, at the outset, on this single issue: How real is the difference between the cell in the tissue and in the culture; does the difference imply any fundamental change in the properties of the cell?

Briefly, the criticism commonly leveled at morphological studies in culture is that disorganization occurs. But, while disorganization connotes an important change, it has been quite erroneously confused, in my view, with dedifferentiation. Disorganization relates to changes of architectural and spatial relationships and not to changes in the physical, chemical and ultrastructural characters of the cells. It is expressed, in the case of cultures of gliomas, only in the erratic behavior of the mesothelial cells from the vascular stroma. But, as for the neuroglia cells, neoplastic and nonneoplastic, the glioma represents an already disorganized tissue growth. In the wider field of general culture cytology, I think it is now widely conceded that biochemically differentiated cells do not dedifferentiate in culture in instances where this has been possible of study (e.g., glycogen, zymogen and pigment production). Even in embryonic material, upon which most of the early work on tissue culture was done and whence the confusion arose, it can be noted that early established morphological differentials are retained in culture; thus, macrophages, neuroblasts and neuroglia cells remain as morphologically characteristic cell races however varied the nutritional conditions we impose.

The cytological studies to be illustrated here were made on over 40 tumors of the astrocytoma-glioblastoma group. By setting up at least 50 explants from each tumor and by making subcultures, it was possible to determine that such neoplasms show a constancy in behavior in culture and that the behavior in culture bears a constant relationship to the histological characters of the neoplasm (Fig. 74). Moreover, in altering the mechanical conditions for cell migration, by growing the cells from a cell suspension of the tumor directly on glass as well as by the standard method of making the cultures in plasma clot, it was found that the forms of the cell in plasma and on glass in fluid medium were not significantly different. Thus it became evident that, although there are no strictly fixed morphological forms (i.e., the number, size and direction of movement of the processes of any individual cell may change from day-to-day and even from hour-to-hour), the tumor cells have a biological individuality from case-to-case. The comparisons between the histology and the cultures were made on the same biopsy sample, usually a fragment of 3 to 4 mm only in diameter. Thus, we are not concerned here with any regional variations in the character of the glioma upon which so much—and, to my mind, too much—stress has been laid in recent years. The cultures and subcultures were all short-term, from a few hours to 2 or 3 weeks old, at most. Since the cultural conditions were good (i.e., with frequent changes of media, air, etc.), we are not concerned here with secondary involutional changes.

In the most fully differentiated astrocytomas, corresponding to

Kernohan's histological Grade 1, dense outgrowths of astrocytic fibers only occur, any accompanying cell bodies that migrate being mesodermal in type. But the tumor tissue has higher survival power than normal adult brain tissue, and even the most minute satellate fragments scattered in the plasma give rise to fibers. Even isolated cell bodies scattered accidentally in this way recover and send out long fine fibers like nerve fibers. There is no question that such cells are astrocytes and not pre-existing neurons, since it is often possible to see the processes growing from clumps of cells with the cell pattern of the neoplastic tissue and not of normal cortex and since the parent tissue is not infrequently from a deep seated astrocytoma in the white matter in which the histological control material shows no nerve cells. On the other hand, while the cells resemble normal adult astrocytes with their long, slender, often anastomosing processes, they differ from the normal cells in that they grow faster and there is a richer pseudopodial activity at the tips of the processes.

Within Grade 1 astrocytomas, there is quite a wide range of growth behavior which must correspond, in my view, to quite a wide biological difference in different members of this grade of gliomas in the intact organ. In the most benign variants of Grade 1 astrocytomas, the cell bodies are almost completely sedentary and it is for this reason that this is the only variety that cannot be successfully subcultured. Higher up in the scale of malignancy between Grades 1 and 2 (Fig. 74A and B) the cell bodies show an increasing tendency to migrate. Isolated satellite cells are also somewhat different in that the processes are more numerous and somewhat shorter, though still slender and tortuous. As many as 40 processes have been counted coming from a single cell body. This great profusion of processes seems to be restricted to this stage of malignancy and, as we enter Grade 2, with its more active emigration of cell bodies, the cells have fewer processes which are finer, more tortuous and often showing marked gliosome formation; characteristically the perikaryon is much more voluminous.

As we ascend Grade 2 and approach Grade 3 astrocytomas, this inversion of the ratio of perikaryon to process is carried farther. The processes are now shorter, often arising from a common trunk, less fibrillary and more protoplasmic. The gliosomes now reveal

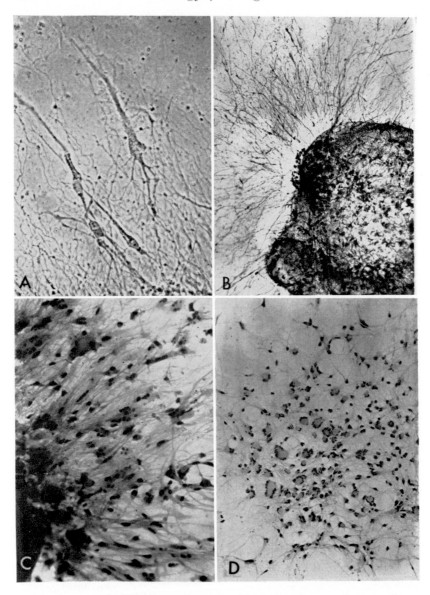

FIGURE 74. A, B. Astrocytoma of Grades 1 and 2 in tissue culture. A shows
the primary living culture by phase contrast; B, the subculture made from
it. Both show the characteristic dense outgrowth of fine glial processes. In
A, 4 migrating cell bodies are seen. C, D. Giant cell glioblastoma; C shows
a primary culture; D, a corresponding subculture. Fixation in formalin-
Ringer solution; Bodian stain.

themselves as rudimentary pseudopodia (Fig. 75). As we enter Grade 3 the type of cell that now predominates in the cultures is the short, bipolar and unipolar astrocyte that corresponds most closely of all neoplastic astrocytes in culture to the embryonic neuroglia cells to which the names astroblast and spongioblast have been given. But in culture it is seen that these are not fixed forms; multipolar cells may become bipolar or even unipolar and vice versa, as they pass from a more sedentary to a more migratory phase. All that is fixed or inherent in them is their particular degree of plasticity.

As we ascend to Grade 3, nuclear abnormalities now dominate the picture more than in the preceding grades. Bi- and multinucleated cells become a pronounced feature but, despite all this nuclear activity, the cytoplasm still possesses a remarkable capacity to form spiderlike processes, even though these are predominantly cytoplasmic and prone to take the form of those in Figure 75.

Finally, in the histological Grade 4 tumors in culture, a rather

FIGURE 75. Neoplastic astrocyte from the outgrowth near the margin of an explant from an astrocytoma of Grades 2 and 3. The cell has about 25 processes arising mainly from 4 trunks of the perikaryon. These show small, knucklelike, pseudopodia. Fixation in formalin-Ringer solution; Bodian stain.

wide range of biological characteristics is revealed. By now we are dealing with cells which migrate rapidly in large numbers within 24 to 48 hours, well ahead of the stromal cells. The neoplastic cells are now greatly dedifferentiated; but their rapid outgrowth, abundant mitoses, multinucleation and grossly aberrant forms of nuclear division (polyploidy, amitosis, etc.) make their distinction from undifferentiated mesenchyme quite easy (Fig. 74 C and D). In culture it is evident that they are neoplastic cells; it is now only their neuroglial lineage which is putative. The cytoplasm forms relatively short, highly fluid prolongations which anastomose to form protoplasmic syncytia. It is visibly evident that their cytoplasm is now very highly plastic and is rapidly synthesized but that, when at any time in the life of the culture it is sufficiently quiescent, it tends to form fibers, thereby revealing its astrocytic affinities. This explains why, amongst a population of predominantly undifferentiated, multinucleated cells, one occasionally sees fairly mature looking astrocytes. It is important to appreciate that, even with these latter cells, reversion to the more plastic form can occur readily later in the culture. Also, since the cytoplasm in these often shows abundant eosinophilic granulation and inclusion formation and since these formations occur also in cells in mitosis, I have no doubt that these are neoplastic cells from the tumor and not the normal astrocytes participating in any reaction around the tumor. These mitoses are abundant and are frequently of aberrant character, often associated with amitotic fragmentation of giant nuclei. The same features are reproduced faithfully in the subcultures (Fig. 74C and D).

Higher in the Grade 4 astrocytomas, the cytoplasm is completely undifferentiated, with no tendency to process formation. It is highly amoeboid and such cells often cannot be distinguished on cytoplasmic characters from ordinary macrophages. Only the giant multiple nuclei give the clue to their neoplastic nature and their neuroglial origin.

DR. COSTERO (discussing Neuroglia Cells in Neoplasms): In the first place, I would like to point out that in the Conference on the Biology of Neuroglia we agreed to start from the basis that there are in the brain, besides neurons and vascular elements, three main varieties of cells—the astrocytes, oligodendrocytes and microgliocytes. From the point of view of the pathologists, however, these three varieties of cells are not at the same biological level and do not suffice to explain the cellular architecture of the brain tumors.

As a matter of fact, astrocytes and oligodendrocytes frequently produce gliomas, astrocytomas and oligodendrogliomas respectively, while microglia cells do not produce similar neoplastic growths or microgliomas. Furthermore, the ependymoma is a perfectly defined tumor species at a biological level similar to the one occupied by astrocytomas and oligodendrogliomas. In addition, microglia cells may be present in any brain tumor, gliomas as well as neuroblastomas, neurilemmomas, melanomas, sarcomas, etc., as an eventual and nonspecific component of the stroma. In other words, astrocytes, oligodendrocytes and ependymocytes represent three biologically similar parenchymatous fixed cells of the adult nerve tissue, while microglia cells are phagocytes resembling the macrophages present in connective tissue. Bailey ('33) was the first to call attention to the presence of microglia cells in glioblastomas and Pomerat ('52) has demonstrated the presence of microglia cells in gliomas, neurilemmomas and melanomas cultured in vitro. A few cases of brain tumors that Polak ('35) considers formed by microglia cells do not invalidate the statement that astrocytes, oligodendrocytes and ependymocytes, on the one hand, and microglia cells, on the other, are four varieties of cells with two completely different biological levels, taking in account their tumor-forming capacities.

Microglia cells always exhibit the same features: ramified cells with continuous movements and intense phagocytic activity (del Río Hortega, '20), provided with extremely active undulating membranes (Costero, '31), transformed, after fixation, into the twiglets and nubbins typical of silver impregnated preparations.

In the second place, as a pathologist I must necessarily consider not two main varieties of neuroglia cells—astrocytes and oligodendrocytes—but four—glioblasts, astrocytes, ependymocytes and oligodendrocytes—as source cells that may produce well defined species of glioma.

The behavior of glioblasts in tumors is very peculiar. a) We always find together in glioblastomas two varieties of neoplastic glioblasts: small, pale, bipolar spongioblasts and large, eosinophilic, piriform astroblasts. These two varieties of neoplastic glio-

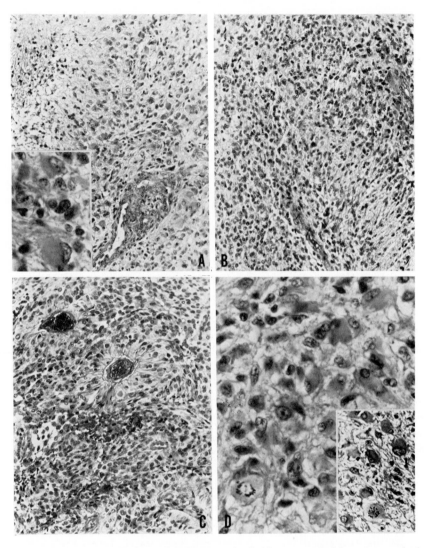

FIGURE 76. Morphological behavior of glioblasts in glioblastoma multi-forme. A. In the upper left-hand corner is an acellular area; in the lower right-hand corner, a vascular proliferation. Hematoxylin-eosin; magnification, 190 ×. The insert shows spongioblasts and astroblasts at higher power (600 ×). B. Glioblastoma formed almost exclusively by spongioblasts (spongioblastoma); note an acellular area extending from the upper left-hand corner to the lower right-hand corner. Hematoxylin-eosin; magnification, 190 ×. C. Glioblastoma formed almost exclusively by astroblasts (astro-blastoma); note the gliovascular systems. Hematoxylin-eosin; magnification, 190 ×. D. Glioblastoma formed almost exclusively by astrocytes (astrocy-

blasts are permanently associated with one another through transition forms (Fig. 76A). b) The small, pale, bipolar spongioblasts produce acellular areas and necrotic zones in the tumor parenchyma and stimulae characteristic vascular proliferation in the stroma (Fig. 76A, B). c) Large, eosinophilic, piriform astroblasts turn their main cytoplasmic prolongation towards capillary vessels forming "gliovascular systems" and tend to become multipolar astrocytes (Fig. 76C, D). d) Another important property of neoplastic glioblasts is their ability to show anaplasia, resulting in adendritic, spheroidal, eosinophilic astroblasts and in multipolar, monstrous, polychromatophilic astrocytes.

In a few special cases the glioblastoma may be formed predominantly by spongioblasts, astroblasts or astrocytes. This cellular polymorphism of glioblastomas may refer to its degree of malignancy and, in a tentatively schematic form, we can state that anaplastic, spongioblastic, astroblastic and astrocytic glioblastomas represent the order from major to minor malignancy. But in every case a minute analysis demonstrates the simultaneous presence of sponglioblasts and astroblasts in glioblastomas. In other words, astrocytes in glioblastomas come from two morphological varieties of glioblasts—spongioblasts and astroblasts—both equivalent from the point of view of their oncogenetical properties and representing two nonseparable progressive grades of maturity in which spongioblasts is the first and astroblasts the last.

Tumor astrocytes show variable behavior in each type of astrocytoma (Fig. 77A). Their origin and meaning have not yet been firmly established. However, tumor astrocytes are conspicuously different from normal astrocytes and from those forming reactional areas of gliosis. Nevertheless, in histological sections it is extremely difficult to differentiate tumor astrocytes of astrocytomas from astrocytes formed in glioblastomas and coming from the spontaneous evolution of neoplastic astroblasts. However, as Dr. Lumsden has just shown, the astrocytes of astrocytomas grow out in tissue cultures following a very simple cellular pattern, not too different from the normal ones, while the astrocytes sometimes

---

toma Grade 2); note the transition forms from astroblasts. Hortega's silver impregnation; magnification, 600 ×. The insert shows a lower power view (190 ×) of the same case stained with hematoxylin-eosin.

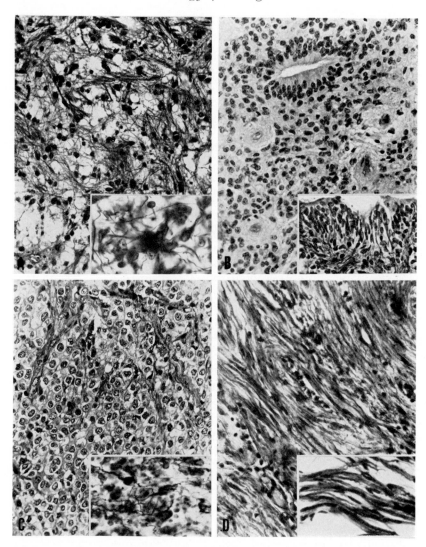

FIGURE 77. Tumor-forming capacity of mature neuroglia cells. A. Astrocytes of a cerebellar astrocytoma. Hematoxylin-eosin; magnification, 310 ×. The insert shows a detail of gliofibrils with Hortega's silver impregnation. B. Ependymal epithelium of a ependymoma of the fourth ventricle. Hematoxylin-eosin; magnification, 310 ×. The insert shows a detail with Hortega's silver impregnation; note internal process in every cell. C. Oligodendrocytes of an oligodendroglioma. Hematoxylin-eosin; magnification, 310 ×. The insert shows a detail with Hortega's silver impregnation; note typical processes. D. Elongated cells of a central neurofibroma. Mallory's stain; magnifi-

present in glioblastomas show wide modulations and frequent transition forms from astroblasts.

The ependymal epithelium is composed of a variety of neuroglia cells which, considered from a pathological point of view, is closely related to the astrocytes but, at the same time, clearly different from it, giving origin to ependymomas (Fig. 77B). The ependymal epithelium preserves in ependymomas, both in vivo and in vitro, its normal property of lining cavities, its internal fiber ending in a vascular foot and its blepharoplasts, proving the biological importance of such morphological characteristics.

Oligodendrocytes in oligodendrogliomas (Fig. 77C) also preserve such basic biological characteristics as the pulsatile movements and the typical distribution of their short processes (Canti, Bland and Russell, '37). Furthermore, it is highly probable that central neurofibromas (von Recklinghausen) be formed by the schwannoid oligodendrocytes (Fig. 77D) described by del Río Hortega ('28; '42) in normal human brain. The simultaneous development of peripheral schwannomas, radicular neurilemmomas and central oligodendrogliomas—both with round cells and with schwannoid cells—in the same patient, gives us a valuable evidence supporting the existence of a close relationship among the corresponding types of neuroglia, i.e., Schwann cells, schwannoid polar oligodendrocytes and classical spheroidal oligodendrocytes.

DR. CAMMERMEYER *(discussing Difficulties in Interpreting Neuropathology of Neuroglia Cells):* Several reasons may be advanced to explain why there are so many controversial concepts of the role played by neuroglia cells in diseases.

The lack of standardized conditions for collecting histological material means that there will be no exact basis for an evaluation of the significance of cell appearance. Efforts to provide for such a basis will often be useless because the quality of material is being influenced by factors which unfortunately are not controllable at the moment of autopsy to the degree possible in animal experimentation. Therefore, aberration in staining quality of nucleus and cytoplasm is not always the expression of pathologi-

---

cation, 310 ×. The insert shows a detail with Hortega's silver impregnation; note similarity with schwannoid oligodendrocytes.

cal functioning of a cell but may often be the result of imperfect technique. In human neuropathological research as opposed to experimental research, the histological characteristics of the normal neuronal, neuroglial and mesodermal elements have to be established anew for each case by careful examination of representative sections.

The occurrence of artificial changes intermingled with pathological changes is a source of erroneous interpretation which may be avoided by better knowledge of the action of fixatives on normal and diseased tissues. Some of the earliest changes produced by formalin consist in the swelling of tissue. The amount of swelling is modified by the varying distribution of myelin, lyophilic colloidal particles and connective tissue, by the temperature of the fixative and by the concentration of formalin. Most important for an evaluation of the appearance of cells is the knowledge that the increased tension caused by hypotonic formalin solutions affects the size and shape of cells, their nuclei and processes. Concomitantly with reduction in size of neuroglia cell nuclei (Fig. 18, p. 62) numerous neurons are affected in a striking manner (Fig. 78B). After fixation with 10 per cent formalin many changes of neurons and neuroglia cells, simultaneously, are produced in histological sections of normal human and animal material which are similar to those often interpreted as cerebral edema, chronic cell change with hyperchromatosis and sclerosis of neuron, and pyknosis of neuroglia cell nuclei. The ill effects tend to strike scattered groups of cells, as in the vicinity of a postmortem cut and of brain compression during removal (Fortuyn, '27; Scharrer, '33; Cox, '36-7), next to petechial agonal blood effusions, within the hippocampus and in the ventral horns. The variability in cell response to fixation and ensuing histological preparations indicates that the principles of so-called equivalent nerve cell pictures and equivalent pictures of neuroglia cells (Nissl, '10) have their limitations in neuropathological research based on routinely prepared material. In view of the fact that both neuronal and neuroglial changes related to the swelling of tissue are avoided by the use of isotonic fixatives (Fig. 78A), they may correctly be considered to be artifacts. Without the precaution of ideal fixation, the demonstration of chromophilic neurons is of no value for an estimation of intensity of cell function or

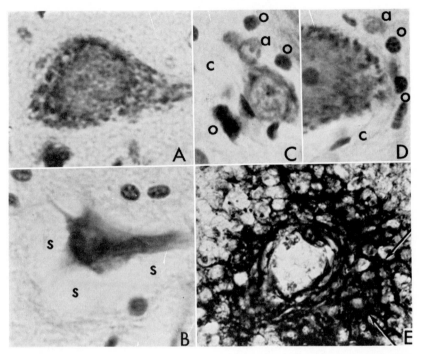

FIGURE 78. A. Ventral horn neuron of cat after physiological perfusion fixation. Gallocyanin stain; paraffin embedded; magnification, 1000 ×. B. Ventral horn neuron of cat with shrinkage of cell body and production of pericellular space *(s)* after immersion fixation in 10 per cent formalin. Gallocyanin stain; paraffin embedded; magnification, 1000 ×. C. Perineuronal astrocyte *(a)* and oligodendrocyte *(o)*, above, and capillary *(c)* between the neuron and group of oligodendrocytes *(o)*, below. Physiological perfusion fixation of cat; gallocyanin stain; paraffin embedded; magnification, 1000 ×. D. Capillary *(c)* situated between a large ventral horn neuron and two oligodendrocytes *(o)*. Physiological perfusion fixation of cat; gallocyanin stain; paraffin embedded; magnification, 1000 ×. E. Fibrin stained material in astrocytes, processes and cell bodies *(arrows)*. Human case Oslo, N. P. 42-1946. Formalin fixation; phosphotungstic acid hematoxylin stain; magnification, 625 ×.

severity of cell damage (Nissl, '10; Massazza, '24; Müller, '30; Koenig, Groat and Windle, '45; Weil, '46; Wolf and Cowen, '49; Meyer, '52), since these neurons always occur along with retracted cytoplasm, dark small nucleus and wide pericellular space. According to a recent idea formulated after the study of experimental venous infarction of brain, the oligodendrocytes become swollen and subsequently contribute to the damage of neurons by compression (Denny-Brown, Horenstein and Fang, '56); the brain fixed in formalin after removal was the site of well-defined pathological changes in addition to others of the appearance discussed herein.

If the brain is frozen immediately after being immersed in formalin, the formation of ice crystals in gray and white matter may result in the cleavage of tissue which disturbs the relationship between cells and produces small dark neuroglia cell nuclei. Changes closely alike in appearance were both illustrated as representative of so-called grapelike disintegration of Buscaino (Jansen, '36; Weil, '46) and referred to as pathological changes (Barten, '34; Dickson, '47; Zeman, '55).

Some of the changes due to prolonged fixation include post-mortem formation of metachromatic plaques with the deposition of birefringent material over a sharply demarcated irregular area where myelin is abnormally stained and neuroglia cell nuclei are dark; similar changes were interpreted as a staining reaction of pathologically changed tissue (Buscaino, '20; '24; Ferraro, '28; Moschel, '56). With continued fixation there is also exchange of ions, loss of NH_2 groups, and changes in histochemical composition. Therefore, it is necessary that all possible factors contributing to the final appearance of the tissue be carefully evaluated in a study of the response of the neuroglial elements to disease processes.

The nonspecific nature of structural changes often results in the formulation of diverse opinions. For astrocytes it is well known that only those bordering an area of necrosis react to diseases with the formation of gliosis (Rand, '52). Similarly, the astrocytes next to the surface of ventricles and brain frequently react with the formation of protruding glial tissue (Cooper and Kernohan, '51). The more recent ideas about the structure of astrocytes seem to indicate that this cell type serves the purpose to fill out gaps between the other tissue elements. The rapidity of astrocyte response would be explained by an ability of the cells to expand readily into their immediate vicinity, where neurons had atrophied or disappeared. The ensuing phases of astrocyte reaction seem to be associated with more profound changes in cell structure manifested by the acquired stainability of the cytoplasm, the permanent enclosure of iron from disintegrated hemoglobin, degenerated ferruginous tissue or diffused serum iron, and local growth potentiality. Possibly as an expression of the intensified activity, the astrocytes are frequently involved in those pathological conditions which are most difficult to classify nosologically, as, for example, diffuse gliomatosis (Einarson and Neel, '40; '42), glioblastomatose *en plaque* (Scherer, '38), syringomyelia (Staemmler, '42), tumors of the infundibulum (Globus, '42a) and ventricular wall (Globus and Kuhlenbeck, '44; Boykin, Cowen, Iannucci and Wolf, '54) and atresia of the Sylvian aqueduct (Globus and Bergman, '46). Also, in instances of acute brain damage there may occur some uncertainties whether the stained material is related to the unusual response of astrocytes (Haymaker and Davison, '50). The study of comparable sections stained by other techniques may be decisive in identifying the material as fibrin distributed in an area of acutely degenerated cells. It is of interest to note that in the narrow perivascular zone of necrosis in gray and white matter the stained material follows closely the structures of the original astrocytes (Fig. 78E, *arrows*); this may be evidence of the site of storage of thromboplastin and other material which, after the disintegration of cell boundaries, were in a condition to convert perivascularly diffused fibrinogen to fibrin.

The reaction of oligodendrocytes to diseases is still much debated (Brownson, '55). Since their number varies with their location and with the condition of the host it is not surprising that it is exceedingly difficult to determine the extent and evaluate the significance of oligodendrocyte response in acute diseases or experiments. This reservation holds for observations made in animals—dogs in particular (Lewis and Swank, '53)—because they are frequently associated with the sequelae of meningo-encephalitis and hydrocephalus. Also, the concept of perineuronal satellitosis may need to be re-examined in the light of the observation that many oligodendrocytes located near neurons are closer to a capillary than a neuron (Fig. 78C, D). Kryspin-Exner ('42-3; '52) has suggested the existence of several types of oligodendrocytes, some of which were similar to those considered by us to be artificial; others, recognized in material of chronic syphilis, were difficult to separate from vacuolated plasma cells. Here, again, a reappraisal of the subject would seem advisable on the basis of information that this conference and symposium have given us.

Chapter 17

Concluding Remarks on Neuroglia Cells in Relation to Neuropathology

ABNER WOLF

NO HARD and fast conclusions have emerged, nor could they as yet, as to the functions of neuroglia cells beyond the well-known reactions of these cells in disease. Adams has reviewed these for us; the hypertrophy and multiplication of astrocytes in glial scarring, the sensitive reaction of oligodendrocytes to adverse tissue conditions and the activation of microglia cells and other histiocytes with the formation of macrophages and rod cells. Questions which are still debated are: Do the oligodendrocytes participate at all in phagocytosis? Are microglia cells or other histiocytes of vascular and meningeal origin the chief source for macrophages in the central nervous system? Is the rod cell merely an intermediate stage in the development of the microglia cell into macrophages, representing a longer persisting interval phase or does it have some other functional significance? The eventual fate of the macrophages in the brain is not precisely known nor have the exact time relations of microgliosis and astrocytosis to tissue degeneration been established in any but the broadest terms. Distortion or elaboration of function of the neuroglia cells in disease may well yield clues to their normal function but the emphasis placed upon them as reactive elements in response to abnormal states of the neuron, and their axons and myelin sheaths may serve to cloud our vision in this direction. We must face the possibility that the neuroglia may have other functions that can be perverted by disease or that the neuroglia cells may be congenitally abnormal and that this, in turn, may adversely affect the neuron with reverberating effects on the neuroglia cells in turn. Such suggestions have been made in the past of a primary abnor-

288

mality of astrocytes manifested most strikingly by changes in their nuclei in Wilson's disease, of a degeneration and disappearance of, or congenital deficiency in the oligodendrocytes as a primary factor in some forms of diffuse sclerosis, of columns of abnormal astrocytes as precursors to a syringomyelia, and of the abnormal growth of astrocytes in tuberous sclerosis. Even the activity of abnormal neuroglia cells in gliomas may suggest some characteristic of nonneoplastic cells of the same series as pointed out by Elliott, Pope and others. Russell first demonstrated the characteristic contractile motion of oligodendrocytes in tissue culture of an oligodendroglioma and Lumsden and Pomerat were able to find the same type of motion in normal oligodendroglia in tissue culture. Studies of the oxygen consumption of oligodendrogliomas by the Warburg technique indicated that these had an oxygen consumption many times that of other glial tumors. This seemed astonishing in cells of a slowly growing benign glioma. Some time later a series of observations by Elliott and others which yielded data as to the probable oxygen consumption of normal oligodendrocytes indicated that it, too, was high and it was deduced that these cells must be much more active metabolically than had been supposed. As Pope pointed out, oligodendrocytes are thus sensitive to hypoxia and it is possible that they may suffer in various hypoxic or anoxic conditions of the central nervous system. As has been suspected and Luse has most recently demonstrated, the oligodendrocytes have an important function in myelin formation in, the central nervous system and it is possible that events in the perinatal and infantile periods that induce cerebral anoxia may lead to interference with the formation of myelin or its breakdown. An interesting corollary to the finding that oligodendrocytes may be metabolically very active cells and thus may have important functions as satellites to the nerve cells and their processes as yet unknown, is the recent finding that the perineuronal satellite cells of dorsal and autonomic ganglia (peripheral glia) are apparently also very active cells. This has been shown by their reduction of neotetrazolium in contrast to the activity of most other cells in the ganglia. It is interesting that De Castro has decribed nerve endings on or in these cells, as the Scheibels at this meeting have suggested for the oligodendrocytes, their sister cells in the central nervous system. As suggested by the Scheibels for the oligodendrocytes each may have a function in relation to the activity to the nerve cell. In this respect the interesting observations by electron microscopy on the perineuronal satellite cells in ganglia are very suggestive. It is thus possible that some ganglionic syndrome might conceivably relate to a dysfunction of such central and peripheral satellite cells which secondarily injures nerve cells. As an aside the relative neglect of the peripheral neuroglia at this conference was somewhat surprising since they offer a more accessible group of cells for study in situ.

The suggestion already made that the astrocytes suffer first in some forms of hepatic disease, coupled with the evidence marshalled at this meeting of the intimate relationship of astrocytes to neurons, as well as their well-known close relationship to blood vessels, and the possibility that some transport from capillary to neuron may be interfered with in abnormal states of the astrocyte, offers the possibility that neuronal damage or an interference with its normal activity may thus result. Further, if, as has been suggested, the cytoplasm of the neuroglia cells is really the path of transport of materials from blood to neuron and constitutes part of the blood-brain barrier, then we must seek in the neuroglia for such changes as modify the barrier and this transport and are significant in disease.

Lumsden's observations of astrocytes in tissue culture suggest that they grow more readily under relatively anaerobic conditions. This suggests, as do the findings of Lindenberg in traumatic lesions of the brain, that one of the stimuli to astrocytic proliferation in an abnormal area may be a relative hypoxia brought about in a variety of ways. This makes it probable that the continuing activity of the astrocytes in an abnormal area in which active breakdown of the tissue no longer exists may still be stimulated by the decreasing vascularity, thus lessening oxygen supply and this might explain the continuing astrocytosis under such circumstances.

Should the motility of the neuroglia cells as observed in tissue culture be found to correspond to a comparable activity of these cells in the intact nervous system, some interesting pathogenetic possibilities would emerge. The number of processes of a single astrocyte which contact a capillary wall, and possibly a neuron, varies from cell-to-cell as seen in fixed tissue preparations. The temporary adhesive contacts of the processes of astrocytes described by Lumsden in tissue cultures suggest that the number of processes of the individual astrocyte contacting the capillary wall may change and might have some functional significance. If, indeed, such processes are pathways of transport to and from the neuron, it is conceivable that abnormal states of the neuron may be induced by pathological states of the astrocyte in which the motility of its processes is impaired. The contractile movements of the oligodendrocytes could possibly have to do with both transport and the making and breaking of contacts, and the modification or interruption of such contacts by disease might again lead to malfunction or destruction of the neuron, axon and myelin sheath. Murray's suggestion that movements of the oligodendrocytes might be affected by chemical mediators presents one possible way in which abnormal states of these neuroglia cells might develop.

The privilege of symposia such as the present one is that of speculation. Many of our proposals will eventually prove to be fancy and a few may in time be demonstrated to be facts. In any case, the testing of the new data concerning the neuroglia on neuropathological material promises to be revealing and rewarding.

Bibliography

Abood, L. G., R. W. Gerard, J. Banks and R. D. Tschirgi: (1952) Substrate and enzyme distribution in cells and cell fractions of the nervous system. Am. J. Physiol., 168:728-738.

Achucarro, N.: (1918) On the evolution of the neuroglia and specially their relations to the vascular apparatus (translator's summary). J. Nerv. Ment. Dis., 48:333.

Adams, R. D. and C. Kubik: (1952) The morbid anatomy of the demyelinative diseases. Am. J. Med., 12:510-546.

Adams, R. D. and J. M. Foley: (1953) The neurological disorder associated with liver disease. Res. Pub. Ass. Res. Nerv. Ment. Dis., 32: 198-237.

Amin, A. H., T. B. B. Crawford and J. H. Gaddum: (1953) The distribution of 5-hydroxytryptamine and substance P in the central nervous system. Abst. Commun. XIX internat. physiol. Cong., Montreal, p. 165.

Angevine, D. M.: (1950) Structure and function of normal connective tissue (ref. pp. 13-43) in "Connective Tissue," C. Ragan, Ed., New York, Macy Found.

Ashby, W., R. F. Garzoli and E. M. Schuster: (1952) Relative distribution patterns of three brain enzymes, carbonic anhydrase, choline esterase, and acetyl phosphatase. Am. J. Physiol., 170:116-120.

Astbury, W. T.: (1933) Some problems in the x-ray analysis of the structure of animal hairs and other protein fibres. Trans. Faraday Soc., 29:193-211.

Astbury, W. T.: (1953) A discussion on the structure of proteins. Introduction. Proc. R. Soc., Ser. B., Biol. Sc., Lond., 141:1-9.

Bailey, P.: (1933) "Intracranial Tumors," xxii + 475 pp. Springfield, Ill., Charles C Thomas.

Bairati, A.: (1947) Osservazioni sulla birefrangenza delle fibre di neuroglia. Boll. Soc. ital. biol. sper., 23:16-17.

Bairati, A.: (1948-9) Osservasioni camparate sulle glioarchitettonica. Mem. Accad. sc. Ist. Bologna, 6:3-28.

Bairati, A.: (1949) Morfologia e struttura dei gliociti. Biol. lat., Milano, 2:601-659.

Bairati, A.: (1955) Ricerche sul meccanismo della colorazione argentica dei tessuti nervosi. Nota I—Dati preliminari. *Riv. Istochim.*, 1:307-312.

BAKAY, L.: *(1956)* "*The Blood-Brain Barrier*," xii + 154 pp., Springfield, Ill., Charles C Thomas.

BARTEN, H.: *(1934)* Eine seltene Fehlbildung des Kleinhirns. *Beit. path. Anat.*, 93:219-237.

BEHNSEN, G.: *(1927)* Über die Farbstoffspeicherung im Zentralnervensystem der weissen Maus in verschiedenen Alterszustanden. *Zschr. Zellforsch.*, 4:515-572.

BENDITT, E. P., R. L. WONG, M. ARASE AND E. ROEPER: *(1955)* 5-hydroxytryptamine in mast cells. *Proc. Soc. Exp. Biol., N.Y.*, 90:303-304.

BENITEZ, H. H., M. R. MURRAY AND D. W. WOOLLEY: *(1955)* Effects of serotonin and certain of its antagonists upon oligodendroglial cells in vitro. *Excerpta med., Sect. VIII*, 8:877.

BENNHOLD, H.: *(1932)* Über die Vehikelfunktion der Serumeiweisskörper. *Erg. inn. Med. Kinderh.*, 42:273-375.

BENNHOLD, H.: *(1953)* Die Rolle der Bluteiweisskörper im Regulationsgeschehen. *Verh. Deut. Ges. inn. Med., 59 Kongress:*135-149.

BERING, E. A., JR.: *(1952)* Water exchange of central nervous system and cerebrospinal fluid. *J. Neurosurg.*, 9:275-287.

BERLINER, R. W., T. J. KENNEDY, JR., AND J. ORLOFF: *(1951)* Relationship between acidification of the urine and potassium metabolism. *Am. J. Med.*, 11:274-282.

BORGHESE, E.: *(1954)* Mammalian hypothalamic nuclei cultivated in vitro. *Texas Rep. Biol. M.*, 12:215-228.

BOYKIN, F. C., D. COWEN, C. A. J. IANNUCCI AND A. WOLF: *(1954)* Subependymal glomerate astrocytomas. *J. Neuropath.*, 13:30-49.

BRODY, T. M. AND J. A. BAIN: *(1952)* A mitochondria preparation from mammalian brain. *J. Biol. Chem.*, 195:685-696.

BROMAN, T.: *(1940)* Über cerebrale Zirkulationsstörungen. *Acta path. microb. scand., suppl.*, 42:1-98.

BROMAN, T.: *(1941)* The possibilities of the passage of substances from the blood to the central nervous system. *Acta psychiat. neur. scand.*, 16:1-25.

BROMAN, T.: *(1949)* "*The Permeability of the Cerebral Vessels in Normal and Pathological Conditions*," 92 pp. + 3 plates, Copenhagen, Ejnar Munksgaard.

BROWNSON, R. H.: *(1955)* Perineuronal satellite cells in the motor cortex of aging brains. *J. Neuropath.*, 14:424-432.

BROWNSON, R. H.: *(1956)* Perineuronal satellite cells in the motor cortex of aging brains. *J. Neuropath.*, 15:190-195.

BUCY, P. C. AND H. KLÜVER: *(1955)* An anatomical investigation of the temporal lobe in the monkey (Macaca mulatta). *J. Comp. Neur.*, 103:151-252.

BURGEN, A. S. V. AND L. M. CHIPMAN: *(1952)* The location of cholinesterase in the central nervous system. *Q. J. Exp. Physiol., Lond.*, 37:61-74.

BUSCAINO, V. M.: *(1920)* Le cause anatomo-patologiche delle manifestazioni schizofreniche nella demenza precoce. *Riv. pat. nerv.*, 25:197-226.

BUSCAINO, V. M.: *(1924)* Nuovi dati sulla genesi patologica delle zolle di disintegrazione a grappolo. Reperti in un caso de demenza precoce catatonica. *Riv. pat. nerv.*, 29:93-128.

CAMMERMEYER, J.: *(1947)* Deposition of iron in paraventricular areas of the human brain in hemochromatosis. *J. Neuropath.*, 6:111-127.

CAMMERMEYER, J.: *(1953)* The effect of water on the human spinal cord in post-mortem experiments. *Mschr. Psychiat., Basel*, 126:229-239.

CAMMERMEYER, J.: *(1955a)* Astroglial changes during retrograde atrophy of the nucleus facialis in mice. *J. Comp. Neur.*, 102:133-150.

CAMMERMEYER, J.: *(1955b)* Volumetric characteristics of spinal cord regions in man, cat, rabbit and opossum. *Anat. Rec.*, 121:272.

CANTI, R. G., J. O. W. BLAND AND D. S. RUSSELL: *(1937)* Tissue culture of gliomata. Cinematographic demonstration. *Res. Pub. Ass. Res. Nerv. Ment. Dis.*, 16:1-24.

CATOLLA-CAVALCANTI, A.: *(1949)* Ricerche istologiche sulla struttura dei capillari cerebrali. *Arch. sc. med., Tor.*, 88:593-623.

CAVANAUGH, J. B., R. H. S. THOMPSON AND G. R. WEBSTER: *(1954)* The localization of pseudocholinesterase activity in nervous tissue. *Q. J. Exp. Physiol., Lond.*, 39:185-197.

CERLETTI, U.: *(1903)* Sulla neuronofagia e sopra alcuni rapporti normali e patologici fra elementi nervosi ed elementi non nervosi. *Ann. Inst. Psichiat. r. Univ. Roma*, 2:91-151.

CLARA, M.: *(1955)* Beiträge zur Morphobiologie des Nucleus supraopticus und Nucleus paraventricularis. *Anat. Anz.*, 102:86-88.

CLEMENTE, C. D. AND E. A. HOLST: *(1954)* Pathological changes in neurons, neuroglia and blood brain barrier induced by x-irradiation of the heads of monkeys. *A.M.A. Arch. Neur. Psychiat.*, 71:66-80.

COBB, S.: *(1952)* "*Foundations of Neuropsychiatry*," 5th ed., Baltimore, Williams and Wilkins.

COHEN, M. M.: *(1955)* Quantitation of phosphorus compounds in the normal and pathologic human brain. *J. Neuropath., 14*:70-83.

COLLIP, J. B. AND P. L. BACKUS: *(1920)* The alkali reserve of the blood plasma, spinal fluid and lymph. *Am. J. Physiol., 51*:551-567.

COOMBS, J. S., J. C. ECCLES AND P. FATT: *(1955)* The electrical properties of the motoneurone membrane. *J. Physiol., Lond., 130*:291-325.

COOPER, I. S. AND J. W. KERNOHAN: *(1951)* Heterotopic glial nests in the subarachnoid space; histopathologic characteristics, mode of origin and relation to meningeal gliomas. *J. Neuropath., 10*:16-29.

COSTERO, I.: *(1931)* Experimenteller Nachweis der morphologischen und funktionellen Eigenschaften und des mesodermischen Charakters der Mikroglia. *Zschr. ges. Neur. Psychiat., 107*:371-406.

COSTERO, I., R. BARROSO-MOGUEL, C. M. POMERAT AND A. CHEVEZ: *(1954a)* Caracterizacion del sistema fibroblastico. II. Fibrogenesis intracellular en tejido conectivo cultivado. *Arch. Inst. card. Mexico, 24*:337-372.

COSTERO, I., R. BARROSO-MOGUEL, A. CHEVEZ AND C. M. POMERAT: *(1954b)* Caracterizacion del sistema fibroblastico. IV. Fibrocitos reticulares. *Arch. Inst. card. Mexico, 24*:539-561.

COSTERO, I. AND C. M. POMERAT: *(1951)* Cultivation of neurons from the adult human cerebral and cellular cortex. *Am. J. Anat., 89*:405-468.

COSTERO, I. AND C. M. POMERAT: *(1952)* Propiedades del tejido nervioso conservado fuera del organismo. *Ciencia, 12*:9-18.

COSTERO, I., C. M. POMERAT, I. J. JACKSON, R. BARROSO-MOGUEL AND A. Z. CHEVEZ: *(1955a)* Tumors of the human nervous system in tissue culture. I. The cultivation and cytology of meningioma cells. *J. Nat. Cancer Inst., 15*:1319-1339.

COSTERO, I., C. M. POMERAT, R. BARROSO-MOGUEL AND A. Z. CHEVEZ: *(1955b)* Tumors of the human nervous system in tissue culture. II. An analysis of fibroblastic activity in meningiomas. *J. Nat. Cancer Inst., 15*:1341-1365.

COTLOVE, E.: *(1954)* Mechanism and extent of distribution of inulin and sucrose in chloride space of tissues. *Am. J. Physiol. 176*:396-410.

COX, A.: *(1936-7)* Ganglienzellschrumpfung im tierischen Gehirn. *Beit. path. Anat., 98*:399-409.
Anat., 94:171-207.

DAVENPORT, H. W.: *(1946)*: Carbonic anhydrase. *Physiol. Rev., 26*: 560-573.

DAVSON, H.: *(1955)* A comparative study of the aqueous humour and cerebrospinal fluid in the rabbit. *J. Physiol., Lond., 129*:111-133.

DAWSON, J. R.: *(1934)* Cellular inclusions in cerebral lesions of epidemic encephalitis. *A.M.A. Arch. Neur. Psychiat.*, 31:685-700.

DE CASTRO, F.: *(1951)* Aspects anatomiques de la transmission synaptiques ganglionnaire chez les mammiferes. *Arch. internat. physiol.*, Par., 59:479-513.

DEITERS, O. F. C.: *(1865)* "*Untersuchungen über Gehirn und Ruckenmark des Menschen und der Saugethiere,*" Braunschweig, F. Vieweg u. Sohn.

DEMPSEY, E. W. AND G. B. WISLOCKI: *(1955)* An electron microscopic study of the blood-brain barrier in the rat, employing silver nitrate as a vital stain. *J. Biophys. Cytol.*, 1:245-256 + 5 pl.

DENNY-BROWN, D., S. HORENSTEIN AND H. C. H. FANG: *(1956)* Cerebral infarction produced by venous distension. *J. Neuropath.*, 15:146-180.

DE ROBERTIS, E. AND J. R. SOTELO: *(1952)* Electron microscopic structure of cultured nervous tissue. *Exp. Cell Res.*, 3:433-452.

DESMEDT, J. E.: *(1956)* A cholinergic "local hormone" mechanism in the cat's brain. *Electroencephalography, Montreal*, 8:701.

DESMEDT, J. E. AND G. LaGRUTTA: *(1955)* Control of brain potentials by pseudo-cholinesterase. *J. Physiol., Lond.*, 129:46P-47P.

DICKSON, W. E. C.: *(1947)* Accidental electrocution: with direct shock to the brain itself. *J. Path. Bact., Lond.*, 59:359-365.

DIEZEL, P. B.: *(1955)* Iron in the brain: a chemical and histochemical examination: "*Biochemistry of the Developing Nervous System,*" H. Waelsch, Ed., xvii + 537 pp. (ref. pp. 145-152), New York, Academic Press.

DRUCKMAN, R.: *(1955)* Review of structural evidence of regeneration of nerve fibers in injury to the human spinal cord. Chap. 22 in "*Regeneration in the Central Nervous System,*" W. F. Windle, Ed., xviii + 311 pp., Springfield, Ill., Charles C Thomas.

DUNCAN, D.: *(1955)* Experimental compression of the spinal cord. Chap. 23 in "*Regeneration in the Central Nervous System,*" W. F. Windle, Ed., xviii + 311 pp., Springfield Ill., Charles C Thomas.

DUNCAN, D. AND S. R. SNODGRASS: *(1943)* Diffuse hypertrophy of the cerebellar cortex (myelinated neurocytoma). *A.M.A. Arch. Neurol. Psychiat.*, 50:677-684.

EINARSON, L. AND A. V. NEEL: *(1940)* Notes on diffuse sclerosis, diffuse gliomatosis and diffuse glioblastomatosis of the brain with a report of two cases. *Acta jutland., Aarhus*, 12:1-56.

EINARSON, L. AND A. V. NEEL: *(1942)* Contribution to the study of diffuse brain sclerosis with a comprehensive review of the problem in general and a report of two cases. *Acta jutland., Aarhus*, 14:1-131.

ELLIOTT, K. A. C.: *(1955a)* The relation of ions to metabolism in brain. *Canad. J. Biochem. Physiol.*, 33:466-477.

ELLIOTT, K. A. C.: *(1955b)* Brain tissue respiration and glycolysis. Chap. 3 in *"Neurochemistry,"* K. A. C. Elliott, J. H. Page and J. H. Quastel, Eds., xii + 899 pp. (ref. pp. 53-93), Springfield, Ill., Charles C Thomas.

ELLIOTT, K. A. C. AND W. PENFIELD: *(1948)* Respiration and glycolysis of focal epileptogenic human brain tissue. *J. Neurophysiol.*, 11:485-490.

FAÑANÁS, J. R.: *(1916)* Contribución al estudio de la neuroglia del cerebelo. *Trab. Lab. Inv. biol., Madr.*, 14:163-179.

FANTIS, A. AND E. GUTMANN: *(1953)* Příspěvek k otázce funkce glie (Concerning the question of the function of the glia). *Česk. morph.*, 1:156-164.

FARQUHAR, M. G.: *(1955)* Neuroglial structure and relationships as seen with the electron microscope. *Anat. Rec.*, 121:291.

FARQUHAR, M. G. AND J. F. HARTMANN: *(1957)* Neuroglial Structure and Relationships as Revealed by Electron Microscopy. *J. Neuropath.*, 16:18-39.

FAWCETT, D. W. AND K. R. PORTER: *(1954)* A study of the fine structure of ciliated epithelia. *J. Morph.*, 94:221-281.

FERRARO, A.: *(1928)* Acute swelling of the oligodendroglia and grape-like areas of disintegration. *A.M.A. Arch. Neur. Psychiat.*, 20:1065-1079.

FERRARO, A.: *(1931)* The origin and formation of senile plaques. *A.M.A. Arch. Neur. Psychiat.*, 25:1042-1062.

FERRARO A. AND L. ROIZIN: *(1951)* Aute and chronic clinicopathologic varieties of experimental allergic encephalomyelitis. *Tr. Am. Neur. Ass.*, 76:126-128.

FERRARO, A. AND L. ROIZIN: *(1954)* Neuropathologic variations in experimental allergic encephalomyelitis. *J. Neuropath.*, 13:60-89.

FLEXNER, L. B.: *(1934)* The chemistry and nature of the cerebrospinal fluid. *Physiol. Rev.*, 14:161-187.

FLEXNER, L. B., E. L. BELKNAP, JR., AND J. B. FLEXNER: *(1953)* Biochemical and physiological differentiation during morphogenesis. XVI: Cytochrome oxidase, succinic dehydrogenase and succinoxidase in the developing cerebral cortex and liver of the fetal guinea pig. *J. Cellul. Physiol.*, 42:151-161.

FOLCH, J., I. ASCOLI, M. LEES, J. A. MEATH AND F. N. LeBARON: *(1951)* Preparation of lipide extracts from brain tissue. *J. Biol. Chem.*, 191:833-841.

FORTUYN, A. B. D.: *(1927)* Histological experiments with the brain of some rodents. *J. Comp. Neur.*, 42:349-391.

FRIEDE, R.: *(1953a)* Über die trophische Funktion der Glia. *Virchows Arch.*, 324:15-26.

FRIEDE, R.: *(1953b)* Gliaindex und Hirnstoffwechsel. *Wein. Zschr. Nervenh.*, 7:143-152.

FRIEDE, R.: *(1954)* Der quantitative Anteil der Glia an der Cortexentwicklung., *Acta anat., Basel.*, 20:290-296.

GASSER, H. S.: *(1955)* Properties of dorsal root unmedullated fibers on the two sides of the ganglion. *J. Gen. Physiol.*, 38:709-728.

GEIGER, A., J. MAGNES, R. M. TAYLOR AND M. VERALLI: *(1954)* Effect of blood constituents on uptake of glucose and on metabolic rate of the brain in perfusion experiments. *Am. J. Physiol.*, 177:138-149.

GEREN, B. B.: *(1954)* The formation from the Schwann cell surface of myelin in the peripheral nerves of chick embryos. *Exp. Cell Res.*, 7:558-562.

GEREN, B. B.: *(1956)* Structural studies of the formation of the myelin sheath in peripheral nerve fibers. Chap. 10, pp. 213-220, in *"Cellular Mechanisms in Differentiation and Growth,"* D. Rudnick, Ed., Princeton, Univ. Press.

GEREN, B. B. AND F. O. SCHMITT: *(1955)* Electron microscope studies of the Schwann cell and its constituents with particular reference to their relation to the axon. Pp. 251-260 in *"Fine Structure of Cells,"* New York, Interscience Publishers, Inc.

GLEES, P.: *(1946)* Terminal degeneration within the central nervous system as studied by a new silver method. *J. Neuropath.*, 5:54-59.

GLEES, P.: *(1955)* *"Neuroglia Morphology and Function,"* xii + 111 pp., Springfield, Ill., Charles C Thomas.

GLOBUS, J. H.: *(1928)* Glia response in chronic vascular disease of the brain. *A.M.A. Arch. Neur. Psychiat.*, 20:14-33.

GLOBUS, J. H.: *(1942a)* Infundibuloma. A newly recognized tumor of neuro-hypophysial derivation with a note on the saccus vasculosus. *J. Neuropath.*, 1:59-80.

GLOBUS, J. H.: *(1942b)* Amaurotic family idiocy. *J. Mount Sinai Hosp. N. York*, 9:451-503.

GLOBUS, J. H. AND P. BERGMAN: *(1946)* Atresia and stenosis of the aqueduct of Sylvius. *J. Neuropath.*, 5:342-363.

GLOBUS, J. H. AND H. KUHLENBECK: *(1944)* The subependymal cell plate (matrix) and its relationship to brain tumors of the ependymal type. *J. Neuropath.*, 3:1-35.

Golgi, C.: *(1873)* Sulla struttura della sostanza grigia del cervello. *Gaz. med. ital. Lombardo, 33*:244-246.

Granick, S. and H. Gilder: *(1945)* The structure, function and inhibitory action of porphyrins. *Science, 101*:540.

Granick, S. and H. Gilder: *(1946)* The porphyrin requirements of *Hemophilus influenzae* and some functions of the vinyl and propionic acid side chains of heme. *J. Gen. Physiol., 30*:1-13.

Grazer, F. and C. D. Clemente: *(1957)* Developing blood brain barrier to trypan blue. *Proc. Soc. Exp. Biol., N. Y., 94*:758-760.

Greenberg, D. M., R. B. Aird, M. D. Boelter, W. W. Campbell, W. E. Cohn and M. Murayama: *(1943)* Study with radioactive isotopes of the permeability of the blood-cerebrospinal fluid barrier to ions. *Am. J. Physiol., 140*:47-64.

Greenfield, J. G.: *(1933)* A form of progressive cerebral sclerosis in infants associated with primary degeneration of the interfascicular glia. *J. Neur. Psychopath., 13*:289-302.

Grontoft, O.: *(1954)* Intracranial haemorrhage and blood-brain barrier problems in the new-born. *Acta path. microb. scand., suppl. C*: 109 pp. + 5 pl.

Grynfeltt, E.: *(1923)* Mucocytes et leur signification dans les processus d'inflammation chronique des centres cérébrauxspinaux. *Compt. rend. Soc. biol., 89*:1264-1266.

Guizzetti, P.: *(1915)* Principali risultati dell'applicazione grossolana a fresco delle reazioni istochimiche del ferro sul sistema nervoso centrale dell'uomo e di alcuni mammiferi domestici. *Riv. pat. nerv., 20*: 103-117.

Hardesty, I.: *(1904)* On the development and nature of the neuroglia. *Am. J. Anat., 3*:229-268.

Hassin, G. B.: *(1924)* A study of the histopathology of amaurotic family idiocy (infantile type of Tay-Sachs). *A.M.A. Arch. Neur. Psychiat., 12*:640,662.

Hassin, G. B.: *(1940)* *"Histopathology of the Peripheral and Central Nervous Systems,"* (ref. p. 17) New York, P. B. Hoeber.

Haymaker, W. and C. Davison: *(1950)* Fatalities resulting from exposure to simulated high altitudes in decompression chambers. A clinicopathologic study of five cases. *J. Neuropth., 9*:29-59.

Held, H.: *(1909)* Ueber die Neuroglia marginalis der menschlichen Grosshirnrinde. *Monatschr. Psychol. Neur., Berl., 26* Ergebenshft.: 360-416 + 12 Taf.

Heller, I. H. and K. A. C. Elliott: *(1954)* Desoxyribonucleic acid content and cell density in brain and human brain tumors. *Canad. J. Biochem. Physiol.*, 32:584-592.

HELLER, I. H. AND K. A. C. ELLIOTT: *(1955)* The metabolism of normal brain and human gliomas in relation to cell type and density. *Canad. J. Biochem. Physiol.*, 33:395-403.

HESS, A.: *(1953)* The ground substance of the central nervous system revealed by histochemical staining. *J. Comp. Neur.*, 98:69-91.

HESS, A.: *(1955a)* Relation of the ground substance of the central nervous system to the blood-brain barrier. *Nature*, 175:387-388.

HESS, A.: *(1955b)* The ground substance of the developing central nervous system. *J. Comp. Neur.*, 102:65-76.

HESS, A.: *(1955c)* Blood-brain barrier and ground substance of the central nervous system. *A.M.A. Arch. Neur. Psychiat.*, 73:380-386.

HILD, W.: *(1954a)* Das morphologische, kinetische und endokrinologische Verhalten von hypothalamischem und neurohypophysärem Gewebe in vitro. *Zschr. Zellfors.*, 40:257-312.

HILD, W.: *(1954b)* Histological and endocrinological observations in tissue cultures of posterior pituitary of dog and rat. *Texas Rep. Biol. M.*, 12:474-488.

HIMWICH, H. E.: *(1951)* "*Brain Metabolism and Cerebral Disorders*," xi + 451 pp. (ref. p. 118), Baltimore, Williams & Wilkins.

HIMWICH, H. E.: *(1954)* Blood-brain barrier. In "*Mechanisms of Congenital Malformation*," x + 137 pp. (ref. pp. 63-70), New York, Ass. Aid Crippled Children.

HINSBERG, K. AND R. AMMON: *(1937)* Die Autoxydation von Leinöl-säure in Pufferlösung in Gegenwart von Porphyrinen. *Hoppe-Seyler Zschr.*, 246:139-148.

HINSBERG, K. AND H. NOWAKOWSKI: *(1939)* Autoxydation von Leinöl-säure in Gegenwart von Porphyrinen. *Biochem. Zschr.*, 300:313-324.

HOLMGREN, H.: *(1938)* Funktion und Chemie der Ehrlich'schen Mast-zellen. *Anat. Anz.*, 85:31-38.

HOLMGREN, H.: *(1939)* Über Vorkommen und Bedeutung der chromo-tropen (metachromatischen) Substanz in menschlichen Feten. *Anat. Anz.*, 88:193-288.

HOLMGREN, H.: *(1940)* Studien über Verbreitung und Bedeutung der chromotropen Substanz. *Zschr. mikr. anat. Forsch.*, 47:489-521.

HOLTER, H. AND K. LINDERSTRØM-LANG: *(1951)* Micromethods and their application in the study of enzyme distribution in tissues and cells. *Physiol. Rev.*, 31:432-448.

HOWE, H. A. AND D. BODIAN: *(1942)* "*Neural Mechanisms in Poliomyelitis*," New York, Commonwealth Fund.

HOWE, H. A. AND R. C. MELLORS: *(1945)* Cytochrome oxidase in normal and regenerating neurons. *J. Exp. M.*, *81*:489-500.

HUDSPETH, E. R., H. G. SWANN AND C. M. POMERAT: *(1950)* Preliminary observations on the effect of various concentrations of oxygen on the *in vitro* growth of spinal cord from embryonic chicks. *Texas Rep. Biol. M.*, 8:341-349.

HUGHES, A.: *(1952)* "*The Mitotic Cycle; the Cytoplasm and Nucleus During Interphase and Mitosis*," viii + 232 pp., London, Butterworths Scientific Publications.

HUNTER, F. E., JR. AND O. H. LOWRY: *(1956)* The effects of drugs on enzyme systems. *Pharm. Rev.*, 8:89-135.

JANSEN, J.: *(1936)* Über Hirnveränderungen bei Holzgeistvergiftung. *Acta path. microb. scand.*, *26*:146-153.

KAPPERS, C. U. A., G. C. HUBER AND E. C. CROSBY: *(1936)* "*The Comparative Anatomy of the Nervous System of Vertebrates, Including Man*," 2 vols., New York, Macmillan.

KENCH, J. E. AND J. F. WILKINSON: *(1946)* Porphyrin metabolism in yeast. *Biochem. J., Lond.*, *40*:660-663.

KETY, S. S.: *(1952)* Cerebral circulation and metabolism. Chap. 3 in "*The Biology of Mental Health and Disease*," xxv + 654 pp. (ref. pp. 20-30), New York, P. B. Hoeber.

KLENK, E.: *(1940)* Beiträge zur Chemie der Lipoidosen. *Hoppe-Seyler Zschr.*, *267*:128-144.

KLÜVER, H.: *(1944a)* Porphyrins, the nervous system, and behavior. *J. Psychol.*, *17*:209-228.

KLÜVER, H.: *(1944b)* Porphyrins and the central nervous system. *Fed. Proc., Balt.*, *3*:25-26.

KLÜVER, H.: *(1944c)* On naturally occurring porphyrins in the central nervous system. *Science*, 99:482-484.

KLÜVER, H.: *(1948)* On a possible use of the root nodules of leguminous plants for research in neurology and psychiatry (preliminary report on a free porphyrin-hemoglobin system). *J. Psychol.*, 25:331-356.

KLÜVER, H.: *(1949)* Isolation of legcoproporphyrin. *Fed. Proc., Balt.*, 8:86-87.

KLÜVER, H.: *(1951)* Functional differences between the occipital and temporal lobes with special reference to the interrelations of behavior and extracerebral mechanisms. "*Cerebral Mechanisms in Behavior*," L. A. Jeffress, Ed. xiv + 311 pp. (ref. pp. 147-182), New York, Wiley & Sons.

KLÜVER, H.: *(1954)* On the use of azaporphine derivatives (phthalocyanines) in staining nervous tissue. *J. Psychol.*, *37*:199-223.

KLÜVER, H.: *(1955)* Porphyrins in relation to the development of the nervous system. In *"Biochemistry of the Developing Nervous System,"* H. Waelsch, Ed., xvii + 537 pp. (ref. pp. 137-144), New York, Academic Press.

KODAMA, M.: *(1926)* Über den Fettgehalt des Globus pallidus (das "Pallidumfett"). *Zschr. ges. Neur. Psychiat., 102*:236-249.

KOELLE, G. B.: *(1955)* Cholinesterases of the central nervous system. *J. Neuropath., 14*:23-27.

KOENIG, H., R. A. GROAT AND W. F. WINDLE: *(1945)* A physiological approach to perfusion-fixation of tissues with formalin. *Stain Techn., 20*:13-22.

KORNMÜLLER, A. E.: *(1950)* Erregbarkeitasteuernde Elemente und Systeme des Nervensystems Grundriss ihrer Morphologie, Physiologie und Klinik. *Fortschr. Neur. Psychiat., 18*:437-467.

KRYSPIN-EXNER, W.: *(1942-3)* Beiträge zur Morphologie der Glia im Nissl-Bilde. *Zschr. Änat. Entw., 112*:389-416.

KRYSPIN-EXNER, W.: *(1952)* Über die Architektonik der Glia im Zentralnervensystem des Menschen und der Säugetiere. *Proc. 1st Internat. Cong. Neuropath., Rome, 3*:504-510.

LESLIE, I. AND J. N. DAVIDSON: *(1951)* The chemical composition of the chick embryonic cell. *Biochem. Biophys. Acta, 57*:413-428.

LEWIS, R. C. AND R. L. SWANK: *(1953)* Effect of cerebral microembolism on the perivascular neuroglia. *J. Neuropath., 12*:57-63.

LEWIS, W. H.: *(1920)* Giant centrospheres in degenerating mesenchyme cells of tissue cultures. *J. Exp. M., 31*:275-292 + 2 pl.

LEWIS, W. H.: *(1931)* Pinocytosis. *Bull. Johns Hopkins Hosp., 49*:17-27.

LHOTKA, J. F. AND B. A. MYHRE: *(1953)* Periodic-acid-Foot stain for connective tissue. *Stain Techn., 28*:129-133.

LI, C. L. AND H. JASPER: *(1953)* Microelectrode studies of the electrical actions of the cerebral cortex in the cat. *J. Physiol., Lond., 121*:117-140.

LINDENBERG, R.: *(1956)* Morphotropic and morphostatic necrobiosis. Investigations on nerve cells of the brain. *Am. J. Path., 32*:1147-1177.

LINDENBERG, R. AND W. NOELL: *(1952)* Ueber die Abhaengigkeit der postmortalen Gestalt der Astrocyten von praemortalem, bioelektrisch kontrolliertem Sauerstoffmangel. *Duet. Zschr. Nervenh., 168*:499-517.

LIU, CHAN-NAO AND W. F. WINDLE: *(1950)* Effects of inanition on the central nervous system of the guinea pig. *A.M.A. Arch. Neur-Psychiat., 63*:918-927.

LOGAN, J. E., W. A. MANNELL AND R. J. ROSSITER: *(1952)* Estimation of nucleic acids in tissue from the nervous system. *Biochem. J., Lond., 51*:470-479.

LOWRY, O. H.: *(1955)* A study of the nervous system with quantitative histochemical methods. In *"Biochemistry of the Developing Nervous System,"* H. Waelsch, Ed. (ref. pp. 350-357), New York, Academic Press.

LUMSDEN, C. E.: *(1955a)* Observations on the morphogenesis and growth rate of astrocytic gliomas in tissue culture. *Excerpta med., sect. VIII, 8*:792-794.

LUMSDEN, C. E.: *(1955b)* The cytology and cell physiology of the neuroglia and of the connective tissue of the brain with reference to the blood-brain barrier. *Excerpta med., sect. VIII, 8*:832-834.

LUMSDEN, C. E.: *(1956a)* Discussion on experimental allergic encephalitis. *Proc. R. Soc. M., Lond., 49*:148-156.

LUMSDEN, C. E.: *(1956b)* The problem of correlation of quantitative methods and tissue morphology in the central nervous system. *Proc. 2nd. Internat. Neurochemical Symp.* (in press).

LUMSDEN, C. E. AND C. M. POMERAT: *(1951)* Normal oligodendrocytes in tissue culture. *J. Exp. Cell Res., 2*:103-114.

LUSE, S. A.: *(1956a)* Electron microscopic observations of the central nervous system. *J. Biophys. Cytol., 2*:531-541.

LUSE, S. A.: *(1956b)* Formation of myelin in the central nervous system of mice and rats, as studied with the electron microscope. *J. Biophys. Cytol., 2*:777-784.

MANERY, J. F.: *(1954)* Water and electrolyte metabolism. *Physiol. Rev., 34*:334-417.

MARINESCO, G.: *(1919)* Recherches histologiques sur les oxydases et les peroxydases. *C. rend. Soc. biol., 82*:258-263.

MARSHALL, W. H.: *(1953)* Physiological basis of the electroencephalogram. Discussion. *Electroencephalography, Montreal, Suppl., 4*:82-83.

MASSARI, F.: *(1954)* Ricerche sui fattori che influenzano la colorazione argentica delle struttura fibrose del connettivo—VI. Influenza di fattori estrinseci alle fibre. *Boll. Soc. ital. biol. sper., 30*:19-21.

MASSAZZA, A.: *(1924)* Sulla resistenze e sul comportamento delle varie categorie di cellule nervose del midollo spinale umano alla putrefazione cadaverica. *Riv. pat. nerv., 29*:460-476.

MASSERMAN, J. H.: *(1934)* Cerebrospinal hydrodynamics. *A.M.A. Arch. Neur. Psychiat., 32*:523-553.

304   Biology of Neuroglia

McFarren, E. F. and J. A. Mills: *(1952)* Quantitative determination of amino acids on filter paper chromatograms by direct photometry. *Analyt. Chem.*, 24:650-653.

McNabb, A. R.: *(1951)* Enzymes of gray matter and white matter of dog brain. The distribution of certain nonoxidative enzymes. *Canad. J. Med. Sc.*, 29:205-215.

Meyer, A.: *(1952)* Critical evaluation of histopathological findings in schizophrenia. *Proc. 1st Internat. Cong. Neuropath.*, Rome, 1:649-666.

Miller, W. H., A. M. Dessert and R. O. Roblin, Jr.: *(1950)* Heterocyclic sulfonamides as carbonic anhydrase inhibitors. *J. Am. Chem. Soc.*, 72:4893-4896.

Moschel, R.: *(1956)* Hirnbefund bei einer tödlich verlaufenden Wochenbettpsychose. *Nervenarzt*, 27:211-215.

Müller, G.: *(1930)* Zur Frage der Altersbestimmung histologischer Veränderungen im menschlichen Gehirn unter Berücksichtigung der örtlichen Verteilung. *Zschr. ges. Neur. Psychiat.*, 124:1-112.

Murray, M. R. and G. Kopech, Eds.: *(1953)* "A Bibliography of the Research in Tissue Culture," 2 vols., New York, Academic Press.

Mustakallio, K. K.: *(1954)* Histochemical demonstration of succinic dehydrogenase activity in human brain. *Ann. med. exp. biol. fenn.*, 32:175-177.

Nakai, J.: *(1956)* Dissociated dorsal root ganglia in tissue culture. *Am. J. Anat.*, 99:81-129.

Needham, J.: *(1942)* "Biochemistry and Morphogenesis," xvi + 787 pp. (ref. p. 598), Cambridge, Univ. Press.

Nissl, F.: *(1910)* Nervensystem. "Enzyklopädie der Mikroskopischen Technik," P. Ehrlich, R. Krause, M. Mosse, H. Rosin and K. Weigert, Eds., 2nd ed., 2 volumes (ref. vol. 2, pp. 243-287), Berlin, Urban & Schwarzenberg.

Nurnberger, J. I. and M. W. Gordon: *(1957)* The cell density of neural tissues: direct counting method and possible applications as a biological referent. Chap. 6 in "Progress in Neurobiology," vol. 2: "Ultrastructure and Cellular Chemistry of Neural Tissue," H. Waelsch, Ed.: New York, P. B. Hoeber.

Olson, N. S. and G. G. Rudolph: *(1955)* Transfer of sodium and bromide ions between blood, cerebrospinal fluid and brain tissue. *Am. J. Physiol.*, 183:427-432.

Opalsky, A.: *(1930)* Über einz besondere Art von Gliazellen bie der Wilson-Pseudosklerose-Gruppe. *Zschr. ges. Neur.*, 124:420-425.

OPPENHEIMER, D. R.: *(1955)* A benign "tumour" of the cerebellum. *J. Neur., Lond., 18*:199-213.

ORD, M. G. AND R. H. S. THOMPSON: *(1952)* Pseudocholinesterase activity in the central nervous system. *Biochem. J., 51*:245-251.

PALAY, S. L.: *(1957)* The fine structure of the neurohypophysis. Chap. 2 in *"Progress in Neurobiology,"* vol. 2: *"Ultrastructure and Cellular Chemistry of Neural Tissue,"* H. Waelsch, Ed.: New York, P. B. Hoeber.

PAPPENHEIMER, A. M., JR.: *(1947)* Bacterial Toxins. *Fed. Proc., Balt., 6*:479-484.

PAPPIUS, H. M. AND K. A. C. ELLIOTT: *(1956a)* Water distribution in incubated slices of brain and other tissues. *Canad. J. Biochem. Physiol., 34*:1007-1022.

PAPPIUS, H. M. AND K. A. C. ELLIOTT: *(1956b)* Factors affecting the potassium content of incubated brain slices. *Canad. J. Biochem. Physiol., 34*:1053-1067.

PATEK, P. R.: *(1944)* The perivascular spaces of the mammalian brain. *Anat. Rec., 88*:1-24.

PEARSE, A. G. E.: *(1953)* *"Histochemistry, Theoretical and Applied,"* viii + 530 pp., London, J. & A. Churchill.

PENFIELD, W.: *(1932a)* Neuroglia and microglia. The interstitial tissue of the central nervous system. Chap. 36. in *"Special Cytology. The Form and Functions of the Cell in Health and Disease,"* E. V. Cowdry, Ed., 2nd ed., New York, P. B. Hoeber.

PENFIELD, W.: *(1932b)* Neuroglia: Normal and pathological. Chap. 9, vol. 2 in *"Cytology and Cellular Pathology of the Nervous System,"* W. Penfield, Ed., 3 vols., New York, P. B. Hoeber.

PENFIELD, W. AND W. CONE: *(1926a)* Acute swelling of oligodendroglia, a specific type of neuroglia change. *A.M.A. Arch. Neur. Psychiat., 16*:131-153.

PENFIELD, W. AND W. CONE: *(1926b)* Acute regressive changes of neuroglia (amoeboid glia and acute swelling of oligodendroglia). *J. Psychol. Neur., 34*:204-220.

PERNIS, B. AND C. WUNDERLY: *(1953)* Quantitative determination of amino acids on filter paper. Staining in two stages. *Biochem. biophys. acta, Amst., 14*:209-214.

PETERS, V. B. AND L. B. FLEXNER: *(1950)* Biochemical and physiological differentiation during morphogenesis. VIII. Quantitative morphological studies on the developing cerebral cortex of the fetal guinea pig. *Am. J. Anat., 86*:133-161.

PHILLIPS, C. G.: *(1956)* Motor threshold and the thresholds and distribution of excited Betz cells in the cat. *J. Exp. Physiol., Lond., 41*:70-84.

PITTS, R. F.: *(1950)* Acid-base regulation by the kidneys. *Am. J. Med., 9*:356-372.

POLAK, M.: *(1935)* Sobre la histopatología de los microgliomas cerebrales. *Arch. histol. norm. pat., B. Aires, 5*:41-66.

POMERAT, C. M.: *(1951)* Pulsatile activity of cells from the human brain in tissue culture. *J. Nerv. Ment. Dis., 114*:430-449.

POMERAT, C. M.: *(1952)* Dynamic Neurogliology. *Texas Rep. Biol. M., 10*:885-913.

POMERAT, C. M.: *(1953a)* Rotating nuclei in tissue cultures of adult human nasal mucosa. *J. Exp. Cell Res., 5*:191-196.

POMERAT, C. M.: *(1953b)* Dynamic cytology in experimental medicine. *U. S. Armed Forces M. J., 4*:11-21.

POMERAT, C. M.: *(1954)* Living human histology. *Proc. XVᵉ Cong. Soc. intl. chirurgie, Lisboa, An. 1953*:236-256.

POMERAT, C. M.: *(1955)* Dynamic neuropathology. *J. Neuropath., 14*:28-38.

POMERAT, C. M. AND I. COSTERO: *(1956)* Tissue cultures of cat cerebellum. *Am. J. Anat., 99*:211-247.

POMERAT, C. M., C. G. LEFEBER AND McD. SMITH: *(1954)* Quantitative cine analysis of cell organoid activity. *Ann. N. York Acad. Sc., 58*:1311-1321.

POPE, A.: *(1952)* Quantitative distribution of dipeptidase and acetylcholine esterase in architectonic layers of rat cerebral cortex. *J. Neurophysiol., 15*:115-130.

POPE, A. AND C. B. ANFINSEN: *(1948)* Histochemical distribution of peptidase activity in the central nervous system of the rat. *J. Biol. Chem., 173*:305-311.

POPE, A. AND H. H. HESS: *(1954)* Quantitative distribution of dipeptidase and cytochrome oxidase in cytoarchitectonic layers of human cerebral cortex. *Fed. Proc., Balt., 13*:275.

POPE, A., H. H. HESS AND J. N. ALLEN: *(1957)* Quantitative histochemistry of proteolytic and oxidative enzymes in human cerebral cortex and brain tumors. Chap. 10 in *"Progress in Neurobiology,"* vol. 2: *"Ultrastructure and Cellular Chemistry of Neural Tissue,"* H. Waelsch, Ed.: New York, P. B. Hoeber.

PRICE, G. R., R. J. FERRETTI AND S. SCHWARTZ: *(1953)* Fluorophotometric determination of uranium. *Analyt. Chem., 25*:322-331.

PRINCE, J. H.: *(1955)* The origin and pattern of oligodendroglial cells in the vertebrate optic nerve. *J. Comp. Neur., 103*:541-563.

PURKINJE, J.: *(1836)* Über Flimmerbewegungen im Gehirn. *Müllers Arch., Jg. 1836:289-290.*

RAMON Y CAJAL, S.: *(1909-11) "Histologie du système nerveux de l'homme et des vertébrés,"* L. Asoulay, Ed., 2 vols., Paris, A. Maloine.

RAMON Y CAJAL, S.: *(1913)* Contribución al conocimiento de la neuroglia del cerebro humano. *Trab. Lab. Invest. biol., Madr., 11:255-315.*

RAMON Y CAJAL, S.: *(1925)* Contibution a la connaissance conocimiento de la névroglie cérébrale et cérébeleuse dans la paralysie générale progressive. *Trab. Lab. Invest. biol., Madr., 23:157-216.*

RAND, C. W.: *(1952)* The role of the astrocyte in formation of cerebral scars. With an introduction to Cajal's contribution to our knowledge of neuroglia. *Bull. Los Angeles Neur. Soc., 7:57-70.*

RAND, C. W. AND C. B. COURVILLE: *(1932a)* Histologic changes in the brain in cases of fatal injury to the head. III. Reaction of microglia and oligodendroglia. *A.M.A. Arch. Neur. Psychiat., 27:605-644.*

RAND, C. W. AND C. B. COURVILLE: *(1932b)* Histologic studies of the brain in cases of fatal injury to the head. IV. Reaction of the classic neuroglia. *A.M.A. Arch. Neur. Psychiat., 27:1342-1379.*

DEL Río HORTEGA, P.: *(1916)* Estructura fibrilar del protoplasma neuróglico y origen de las gliofibrillas. *Trab. Lab. Inv. biol., Madr., 14:269-307.*

DEL Río HORTEGA, P.: *(1920)* La microglía y su transformación en células en bastoncito y cuerpos gránulo-adiposos. *Trab. Lab. Inv. biol., Madr., 18:37-82.*

DEL Río HORTEGA, P.: *(1921)* La glía de escasas radiaciones (oligodendroglía). *Bol. r. Soc. Españ hist. nat., 21:63-92.*

DEL Río HORTEGA, P.: *(1928)* Tercera apórtacion al conocimiento morfólogico e interpretación functional de la oligodendroglía. *Mem. r. Soc. Españ. hist. nat., 14:5-122.*

DEL Río HORTEGA, P.: *(1932)* Microglia. Sect. X, vol. 2 in *"Cytology and Cellular Pathology of the Nervous System,"* W. Penfield, Ed., 3 vols: New York, P. B. Hoeber.

DEL Río HORTEGA, P.: *(1942)* La neuroglia normal. *Arch. histol. norm. pat., B. Aires, 1:5-71.*

DEL Río HORTEGA, P.: *(1943)* Ensayo de clasificacíon de las alteraciones celulares del tejido nervioso: alteraciones de las celulas neuroglicas. *Arch. histol. norm. pat., B. Aires, 2:5-100.*

DEL Río HORTEGA, P.: *(1949)* Art and artifice in histologic science. *Texas Rep. Biol. M., 7:363-390.*

ROBERTSON, J. D.: *(1955)* The ultrastructure of adult vertebrate peripheral nerve fibers in relation to myelinogenesis. *J. Biophys. Cytol., 1:271-278 + 3 pl.*

308   Biology of Neuroglia

ROBERTSON, W. F.: (1900) "A Textbook of Pathology in Relation to Mental Diseases," Edinburgh, W. F. Clay.

RODRIGUEZ, L. A.: (1955) Experiments on the histologic locus of the hematoencephalic barrier. J. Comp. Neur., 102:27-45.

ROIZIN, L.: (1949) Histopathologic and histometabolic correlations in some demyelinating diseases. J. Neuropath., 8:381-399.

ROIZIN, L.: (1952) Essays on histometabolic activity of the neuroglia of the central nervous system. J. Neuropath., 11:94.

ROIZIN, L.: (1954) Histometabolic aspects of tissue reaction patterns (neurophagia). J. Neuropath., 13:403.

ROIZIN, L.: (1955) Comparative histologic and histochemical findings of the intraneuronal inclusions in Myoclonus epilepsy. Excerpta med., sect. VIII, 8:774.

ROIZIN, L. AND A. FERRARO: (1942) Myoclonus epilepsy. Clinico-pathologic report of a case. J. Neuropath., 1:297-311.

ROIZIN, L., M. HELFAND AND J. MOORE: (1946) Disseminated, diffuse and transitional demyelination of the central nervous system. A clinico-pathologic study. J. Nerv. Ment. Dis., 104:1-50.

ROIZIN, L. AND F. KALLMANN: (1956) A review of neuropathological histochemical and genetic aspects of Alzheimer's and Pick's diseases. "Symposium on Presenile Dimentia," Am. Soc. Human Genet., Storrs, Conn., Aug. 27, 1956.

ROMEIS, B.: (1940) Hypophyse. In v. Möllendorff, "Handbuch der mikroskopischen Anatomie des Menschen," Berlin, Julius Springer, VI/3, pp. 393-430.

ROSSITER, R. J.: (1955) Chemical constituents of brain and nerve. Chap. 2 in "Neurochemistry," K. A. C. Elliott, I. H. Page and J. H. Quastel, Eds., (ref. p. 28), Springfield, Ill., Charles C Thomas.

ROWLEY, D. A. AND E. P. BENDITT: (1956) 5-hydroxytryptamine and histamine as mediators of the vascular injury produced by agents which damage mast cells in rats. J. Exp. M., 103:399-412.

SCHALTENBRAND, G. AND P. BAILEY: (1928) Die perivaskuläre Piagliamembran des Gehirns. J. Psychol. Neur., 35:199-278.

SCHARRER, E.: (1933) Bemerkungen zur Frage der sklerotischen Zellen im Tiergehirn. Zschr. ges. Neur. Psychiat., 148:773-777.

SCHEIBEL, M. E.: (1955) Axonal efferent patterns in the bulbar reticular formation. Anat. Rec., 121:363.

SCHEIBEL, M. E. AND A. B. SCHEIBEL: (1955) The inferior olive. A Golgi study. J. Comp. Neur., 102:77-132.

SCHERER, H. J.: (1933) Zur Frage der Beziehungen zwischen Leber- und Gehirnveranderungen. Virchows Arch., 288:333-345.

SCHERER, H. J.: (1938) La "Glioblastomatose en plaques." Sur les limites anatomiques de la gliomatose et des processus sclérotiques progressifs (sclérose en plaques, sclérose diffuse de Schilder, sclérose concentrique). *J. belge neur. psychiat.*, 38:1-17.

SCHERER, H. J.: *(1944) "Vergleichende Pathologie des Nervensystems der Säugetiere unter besonderer Berücksichtigung der Primaten,"* viii + 336 pp. (ref. pp. 21, 185 & 313), Leipsig, Georg Thieme.

SCHMIDT, W. J.: *(1942)* Zur Doppelbrechung des Gliagewebes, inbesondere der Müllerschen Stützfasern der Netzhaut. *Zool. Anz.*, 138:93-96.

SHAW, E. AND D. W. WOOLLEY: *(1954)* Pharmacological properties of some antimetabolites of serotonin having unusually high activity on isolated tissues. *J. Pharm. Exper. Ther.*, 3:43-53.

SMITH, J. D.: *(1949)* Haemoglobin and the oxygen uptake of leguminous root nodules. *Biochem. J., Lond.*, 44:591-598.

SOLOMON, A. K.: *(1949)* Equations for tracer experiments. *J. Clin. Invest.*, 28:1297-1307.

SPATZ, H.: *(1922a)* Über den Eisennachweis im Gehirn, besonders in Zentren des extrapyramidal-motorischen Systems. I. Teil. *Zschr. ges. Neur. Psychiat.*, 77:261-390.

SPATZ, H.: *(1922b)* Über Stofwechseleigentümlichkeiten in den Stammganglien. *Zschr. ges. Neur. Psychiat.*, 78:641-648.

SPATZ, H.: *(1933)* Die Bedeutung der vitalen Färbung für die Lehre vom Stoffaustausch zwischen dem Zentralnervensystem und dem übrigen Körper. *Archiv. Psychiat., Berl.*, 101:267-358.

SPIELMEYER, W.: *(1922) "Histopathologie des Nervensystems,"* Berlin, Julius Springer.

STAEMMLER, M.: *(1942) "Hydromyelie, Syringomyelie und Gliose. Anatomische Untersuchungen über ihre Histogenese,"* Berlin, Springer-Verlag.

STRASSMANN, G.: *(1945)* Hemosiderin and tissue iron in the brain, its relationship, occurrence and importance. A study on ninety-three human brains. *J. Neuropath.*, 4:393-401.

SWEET, W. H. AND H. B. LOCKSLEY: *(1953)* Formation, flow, and reabsorption of cerebrospinal fluid in man. *Proc. Soc. Exp. Biol., N. Y.*, 84:397-402.

SWEET, W. H., B. SELVERSTONE, S. SOLOWAY AND D. STETTEN, JR.: *(1950)* Studies of formation, flow, and absorption of cerebrospinal fluid. *Surg. Forum*, 1:376-381.

SYLVÉN, B.: *(1941)* Über das Vorkommen von hochmoledularen Esterschwefelsäuran im Granulationsgewebe und bei der Epithelregeneration. *Acta chir. scand., suppl. 66*, 86:1-151.

SYLVÉN, B.: *(1945)* Ester sulphuric acids of high molecular weight and mast cells in mesenchymal tumors. *Acta. radiol., Stockh., suppl.* 59:1-99.

TASAKI, I.: *(1953)* "*Nervous Transmission*," Springfield, Ill., Charles C Thomas.

THANNHAUSER, S. J.: *(1950)* "*Lipoidoses; Diseases of the Cellular Lipid Metabolism*," H. A. Christian, Ed., 2nd ed., 595 pp., New York, Oxford University Press.

TSCHIRGI, R. D.: *(1952)* Blood-brain barrier. Chap. 4 in "*The Biology of Mental Health and Disease*," xxv + 654 pp. (ref. pp. 34-46), New York, P. B. Hoeber.

TSCHIRGI, R. D., R. W. FROST AND J. L. TAYLOR: *(1954)* Inhibition of cerebrospinal fluid formation by a carbonic anhydrase inhibitor, 2 acetylamino-1, 3, 4-thiadiazole-5-sulfonamide (Diamox). *Proc. Soc. Exp. Biol., N. Y.*, 87:373-376.

VALENTIN, G.: *(1836)* Fortgesetzte Untersuchungen über die Flimmerbewegung. *Repertorium f. Anat. Physiol.*, 1:148-159.

VAN BOGAERT, L.: *(1945)* A subacute sclerosing leucoencephalitis. *J. Neur., Lond.*, 8:101-120.

VAN BREMEN, V. L. AND C. D. CLEMENTE: *(1955)* Silver deposition in the central nervous system and the hematoencephalic barrier studied with the electron microscope. *J. Biophys. Cytol.*, 1:161-166.

VICTOR, J. V. AND A. WOLF: *(1937)* Metabolism of brain tumors. *Res. Publ. Ass. Res. Nerv. Ment. Dis.*, 16:44-58.

VIRCHOW, R.: *(1846)* Ueber das granulierte Ansehen der Wanderungen der Gehirnventrikel. *Allg. Zschr. Phyciat., Berl.*, 3:242-250.

VIRCHOW, R.: *(1851)* Ueber Blut, Zellen und Fasern. Eine Antwort an Herrn Henle. *Virchows Arch.*, 3:228-248.

WALLACE, G. B. AND B. B. BRODIE: *(1939)* The distribution of iodide, thiocyanate, bromide, and chloride in the central nervous system and spinal fluid. *J. Pharm. Exp. Ther.*, 65:220-226.

WALLACE, G. B., B. B. BRODIE, M. M. FRIEDMAN AND D. BRAND: *(1937)* The distribution of administered iodide and thiocyanate in comparison with chloride and their relation to body fluids. *J. Pharm. Exp. Ther.*, 61:397-411.

WALLACE, G. B., B. B. BRODIE, M. M. FRIEDMAN AND D. BRAND: *(1939)* The distribution of administered bromide in comparison with chloride and its relation to body fluids. *J. Pharm. Exp. Ther.*, 65:214-219.

WALSER, M., D. W. SELDIN AND A. GROLLMAN: *(1954)* Radiosulfate space of muscle. *Am. J. Physiol.*, 176:322-324.

WEED, L. H.:*(1923)* The absorption of cerebrospinal fluid into the venous system. *Am. J. Anat.*, 32:191-221.

WEIGERT, F.: *(1895)* *"Beiträge zur Kenntniss der normalen menschlichen Neuroglia. Festschrift zum fünfzigjährigen Jubiläum des ärztlichen Vereins zu Frankfurt a. M,"* S. 149 + 13 Taf., Frankfurt a. M., A. Weisbrod.

WEIL, A.: *(1946)* *"Text book of Neuropathology,"* 2nd ed., xvi + 356 pp., London, William Heinemann.

WEIL, A.: *(1948)* A chemical analysis of the phospholipid of the brain in disseminated sclerosis. *J. Neuropath.,* 7:453-456.

WENDEROWIĊ, E.: *(1925)* Über Leitungs- und Zellveränderungen der Hemisphären bei Sclerosis cerebello-pyramido-intercorticalis und über interstitielles sphärisches Fett im Zentralnervensystem. *Arch. Psychiat., Berl.,* 75:490-549.

WENDEROWIĊ, E. AND M. NIKITIN: *(1913)* Über die Verbreitung der Faserdegeneration bei amyotrophischer Lateralsklerose mit besonderer Berücksichtigung der Veränderungen im Grosshirn. *Arch. Psychiat., Berl.,* 52:300-334.

WERSÄLL, J.: *(1956)* Studies on the structure and innervation of the sensory epithelium of the cristae ampullares in the guinea pig. *Acta otolar., Stockh., suppl. 126.*

WILKE, G. UND E. KIRCHER: *(1952)* Über röntgenographische Untersuchungen zur Frage der Gliafaserbildung. *Deut. Zschr. Nervenh.,* 167:391-406.

WILLIAMS, S. C.: *(1930)* Regeneration of peripheral nerves in amphibia studied with the aid of a vital stain. *J. Exp. Zool.,* 57:145-181.

WISLOCKI, G. B. AND E. H. LEDUC: *(1952)* Vital staining of the hematoencephalic barrier by silver nitrate and trypan blue, and cytological comparisons of the neurohypophysis, pineal body, area postrema, intercolumnar tubercle and supraoptic crest. *J. Comp. Neur.,* 96:371-413.

WISLOCKI, G. B. AND E. H. LEDUC: *(1954)* The cytology of the subcommissural organ, Reissner's fiber, periventricular glial cells and posterior collicular recess of the rat's brain. *J. Comp. Neur.,* 101:283-310.

WISLOCKI, G. B. AND T. J. PUTNAM: *(1920)* Note on the anatomy of the areae postremae. *Anat. Rec.,* 19:281-286.

WITTENBERG, J. B., S. R. KOREY AND F. H. SWENSON: *(1956)* The determination of higher fatty aldehydes in tissues. *J. Biol. Chem.,* 219:39-47.

WOLF, A. AND D. COWEN: *(1949)* Pathology. *"Selective partial ablation of the frontal cortex,"* F. A. Mettler, Ed., (ref. pp. 453-472), New York, P. B. Hoeber.

WOOLLAM, D. H. M. AND J. W. MILLEN: *(1955)* The perivascular spaces of the mammalian central nervous system and their relation to the perineuronal and subarachnoid spaces. *J. Anat., Lond.*, 89:193-200.

WOOLLEY, D. W. AND E. N. SHAW: *(1954a)* A biochemical and pharmacological suggestion about certain mental disorders. *Proc. Nat. Acad. Sc., U. S., 40*:228-231.

WOOLLEY, D. W. AND E. SHAW: *(1954b)* Some neurophysiological aspects of serotonin. *Brit. Med. J., 2*:122.

WOOLLEY, D. W. AND E. N. SHAW: *(1957)* Evidence for the participation of serotonin in mental processes. *Ann. N. Y. Acad. Sc. 66*:649-667.

WYCKOFF, R. W. G. AND J. Z. YOUNG: *(1954)* The organization within neurons. *J. Anat., Lond.*, 88:568.

ZEMAN, W.: *(1955)* Electrische Schädigungen und Veränderungen durch ionisierende Strahlen. In *"Handb. spez. path. Anat. Histol.,"* O. Lubarsch, F. Henke and R. Rossle, Eds., vol. 13, part 3, (ref., pp. 327-362), Berlin, Springer-Verlag.

Index

313

Lipoidoses, 273
Lipoids, 157
  solubility, 132
  in tumor astrocytes, 155
Liquefactive necrosis, 256
Liu, C. N., 251, 302
Liver
  cirrhosis, 47
  disease, 249
    encephalopathy, 255
    fatal, 255
  and glucose content of cerebral cortex, 138
  sinusoids of, 118
Lobectomy, bilateral temporal, 231
Lobotomies, 174
Local chemical gradients, 23
Locksley, H. B., 132, 309
Locus minoris resistentiae, 93
Logan, J. E., 208, 302
Lowry, O. H., 134, 217, 220, 222, 301, 303
Lumsden, C. E., 141-161, 174, 178, 303
Luse, S. A., 31, 37, 57-59, 99-129, 303

M

Macro-biochemical analyses, 213
Macrophages, xii, 115, 212, 247, 250-251, 257, 259-260, 278
  source of, 288
  system, 161
Magnes, J., 138, 298
Malaria, falciparum, 260
Malignancy
  grading of, 141
neoplasms, 119
Manery, J. F., 132, 303
Manhattan Project, 41
Mannell, W. A., 208, 302
Marginal neuroglia of Held, 88
Marinesco, G., 215, 303
Marsalid, 181
Marshall, W. H., 241, 303
Massari, F., 95, 303
Massazza, A., 284, 303
Masserman, J. H., 137, 303
Mast cells, serotonin, 180
McNabb, A. R., 220, 304
McFarren, E. F., 71, 303

Meath, J. A., 208, 297
Medullated sheaths and oligodendrocytes, 53
Melanomas, 279
Mellors, R. C., 216, 300
Meningeal inflammation, 261
Meninges, fungous infections of, 261
Meningitis, 116
Meningo-encephalitis, 287
Mental disturbance, 242
  serotonin, 176, 180
Mesencephalon, 90
Mesenchyme, 278
  cells, in vascular adventitia, 143
  from brain tissue, 142
  from gliomas, 142
Mesodermal cells, 144-145, 152
  neuroglia cells, 143
Mesoglia cells, xii (*See also* Microglia cells)
Metabolin of astrocytes, 237
Metabolism, 110, 228, 232
  arborization of neuroglia cells, 239
  carbon dioxide, 137
  central nervous cellular, 134
  of cerebral cortex, 229-230
  disorders, neuroglia in, 266-270
  enzymes of general, 228
  increase, 79
  interrelationships between neuroglia cells and neurons, 42
  maintenance of, 118
  of neuroglia, 63, 129, 213, 215, 239
    implication of histochemical studies, 211-233
  neuronal, 45, 239
  oxidative rates in neuroglia cells, 63
  porphyrins as regulators, 41
  rate, neuroglia cells, 215
  seasonal variations, 239
  studies, 203
Metabolites, diffusion gradient, 22
Metachromasia of neuropil, 119
Metachromatic leucoencephalopathies, 255
Metachromatic plaques, 286
Metallic substances, deposition of, 164
Meyer, A., 284, 304
Michaelis, L., 39

area influenced by, 62
description of, 57
in oligodendrogliomas, 282
and oxidation reduction system, 39
oxidative metabolism rate, 218
pale processes, 105-106
as perineuronal satellites, 53
penineuronal satellitosis, 251
perinuclear cytoplasm, 172
phagocytosis, 288
pinocytosis, 174
porphyrins in, 21-22, 38-39
free, 41
preparation of material, 61
presenile and senile processes, 267
proteolytic activity, 235
pseudocholinesterase in, 21
pulsating activity of, 170, 174, 178, 242
pure cultures of, 23
reactions, 288
to disease, 287
del Río Hortega's types, 15
role in central nervous system, 22
respiration, 231
respiratory activity of white matter, 217
response to vaso-constrictor, 177
rhythmic pulsatile activity, 174
satellite, 11, 46, 237
to blood vessel surface, 58
sensitivity to changes in cerebral homeostasis, 221
serotonin
effect of, on fetal, 179
response to, 174, 176-190
schwannoid, 282-283
silver carbonate methods, 6
spasmodic contraction of, 176
spheroidal, 282
nucleus, 100
storing memory, 242
structural interrelationships, 23
swelling of, 251, 254, 265
synapselike contact, 13
tonic contraction, 176
transmitting information to, 17
tumors, action in, 81
types of, 287

and unmyelinated axon terminals, 15
and unmyelinated long tract fibers, 15
virus infections, 260
volume fraction, 226
Oligodendrocytosis, 251, 254
Oligodendroglia
chemistry of, 21
tumors, 57-58
Oligodendrogliomas, 81, 101, 174, 230, 279, 289
cytochrome oxidase content, 217
oligodendrocytes in, 282-283
oxygen consumption, 217, 289
respiration, 229
Olson, N. S., 125-126, 304
Ontogeny, 239
Opalsky, A., 249, 304
Oppenheimer, D. R., 82, 304
Optic nerve fibers, 42
Orange staining bodies from Golgi technique, 5-6
Ord, M. G., 220, 305
Organelles, 31
Organoids, neuroglia cells, 174
Orloff, J., 138, 293
Osmosis, 184
Osmotic equilibrium, 135
Osmotically active particles in extra-vascular fluids, 137
Osmotically obligate water, 137
Oxidation, 40
rate of, 38
reduction system, 39
Oxidative phosphorylation, 214
Oxygen
consumption, 214
deficiency, glial proliferation, 264
diminished, 250
lack of, in cells, 40
uptake, 228-229, 232
low, 40

P

Palay, S. L., 24-49, 305
Pallidum, 118
free fat in, 119
Pappenheimer, A. M., Jr., 40, 305
Pappius, H. M., 111, 128, 305